RISK AND UNCERTAINTY

Other International Economic Association symposia

Conference on

RISK AND UNCERTAINTY

Proceedings of a Conference
held by the International Economic Association

EDITED BY
KARL BORCH
AND
JAN MOSSIN

MACMILLAN
London · Melbourne · Toronto
ST MARTIN'S PRESS
New York
1968

© The International Economic Association 1968

Published by
MACMILLAN AND CO LTD
Little Essex Street London W C 2
and also at Bombay Calcutta and Madras
Macmillan South Africa (Publishers) Pty Ltd Johannesburg
The Macmillan Company of Australia Pty Ltd Melbourne
The Macmillan Company of Canada Ltd Toronto
St Martin's Press Inc New York

Library of Congress catalog card no. 68–29940

Printed in Great Britain by
R. & R. CLARK LTD
Edinburgh

out our section by supporting Community Tennis Association (CTA's) like CNYTA. We are excited and look forward to collaborating with you to keep tennis in communities.

Eastern realized the CTA's are the cornerstone of our efforts and partnering with them creates the win-win combination that benefits all. Promoting tennis and making it accessible cannot be done from our sectional office. We need organizations like yours to support tennis in communities. Eastern will help you build on the strengths that exist and help plan and explore new areas of the game. Our many tennis resources are available to your organization and we welcome the opportunity to work together.

ood Food, Good Friends, Good Tennis
Sandy Sulik & Marylou Watson

HD69/D4/B58.

CONTENTS

v

Contents

Contents

ACKNOWLEDGEMENTS

THE International Economic Association wishes to express its gratitude to all those organizations and persons who helped in arranging the Conference reported in this volume. The Conference was held and this volume has been prepared and published with the aid of funds made available to the Association by UNESCO and by the Ford Foundation. To both those bodies the Association owes great gratitude for their support over a long period of years. A particular word of thanks is due to the Czechoslovak Academy of Sciences, who made it possible to hold the Conference in the beautiful setting of Smolenice Castle, fifty kilometres north of Bratislava.

Our sincere thanks are due to those who wrote the papers for the Conference, and to those who contributed to the discussions. A special word of gratitude is due to Dr. Jana Sereghyova of the Economic Institute of the Czechoslovak Academy of Sciences, who was in charge of the secretariat and the local arrangements for the Conference.

28 November 1966

LIST OF PARTICIPANTS

Professor Karl Borch (*Chairman*), Norwegian School of Economics and Business Administration, Bergen, Norway.

Mr. F. Bessière (*Vice-Chairman*), Électricité de France, Paris, France.

Professor Jaromir Walter (*Vice-Chairman*), Vysoká Škola Ekonomická, Prague, Czechoslovakia.

Professor Luc Fauvel (*Secretary-General*), Université de Paris, France.

Dr. Jan Mossin (*Rapporteur*), Norwegian School of Economics and Business Administration, Bergen, Norway.

Mr. M. Baret, Shell, Paris, France.

Mr. Edmond Baudier, Cermap, Paris, France.

Professor Hans Bühlmann, Federal Institute of Technology, Zürich, Switzerland.

Professor Myron J. Gordon, University of Rochester, Rochester, U.S.A.

Dr. Arkadiy A. Gretchikhin, Association of Soviet Scientific Economic Institutions, Moscow, U.S.S.R.

Professor Donald D. Hester, Yale University, U.S.A.

Dr. Petru L. Ivanescu, Academia R.S.R., Bucharest, Rumania.

Professor Anton Klas, Vysoká Škola Economická, Bratislava, Czechoslovakia.

Dr. J. Koerts, Econometrisch Instituut, Rotterdam, Netherlands.

Dr. Werner Leinfellner, Institut für Höhere Studien, Vienna, Austria.

Mr. Björn Leonardz, Stockholm University, Stockholm, Sweden.

Professor Kenneth R. MacCrimmon, Carnegie Institute of Technology, Pittsburgh, U.S.A.

Dr. Zbigniew Madej, Polish Economic Society, Warsaw, Poland.

Professor Thomas A. Marschak, University of California, Berkeley, U.S.A.

Professor G. Menges, Universität des Saarlandes, Saarbrücken, West Germany.

Dr. Pavel Pelikán, Academy of Sciences, Prague, Czechoslovakia.

Professor Richard N. Rosett, University of Rochester, Rochester, U.S.A.

Dr. Reinhard Selten, Goethe Universität, Frankfurt am Main, West Germany.

Professor Ivan M. Siroyezhin, Leningrad University, Leningrad, U.S.S.R.

Mr. C. A. Staël von Holstein, Stockholm University, Stockholm, Sweden.

Dr. Sten Thore, Norwegian School of Economics and Business Administration, Bergen, Norway.

Dr. Milan Ullrich, Academy of Sciences, Prague, Czechoslovakia.

List of Participants

Dr. Ladislav Unčovský, University of Bratislava, Bratislava, Czechoslovakia.

Dr. Christopher B. Winsten, Nuffield College, Oxford, England.

INTRODUCTION

BY

KARL BORCH

THE papers in this volume were presented at a Conference on Risk and Uncertainty, organized by the International Economic Association, and held at Smolenice Castle from 29 March to 6 April 1966. The papers were extensively and intensively discussed at the Conference. Dr. Mossin has prepared a summary report of the discussions, which, in an admirable manner, captures the highlights and reflects the spirit of friendly, constructive criticism which prevailed during the whole discussion.

It was Frank H. Knight who first used 'risk' and 'uncertainty' as two different, well-defined concepts. His book *Risk, Uncertainty and Profit*, which appeared in 1921, opened the way for systematic studies of the uncertainty elements in economics, and Knight's terminology has been widely accepted by a whole generation of economists. It seems, however, that it no longer serves any useful purpose to distinguish between risk and uncertainty. The distinction is used only occasionally in the papers presented at the Conference, and nowhere does it appear essential to the argument which the author wants to present. 'Risk and Uncertainty' was, however, the official subject of the Conference, and it is appropriate that it should remain as the title of this volume.

The presence of risk and uncertainty means that the outcome of an action cannot be predicted with certainty. In such situations it may be possible to specify the set of all possible outcomes. If we want to analyse these situations further, it seems that we are forced to introduce assumptions about how likely the different outcomes are. This means, however, that we introduce a probability measure — or something equivalent — over the set of possible outcomes. Once we have accepted this step as inevitable, or expedient, we can develop a theory in which there is no need for a distinction between risk and uncertainty. This does not mean that we have solved all philosophical problems concerning the real meaning of probability. Practical people may — rightly or wrongly — dismiss such problems as unimportant, and may be surprised or disappointed to see that they got so much attention during the discussion at the Conference.

The step from a deterministic to a probabilistic economic theory implies a step to a much higher level of mathematical abstraction. In a deterministic theory, prices, quantities, and other variables can be represented by familiar scalar numbers. These variables can be 'measured', and the relationship between them can be expressed by ordinary equations. The deterministic theory has a dynamic version, where the variables are defined as functions of time. The relationships are then defined by systems of differential equations, which may be of an intricate nature, although well within the borders of classical mathematical analysis.

In a probabilistic economic theory, the scalars from the deterministic case will have to be replaced by stochastic variables, and stochastic processes must take the place of the functions in the dynamic theory. These new concepts cannot be handled by elementary mathematics. They are difficult even to define, and their intuitive contents cannot in general be illustrated by the graphs and figures which have held an honoured place in economic textbooks for more than a century.

The papers in this volume indicate the level of mathematics which we shall need to master the economics of uncertainty. The papers also indicate that we have a long way to go before we are masters of this subject.

Most economists who have written about the subject seem to have assumed that market prices constitute the main source of risk and uncertainty. This is a natural assumption if one begins the analysis by considering the problem as it is seen by a businessman. The assumption implies, however, that uncertainty is of minor importance in a centrally directed economy, where prices are determined by planners and not by market forces.

The Conference made it clear that this point of view now belongs to the past. Both the papers and the discussion show that prices cannot be the basic source of uncertainty. Prices are determined within the economic system by other factors, which in some sense are more fundamental. It is among these factors that we must seek the sources of uncertainty. This argument leads us to consider the following two factors as potential basic sources of uncertainty :

(i) *The technology.* The classical production function is obviously a fiction. In a realistic theory we must assume that given inputs can determine the output only in a probabilistic sense.

(ii) *The behaviour* of consumers and other decision-makers. It is generally accepted that this behaviour can be erratic — people make mistakes. In addition we know from the theory of games that 'mixed strategies' may be optimal in certain situations. This means that rational people may behave in an erratic manner in order to advance their own interests.

The first of these sources of uncertainty will exist in any agricultural or industrial society, and it will be important under any economic system. The second of the sources can obviously be important only in a society where economic decisions are decentralized.

From these considerations it follows that some uncertainty is inevitable under any economic system. This uncertainty cannot be 'assumed away' — for instance by an appeal to the Law of Large Numbers — as one did so often in classical theory.

It also follows that some sources of uncertainty will disappear in a society, if the process of decision-making is centralized. It does not follow, however, that centralization necessarily leads to increased economic efficiency, although it may be tempting to jump to this conclusion.

It appears, on the other hand, that some decentralization — for instance, freedom of choice for the consumer — is considered desirable, even at the cost of some inefficiency. The problem is then to find the right, or optimal, balance between freedom and efficiency. This may well be considered the most important and challenging problem that our age presents to economists. It is hoped that this volume will stimulate research, and lead to further discussion of this problem.

PART I
ECONOMIC DECISIONS UNDER UNCERTAINTY

Chapter 1

DESCRIPTIVE AND NORMATIVE IMPLICATIONS OF THE DECISION-THEORY POSTULATES

BY

KENNETH R. MacCRIMMON

I. INTRODUCTION

MOST decisions of importance are made under conditions of uncertainty. In choosing among various courses of action we are not sure what the outcome of any particular action will be. A number of decision-making theories have been proposed for such situations. In this paper we shall deal with one particular theory of decision-making under uncertainty. This theory is based on the concepts of personal probability and utility and may be stated in the form of a set of postulates. Various sets of postulates have been formulated; the postulates we shall use are essentially the same as those of L. J. Savage (1954).

This decision theory is normative rather than descriptive. That is, it is a theory of how individuals *should* make decisions rather than how they *do* make decisions. Several challenges to the normative implications of the theory have been made in the form of conjectures and 'paradoxes'. These have generally been unsupported by empirical evidence. On the other hand, some researchers have supposed the theory to be descriptive and have generated much data. Unfortunately, many of these studies do not have the presumed relevance to the theory. In this study we attempt to discover the degree to which the postulates are good descriptions (of actual behaviour) and the degree to which they seem to be good norms.

A descriptive theory can be judged by its explanatory or predictive ability. It is more difficult, though, to judge a normative theory. Presumably, adopting a good normative theory will lead to 'better' results. But 'better' in what sense? The criteria must be specified and will often be part of the theory itself. One condition we might

3

expect a good normative theory to satisfy is that it should seem reasonable to individuals with expertise in the domain of usage. Thus, we should expect a good normative theory of decision to seem reasonable to successful, practising decision-makers.

To this end we present some experimental results based on decision problems given to a group of business executives. These executives were drawn from the Executive Development Programme at the University of California, Los Angeles. This programme trains upper-middle-level executives for top management positions. The average [1] executive can be described as forty-two years of age, holding a college degree, and earning $25,000 a year as a division manager in a company of about 6,000 employees.

In a series of four experimental sessions (of about one hour each) held in March and April 1964, decision problems based on each of the postulates were given to the subjects. Thirty-eight executives became regular subjects, and with only a couple of minor exceptions completed all the material. In this paper we can only briefly summarize the experiments and the results. For completeness we shall mention the results for each postulate. We shall, however, particularly emphasize those experiments and results having the greatest relevance to the topic of uncertainty. For a more complete treatment the reader is referred to MacCrimmon (1965) and a series of forthcoming working papers.

In order to probe the normative implications of the postulates, we were not only concerned with the subjects' initial response to the decision problems, but we were interested in their behaviour when they were given an opportunity to reflect on their answers — and especially after they were presented with arguments conforming to, and conflicting with, the postulates.[2] For this reason, the decision problems were especially constructed so that the strongest possible counter-argument to each postulate could be made. This puts the postulates to a very severe test, perhaps more severe than would arise in most real-world decision situations.

Although it is desirable to present as much experimental material as possible in a written form (to allow replication by other researchers), it is very important in experiments such as these to have an opportunity to follow-up on interesting or confusing written responses. Thus, after all the written experimental material had been completed,

[1] The figures are based on median values for each characteristic.
[2] These arguments were presented in a written form and will be described in more detail in later sections of this paper.

4

a terminal interview (of median length thirty minutes) was held with each subject individually. These interviews are an important part of this study, but because of constraints on the length of this paper it is feasible to present only a small part of the interview results. The interested reader is referred to the reports mentioned above.

In the next six sections of this paper, we shall state the appropriate postulate, present one of the experiments based (primarily) on that postulate, describe the experimental procedures, and discuss the results of the relevant experiments. Before presenting this material, however, we need to introduce the following basic concepts.

Alternatives (also acts or actions):

$a, b, c \in A$, the set of all possible actions.

States:

$x \in X$, the set of all possible states of the world.

Events:

$z \subseteq X$

If $\bigcup_{i=1}^{n} z_i = X$ and $z_i \cap z_j = \emptyset$ (all $i, j, i \neq j$),

we call $\{z_i\}$ an n-fold partition of X.

$z^c = \{x \notin X : x \notin z\}$, and is called the complement of z.

Consequences (also outcomes or rewards):

$(a, x) \in A \times X$.

If (a, x) is a constant for all $x \in z$, we write (a, z).

These concepts plus the relation of preference provide the basis for the postulates. The preference relation is defined as follows: if the decision-maker chooses b when both a and b are available, we say that a 'is not preferred to' b, and write $a \leqslant b$. As a corollary, if $a \leqslant b$ and also $b \leqslant a$, we say that the decision-maker 'is indifferent between' a and b, and write $a \sim b$; if $a \leqslant b$ but it is not true that $b \leqslant a$, we say that b 'is strictly preferred to' a, and write $a < b$. We later (Postulate 4) use the preference relation to develop the relation 'is not more probable than' between events. This relation is denoted as $\leqslant \cdot$.

II. POSTULATE 1: COMPLETE ORDERING

The first postulate we consider asserts that all alternatives are comparable and that choices are transitive. A formal statement of the postulate is given below.

Postulate 1: For every *a, b, c* ∈ *A*,
(1) $a \leqslant b$ or $b \leqslant a$.
(2) If $a \leqslant b$ and if $b \leqslant c$, then $a \leqslant c$.

The first part of the postulate (comparability) was not an explicit part of our experiments. We note though that at no point did a subject refuse to make a choice. The second part of the postulate (transitivity) was the basis for a particular set of experiments. These experiments will be treated only briefly in this paper because although transitivity is a very important concept, it is not a notion especially concerned with the topic of uncertainty.

As an example of the experiments used, the context of the first experiment was as follows :

Assume you are President of a company that makes small appliances. Suppose your company has extensively redesigned and improved one item in your product line. You must now make the final decision on the new price.

You feel that the important criteria in evaluating a pricing policy are expected return and expected share of market. You have directed your market-research staff to prepare these figures for the various possible pricing policies. You have every reason to believe in the reliability of the figures.

The subject was asked :

Which of the following pricing policies, A or B, do you prefer ? Please circle your choice.

A.	Expected return	10 %
	Expected share of market	40 %
B.	Expected return	20 %
	Expected share of market	20 %

A total of 4 distinct alternatives were used (the others being: C. Expected return 5 per cent, Expected share of market 50 per cent; and D. Expected return 15 per cent, Expected share of market 30 per cent). All 6 binary combinations of these 4 alternatives were presented (interleaved with some other transitivity experiments). This structure means that the subject had 4 chances to make 2 intransitivities on this experiment (May 1954).

After being presented with these binary choices the subject was asked to rank the four alternatives. Thus in addition to observing intransitivities (i.e. circular triples), we can compare his binary choices with his ranking of the 4 alternatives. A discrepancy

6

between the binary choice and the ranking will be called a 'choice instability'. [1]

In the experiment described, only 2 of the 38 subjects had an intransitivity while 18 of the subjects had 'choice instabilities'. In the other two transitivity experiments (with a similar structure to the one described) 1 subject in the second experiment and 5 subjects in the third had intransitivities, while 15 and 11 subjects, respectively, had 'choice instabilities' in these experiments. No subject had an intransitivity in more than one experiment. Thus, of the 114 subject-experiments (38 × 3), 8 subjects had intransitivities.

During the interview, 6 of these 8 subjects quickly acknowledged that they had made a 'mistake' in their choice and expressed a desire to change their choices. The remaining 2 subjects persisted in the intransitivity, asserting that they saw no need to change their choices because they focused on different dimensions for different choice pairs. The fallacy of this reasoning was not apparent to them in a five-minute discussion.

Only 8 of the 38 subjects had no 'choice instabilities' in the three experiments. The other 30 subjects (except for the 2 who persisted in intransitivities) all wished to change their choice (most would change the binary choice, but the difference was not significant). They generally attributed the 'choice instability' to carelessness in their reading or thinking.

III. POSTULATE 2: (a) THE IRRELEVANCE OF IDENTICAL OUTCOMES

Two implications of Postulate 2 will be discussed in this paper. The first, which may be called 'the irrelevance of identical outcomes', is the subject of this section, and the second implication will be covered in the next section (IV). Postulate 2 is formally stated below.

Postulate 2: If $(a, x) = (a', x)$ and $(b, x) = (b', x)$ for every $x \in z$, and if $(a, x) = (b, x)$ and $(a', x) = (b', x)$ for every $x \in z^c$, then $a \leqslant b$ if, and only if, $a' \leqslant b'$.

Three experiments concerning the 'irrelevance' implication of Postulate 2 were given to the subjects. The first experiment read as follows.[2]

[1] An intransitivity implies a 'choice instability', but the converse is not true.
[2] Slight changes have been made in notation and format, so that the current reader can more easily relate the experiment and Postulate 2.

7

Assume you are the President of a medium-sized company, and you have to choose among alternative investments in a production process involving uncertain outcomes. Suppose further that the uncertainty can be related to drawing a ball out of an urn containing 100 balls numbered from 1 to 100. The ball drawn will determine the outcome.

Which of the following two investments do you choose ? (Please give reasons for your choice.)

Investment a: Invest in a production process such that if ball numbered 1–10 is drawn, it corresponds to getting a return of 500 per cent ; if ball number 11 is drawn, it corresponds to failure of the process and your company will go bankrupt ; and finally if ball numbered 12–100 is drawn, it corresponds to getting a return of 5 per cent.

Investment b: Invest in a production process such that no matter which ball (numbered 1–100) is drawn, it corresponds to getting a return of 5 per cent.

After making a choice between *a* and *b*, the subject was then asked :

Making the same assumptions as above, if instead of investments *a* and *b* you are faced with investments *a '* and *b '*, which would you choose ? (Please give reasons for your choice.)

Investment a ': Invest in a production process such that if ball numbered 1–10 is drawn, it corresponds to getting a return of 500 per cent ; however, if ball numbered 11–100 is drawn, your company will go bankrupt.

Investment b ': Invest in a production process such that if ball numbered 1–11 is drawn, it corresponds to getting a return of 5 per cent ; however, if ball numbered 12–100 is drawn, your company will go bankrupt.

For the reader's convenience this experiment is shown in the payoff matrix below.

	Balls 1–10	Ball 11	Balls 12–100
Investment *a*	500% return	bankruptcy	5% return
Investment *b*	5% return	5% return	5% return
Investment *a'*	500% return	bankruptcy	bankruptcy
Investment *b'*	5% return	5% return	bankruptcy

Postulate 2 asserts that a choice of *b* over *a* should lead to a choice of *b'* over *a'*, and conversely. (Note that event z corresponds to balls 1–11, and event z^c corresponds to balls 12–100.)

8

This type of problem has been suggested by M. Allais (1953a, 1953b) and G. Morlat (1953). They conjecture that individuals when confronted with such situations will choose alternative b over a, and alternative a' over b'. The assertion is made (Allais, 1953a) that even upon reflection individuals will maintain such a choice. Persistence in such a choice (or in a and b') is, of course, in conflict with Postulate 2.

In our experiments, after answering the above questions the subject was presented with two prepared answers to the same problem. He was told both answers had been given by executives in a previous session. He was asked to provide a critique of each answer and to select the one that was more logical.

One prepared answer conformed with Postulate 2. It chose alternatives b and b' and gave reasons to the effect that the outcomes for the pair a and b, and for the pair a' and b', were identical if a ball numbered 12 through 100 was drawn, and, on the basis of taste, b was preferred to a when considering balls 1–11, but since b' is identical to b, and a' is identical to a, this implied b' should then be chosen over a'.

The other prepared answer had choices that conflicted with Postulate 2. The reasons presented were similar to those suggested by Allais (1953a). The choices made were b and a'. The justification for b was that it was safer — i.e. why take a chance on bankruptcy — whereas the justification for a' was that both a' and b' involved a high (and almost indistinguishable) chance of bankruptcy and so one might as well aspire to a 500 per cent return.

In the decision problem described above (the first of three quite similar experiments), slightly over 60 per cent of the (36 participating) subjects gave initial answers consistent with Postulate 2. Thus almost 40 per cent had answers in conflict with Postulate 2. These same percentages of conformity-conflict responses were found in the other two similar experiments. (The second experiment changed some of the material to a qualitative form, and the third experiment reversed the ball numbers and narrowed the quantitative outcomes.) A high degree of apparent conflict with Postulate 2 thus exists in the actual responses of the subjects.

Information on the extent to which the figures represent accidental conformity or accidental violation may be obtained from the (written) responses to the prepared answers. On the first experiment, only about 20 per cent of the subjects selected the conforming answer, while about 80 per cent selected the conflicting answer as

9

being the more logical one. Note then that many individuals who themselves gave conforming answers disagreed with the prepared conforming answer. (It is also true that some subjects initially giving violating answers disagreed with the prepared violating answer.) These percentages shifted towards conformity on the second experiment, with about 50 per cent of the subjects selecting the conforming answer and about 50 per cent of the subjects selecting the violating answer. (There was no presentation of prepared answers in the third experiment.)

Some logical lapses on the part of the subjects are thus apparent. Even though an individual himself may conform or violate Postulate 2, he apparently cannot recognize a complementary conforming or violating answer. Perhaps the prime reason for this response pattern was uncovered during the interview. The subjects had great difficulty separating logical deductions from a set of premises (the operation that was requested here) from the beliefs underlying the premises themselves. Thus, for example, if an individual selected a and a' (a conforming answer) he may select the violating prepared answer b and a' because the prepared conforming answer, b and b', is composed of two completely different actions. Reasons given for this choice would often be that the (b, b') prepared answer was 'too conservative', rather than asserting that it was less logical than the other prepared answer. (Analogous responses were given in the other cases.) Reasons given for the prepared-answer choice often had no connection with the subject's own answers and reasons given just a few minutes earlier.

The oral interview provided an opportunity to clear up some of this confusion between beliefs and logical deductions. After such a discussion most of the subjects tended to move towards conformity with the postulate-based reasoning. This trend can even be noted in the strictly written part of the experiment by comparing the figures given above for the responses to the prepared answers in the first and second experiments. The shift became more pronounced during the interview, with about 75 per cent of the subjects indicating their complete agreement with the postulate-based reasoning. Another 11 per cent indicated agreement for all instances except where one alternative has a sure outcome (for example, in the experiment described earlier, alternative b always gives a 5 per cent return).

Approximately 14 per cent of the subjects indicated their continued disagreement with the applicability of the postulate-based reasoning to such decision problems. The reason most often given by these subjects was that the problem could not be decomposed as the postulate-based reason implied. Comments such as 'You can't disregard what happens if balls 12–100 are drawn', 'You can't ignore such a big part of the problem', and 'You're only looking at part of the picture', were typical of this group. Attempts to explain that events were not being 'ignored' were unsuccessful. It should be observed though that all these subjects would be willing to conform to Postulate 2 if the event having identical outcomes was not so probable. Thus, that we get persistent violation of Postulate 2 is primarily due to the very special nature of these constructed situations.

IV. POSTULATE 2: (b) RISK VERSUS UNCERTAINTY

In this section we shall consider another implication of Postulate 2 (formally stated on p. 17). This interpretation may be called 'risk versus uncertainty'. We can develop the meaning of this most usefully in the context of one of the three experiments actually given to the subjects. The core of the first experiment read as follows:

1. Which of the following wagers do you prefer?
   (a) $1,000 if the top card in an ordinary, well-shuffled deck of playing cards is *red*; $0 if *black*.
   (b) $1,000 if the closing price tomorrow of Pierce Industries on the American Stock Exchange is *higher* than the closing price today; $0 if *not higher*.
   (c) Either (a) or (b).
   Please give reasons for your choice.

2. Which of the following wagers do you prefer?
   (a) $1,000 if the top card in an ordinary, well-shuffled deck of playing cards is *black*; $0 if *red*.
   (b) $1,000 if the closing price tomorrow of Pierce Industries on the American Stock Exchange is *not higher* than the closing price today; $0 if *higher*.
   (c) Either (a) or (b).
   Please give reasons for your choice.

This abbreviated form of the first experiment can serve to demonstrate the main focus of our interest in this section, that is, a 'risk/uncertainty' implication of Postulate 2.

The applicability of Postulate 2 to this experiment can perhaps best be seen by considering the payoff matrix representation below.

Actions \ Events	Stock higher and Card black	Stock not higher and Card red	Stock higher and Card red	Stock not higher and Card black
1(a)	$0	$1,000	$1,000	$0
1(b)	$1,000	$0	$1,000	$0
2(b)	$0	$1,000	$0	$1,000
2(a)	$1,000	$0	$0	$1,000

Making a correspondence with the notation of Postulate 2, let us now associate the (joint) events 'stock higher and card black' and 'stock not higher and card red' with z, the (joint) events 'stock higher and card red' and 'stock not higher and card black' with z^c. Let us further associate the actions 1(a) with a, 1(b) with b, 2(b) with a', and 2(a) with b'. For convenience in the following discussion let us refer to 1(a) as a 'bet' on the card being red, 1(b) as a 'bet' on the stock price being higher, (2b) as a 'bet' on the stock price not being higher, and 2(a) as a 'bet' on the card being black.[1]

Using these correspondences, Postulate 2 asserts that if you prefer a bet on the card being red to a bet on the stock price being higher, you then should prefer a bet on the stock price not being higher to a bet on the card being black. Note that the event 'black' is the complement of the event 'red', and the event 'not higher' is the complement of the event 'higher'. Postulate 2 thus asserts that if you prefer a bet on one event over a bet on a second event, then you should prefer a bet on the complement of the second event over a bet on the complement of the first event (given the same reward conditions). This relationship holds regardless of the nature of the events. Thus, within the context of this theory it is not meaningful to distinguish between the nature of events.

A notion that is in conflict with this is the dichotomy between 'risky events' and 'uncertain events' that is sometimes made. Under such a view, the card events would be called 'risky' because most people would be willing to assign a (common) relative frequency to them, while the stock events would be called 'uncertain' because most people would not assign (common) relative frequencies. This leads to an incomparability between 'risky events' and 'uncertain events' and to a different procedure for dealing with them. Thus, with such

[1] By a bet on an event we mean an alternative such that the decision-maker gains more if that event occurs than he does if it does not occur.

a view, it would not be inconsistent to prefer the bet on 'red' to the bet on 'higher' and then to prefer the bet on 'black' to the bet on 'not higher'.

This conclusion, and the type of experiment itself, has been suggested by D. Ellsberg (1961) as a situation in which people do not act in a manner consistent with Postulate 2. He contends that on the basis of presenting similar, but informal, problems to some top decision theorists, these individuals generally do choose actions 1(*a*) and 2(*a*), i.e. the bets on the 'risky events' over the bets on the 'uncertain events'. Ellsberg further claims that even upon reflection individuals will tend to persist in these choices.

In our experiments the subject was asked to make choices and give reasons in each of the six possible pairs of wagers (i.e. bets on two events and their complements taken pairwise) with the (identical) reward conditions used in the example at the beginning of this section. However, it should be noted that a choice of a bet on 'red' may not indicate strict preference but only indifference. Thus, a choice of a bet on 'red' *and*, in a later pair, a choice of a bet on 'black' may not be inconsistent with Postulate 2 if they merely indicate indifference. Therefore, a second set of reward conditions was also used. Under these conditions the stock bets still paid off $1,000 if correct, but the payoff on the card bets was reduced to $990. It is easily seen that a choice of both the 'red' and 'black' bets under these conditions is inconsistent with Postulate 2. Altogether, then, twelve pairs of wagers were presented to the subject in a single experiment.

Three 'risk/uncertainty'-type experiments were given to the subjects. The first has been discussed as the example in this section. The third was very similar, the only change being a replacement of the card events ('red' or 'black') by coin events ('heads' or 'tails') and a replacement of the stock events ('higher' or 'not higher') by GNP events ('U.S. 1964 GNP less than $620 billion' or 'U.S. 1964 GNP at least $620 billion'). The second experiment involved investments in two foreign countries with historical frequencies being given for one country (a 'risky' case) while no probabilities were assigned for the other country (a case of 'uncertainty').

In addition to asking for the subject's own responses on the first experiment, two different sets of choices and reasons were presented (in written form) to him for his critique. One set was consistent with Postulate 2, using informal probability-type arguments, while the other was inconsistent with Postulate 2 in that it gave 'risk/uncertainty'-type arguments — stating that the card odds were known whereas the stock odds were not known. Both sets of written reasons were entirely verbal in form.

Thirty-five of the 38 subjects completed the three experiments and the corresponding part of the terminal interview. Various kinds of answers inconsistent with Postulate 2 can be identified (Mac-Crimmon, 1965), but here we shall only be concerned with the 'risk/uncertainty' ones. (Most of the others were later labelled as 'mistakes' by the subjects.)

In the first experiment (the example at the beginning of this section), only 3 subjects had 'risk/uncertainty' violations of Postulate 2, in the third experiment only 5 subjects had such violations, while in the second experiment 19 subjects had 'risk/uncertainty' violations. Later questioning of the subjects indicated that, while the second experiment provided a less artificial decision context, it afforded an opportunity to make many irrelevant and changing assumptions that led to an unusually high degree of conflict with Postulate 2.

Considering all three experiments (even though the second has the defects mentioned above), no subjects had three 'risk/uncertainty' violations, only 3 subjects had two 'risk/uncertainty' violations, and 11 subjects had no 'risk/uncertainty' violations. The remaining 21 subjects had one 'risk/uncertainty' violation, with 17 of these occurring on the second experiment. If we separately consider only the first and third experiments (the two most closely corresponding to Ellsberg's), we find that 28 subjects had no 'risk/uncertainty' violations, 6 subjects had one, while only 1 subject had a 'risk/uncertainty' violation in both experiments.

In the first experiment a relatively higher proportion agreed with the violating answer than gave violating answers themselves; however, a majority still thought that the conforming answer was more logical. Eighteen subjects selected the conforming answer, 11 subjects selected the 'risk/uncertainty' violating answer, while the other 6 subjects thought neither was logical. Contrary to the responses to the prepared answers for the experiments discussed in the previous section, there was an insignificant amount of 'cross-over' (i.e. subjects giving one response themselves, then later selecting the other).

At the terminal interview, the reasons for the subject's particular choices were pursued, with emphasis being placed on those seemingly distinguishing between 'risk' and 'uncertainty'. The only subject giving 'risk/uncertainty' choices in his written answers to the first and third experiments persisted in this distinction during the interview. He insisted that he knew the odds on card and coin bets but not on bets involving stock-price increases or the level of GNP; and he further stated that he would select bets in which he knew the odds — even at a slight penalty (in terms of the payoffs). Of the other 6 subjects having (single) 'risk/uncertainty' violations in either the first or third experiment, all but one (with a second subject unsure) concluded that such a distinction was not reasonable, and they indicated a wish to change their choices. However, in the second experiment, slightly over half (10 of 19 subjects) did not wish to change a 'risk/uncertainty' violation. In general, this may be related to ambiguity in the problem statement, clarification of which the subjects would not accept. Of the other subjects — those initially giving non-'risk/uncertainty' violating answers, almost all attributed their answers to 'mistakes' and agreed completely with the applicability of Postulate 2.

In general, then, subjects do not persist in making distinctions between 'risky' and 'uncertain' events when given an opportunity to reflect on their answers — and this in an experiment especially designed to elicit such violations! Persistent violators are probably rare, but one can agree with Ellsberg (1963) that they are a particularly interesting group to study further.

V. POSTULATE 3: ADMISSIBILITY

Postulate 3 [1] introduces a very important concept, admissibility (also called 'dominance'). This notion has general interest beyond a particular theory of decision such as that considered here. This postulate is formally stated as follows:

Postulate 3: If $\{z_i\}$ is an n-fold partition of z, and if $(a, z_i) \leqslant (b, z_i)$ for all $z_i \in \{z_i\}$, $i = 1, 2, \ldots, n$, then $a \leqslant b$ given z. If, in addition, $(a, z_{i_0}) < (b, z_{i_0})$ for some non-null $z_{i_0} \in \{z_i\}$, then $a < b$ given z.

When the above conditions hold we say that alternative a is 'inadmissible', or that alternative b 'dominates' alternative a.

The concept of admissibility appeals very strongly to one's common sense. It also can have great practical significance in decision problems. It gives us a way of choosing among complex actions in

---

[1] Corresponding to Savage's Theorem 3 (1954, p. 26).

particular situations after having established a preference among consequences.

As part of the experiments on the independence of beliefs and tastes (to be discussed in the next section), material dealing with admissibility was included. In these experiments the subjects were asked to rank a number of alternative wagers from the one they preferred most to the one they preferred least. Of the six pages of wagers only the last three are of relevance here ; they each contained twelve wagers.

Three pairs of wagers form the test of admissibility.

(a_1) Win $1,200 if the Gross National Product for 1964 is over $610 billion ; lose $400 otherwise.

(b_1) Win $1,200 if the Gross National Product for 1964 is over $600 billion ; lose $400 otherwise.

(a_2) Win $1,200 if Goldwater receives the Republican nomination for President in 1964 ; lose $400 otherwise.

(b_2) Win $1,200 if Goldwater or Rockefeller receives the Republican nomination for President in 1964 ; lose $400 otherwise.

(a_3) Win $1,200 if the price of Syntex on the American Stock Exchange is at least twice its current price by the end of this year ; lose $400 otherwise.

(b_3) Win $1,200 if the price of Syntex on the American Stock Exchange is higher than its current price by the end of this year ; lose $400 otherwise.

On each of the three pages, two of these pairs appeared ; each pair was thus presented twice. Different reward conditions were used on each page.

The applicability of the postulate of admissibility to the above pairs should be quite apparent. In each case the *b* alternative dominates the *a* alternative (i.e., $a_i \leqslant b_i$ for $i = 1, 2, 3$).[1] Ranking the *a* alternative higher than the *b* alternative is thus a violation of the admissibility postulate.

Thirty-seven of the 38 regular subjects completed the admissibility experiment and participated in the interview. Of the 37 subjects, 12 had at least one inadmissibility, and 5 of the 12 had multiple inadmissibilities. Four of the 5 had two inadmissible choices, while the other subject had four inadmissibilities. (The maximum number of inadmissibilities possible, of course, was six, that is, three pairs of wagers presented twice.)

[1] Assuming a larger money amount is preferred to a smaller amount.

Because convincing written counter-arguments to the concept of admissibility could not be constructed, the subjects were not forced to reflect on their answers until the interview. After giving the subjects such an opportunity during the interview, almost all subjects with inadmissibilities quickly indicated that they would revise them. They made comments such as, 'That's just a mistake', 'I misread it', and 'That other one is obviously better'.

Two subjects did not recognize the inadmissibility immediately and they were questioned further about their choices (e.g. questions such as 'Do you know what happens if GNP is between 600 and 610 ?'). These subjects then perceived the inadmissibility. One subject stated that 'It seems obvious now . . . but I didn't look at it that way.' The other subject said, 'I don't know what I could have been thinking of.'

Thus no subject persisted in an inadmissible choice. Those subjects initially giving inadmissible choices generally attributed them to carelessness in their reading or thinking about the problem.

VI. POSTULATE 4: INDEPENDENCE OF BELIEFS AND TASTES

The postulate we deal with in this section asserts that the decision-maker's beliefs should be independent of his tastes. He should be subject neither to wishful thinking nor to persecution mania. Postulate 4 may be formally stated as follows :

Postulate 4 : For every a, $b \in A$ and z_1, z_1^c, z_2, $z_2^c \subset X$, if (a, z_1^c) $\sim(b, z_2^c) < (a, z_1) \sim(b, z_2)$, then $z_1 \leqslant z_2$ if, and only if, $a \leqslant b$.

The alternatives a and b may be thought of as 'bets' on events z_1 and z_2, respectively, in the same sense as the term was used in Section IV.

Subjects were asked to rank, from most preferred to least preferred, all bets on a page containing either eight or twelve bets. There were six such pages. The bets were grouped into quadruples and various combinations of quadruples were presented in a random order on a page. Each *bet* on the same page had identical reward conditions, but each *page* had a different set of rewards. The reward conditions comprised all possible combinations of losses and gains, and positive and negative expected money values.

An example of the type of quadruple and reward condition used is given below.

B   17

(a) Win $1,200 if a fair coin falls heads up ; lose $400 otherwise.

(b) Win $1,200 if the gold outflow exceeds the gold inflow in the U.S. this year ; lose $400 otherwise.

(c) Win $1,200 if Britain enters the Common Market this year; lose $400 otherwise.

(d) Win $1,200 if the price of the stock Syntex on the American Stock Exchange at the end of this year will be at least twice its current price ; lose $400 otherwise.

A total of four such quadruples was used.

Postulate 4 asserts that these bets should be ranked in the same order irrespective of the particular reward conditions (so long as the first is preferred to the second — for example, when 'win $1,200, lose $400' are replaced by 'win $0, lose $300' respectively). Thus, on each page that a quadruple appears it should be ranked in identical order. The bets in a given quadruple always appeared mixed in with those of one or two other quadruples (the quadruples combined differed from page to page). Subjects were not allowed to look back or to keep notes.

Thirty-seven subjects completed this experiment. Only 2 subjects had as many as 2 of the 4 quadruples ranked identically over the 3 or 4 times the quadruple was presented. Sixteen subjects had none of the 4 quadruples ranked identically. This is an unexpectedly high degree of apparent disagreement with the independence of tastes and beliefs postulate. That is, most subjects do apparently let their tastes influence their beliefs.

However, during the interview there was a unanimous swing towards identical rankings (by each subject for the quadruples presented). None of the 37 subjects wished to maintain even one different ranking — some even said specifically that 'the probabilities don't change'. The violation was primarily attributed to mistakes they had made and the complexity of the experiment. As one executive said, 'I mainly consider at most 3 or 4 alternatives at a time, not 8 or 12!' There was complete agreement (after the interview) on the reasonableness of the implications of Postulate 4.

VII. POSTULATE 5: EQUIVALENT n-FOLD PARTITION

The fifth postulate [1] is primarily a structural one. It asserts that the decision-maker should be able to construct an *n*-fold equivalent

---
[1] Corresponding to Savage's Postulate 6.

18

partition of the universal state. The meaning of this is implicitly defined in the following formal statement of the postulate.

Postulate 5: For any n, there exists an n-fold partition $z = \{z_1, z_2, \ldots, z_n\}$ of X such that for some $a_1, a_2, \ldots, a_n \in A$, (1) $(a_i, z_i^c) = s < t = (a_i, z_i)$, and (2) $a_1 \sim a_2 \sim \ldots \sim a_n$.

In the experiments we deal only with a special case of Postulate 5, the case where $n = 2$. Thus we are examining only the subject's ability to make an equivalent binary partition. Consider the following series of wagers.

Please indicate your choice among the following sets of wagers:

(*a*)   Win $1,000 if the Dow Jones industrial average (of stocks on the New York Stock Exchange) at the end of this year is at least x; win $0 otherwise.

(*b*)   Win $1,000 if the Dow Jones industrial average at the end of this year is less than x; win $0 otherwise.

(*c*)   Neither or either (please explain).

The variable x takes on the values 600, 1,000, 800, 700, 900, 650, 950, 750, and 850 in that order. The value of the Dow Jones industrial average at the time of the experiments was around 800.

Consistent responses would select the 'at least' bet for x less than some value x_0, and would switch to the 'less than' bet for x greater than x_0. This experiment roughly indicates a zeroing-in procedure for obtaining equivalent partitions; however, note that we deal only with the special case, $n = 2$, and only coarse intervals are used.

Of the 37 subjects who completed this experiment, 32 gave choices (of the above form) from which a unique, equivalent twofold partition could be made. Of the other 5 subjects, 2 gave an 'indifference band' (i.e. chose wager (*c*) for $x = 800$ and $x = 850$), one had a 'less than' choice among the 'at least' choices (i.e. chose the 'at least' bets for $x = 600$, 650, 750, 800, and 850, but the 'less than' bet for $x = 700$),[1] and the other 2 subjects chose the same bet all nine times (one subject always chose the 'at least' bet,[2] while the other always chose the (*c*), or indifference, bet).

Four of these 5 subjects recognized their inconsistent responses during the interview. They attributed their choice to carelessness and all four indicated a desire to modify their choices. The subject

---

[1] This is also an inadmissible choice — a violation of Postulate 3.

[2] This choice is not inconsistent if the subject thought that the value would be greater than 1,000, but information obtained during the interview indicated that this was not so.

who always chose the indifference bet did not seem to understand the implications of his choice, and insisted that he would always choose the (c) wager — even if the values used in the experiment were replaced by much larger values. He stated that he had chosen the indifference wager 'for consistency' and refused to discuss the experiment any further.

VIII. CONCLUSIONS

This study should be viewed as an exploratory one — an initial attempt to probe the normative implications of the decision-theory postulates. Several characteristics of this study serve to distinguish it from others. The focus was on the level of the individual postulates rather than on the level of the expected utility theorem. The various counter-arguments to the postulates were examined in the context of controlled experiments. The subjects of these experiments were experienced, practising decision-makers, that is, high-level business executives. In addition to gathering evidence on the extent to which these decision-makers conform to the theory in their actual decision behaviour, a systematic follow-up was made on some normative implications of the postulates. In the process some preliminary indications of the teachability of the theory were obtained. The results pertaining to each of these points will be summarized below.

Not surprisingly, we find that the personal probability/utility theory is not a very good description of the decision-making behaviour of the subjects. From the previous sections of this paper, one can note a high degree of inconsistency between the actual choices of the subjects and those choices prescribed by the appropriate postulate. In addition, an examination of the responses over all experiments by each subject (see chap. 10 of MacCrimmon, 1965) shows that the choices of each subject were inconsistent with at least one of the postulates. It follows logically then that no subject acted as if he maximized expected utility over all experiments.

In attempting to generalize this conclusion, two characteristics of the experiments must be considered. First, the decision problems were specially constructed in order to elicit violations of particular postulates. This suggests that the postulates might better describe more ordinary situations — that is, the less structured ones that we should expect to confront in the real world. On the other hand, the decision problems were very simple and somewhat transparent and should make conformity with the postulates much easier than in the more complex real-world decision problems.

The results presented in this paper show that there was a high degree of apparent violation across most of the postulates in the actual written choices of the subjects. Later, when confronted with the written prepared answers, they tended to select those most similar to their own, although there was a slight trend towards the conforming answer. However, during the interviews, under a neutral form of questioning,[1] there were large shifts towards conforming with the postulates. In many cases the subjects themselves expressed a desire to change their choices even before the particular experiments were discussed. The violations were generally labelled as 'mistakes' by the subjects and in one or two cases may be attributed to undue complexity or ambiguity in the experiments themselves. Thus there was little persistent violation of the postulates. Most of the persistent violation that did occur involved Postulate 2. This tends to justify the interest in, and attention to, Postulate 2 (Savage's so-called 'sure-thing principle') in the literature.

Most of the persistent violation, and also the highest degree of violation in the actual choices, occurred among the lower-level executives. The higher-level executives tended to have both a higher degree of conformity in their actual choices and a better acceptance of the applicability of the postulate-based reasoning. The higher-level executives were less defensive in discussing their choices, and were able to draw on their own real-world decision-making experiences — a subject that was pursued in the latter part of the interviews. In addition, these executives (earning over $30,000 a year) recognized the need for studies of decision-making involving uncertainty, and were, in general, enthusiastic about the teachability of some of the decision-theory concepts. This study should demonstrate that using business executives (especially high-level ones) as subjects in decision-making experiments is not only feasible but highly desirable. The opportunities lost by using college students, or some similar group, in decision-making studies should be recognized.

Perhaps the most important conclusion to be drawn from this study is the desirability of using the personal probability/utility postulates

[1] The interview results show that the subjects did not know the context of the experiments. It had been repeatedly emphasized that there was no right or wrong answer to the decision problems with which they were presented. For details on the exact form of the interview see MacCrimmon (1965).

in training decision-makers. As noted above, the most successful executives were especially enthusiastic about this possibility. Even though training was not an overt part of this study, that is, no pressures were applied to get the subjects to adopt the decision-theory approach, we see that simple exposure, as described in this paper, led to a large shift towards acceptance of the postulates. More direct training methods can easily be constructed; some can be inferred from this paper. Future studies should systematically examine methods for training people how to structure decision problems and how to police their own decisions within the decision-theory framework.

REFERENCES

Allais, M. (1953*a*), 'Fondements d'une théorie positive des choix comportant un risque et critique des postulats et axiomes de l'école américaine', *Économétrie*, Paris : Centre National de la Recherche Scientifique, pp. 257–332.

— (1953*b*), 'Le Comportement de l'homme rationnel devant le risque : critique des postulats et axiomes de l'école américaine', *Econometrica*, 21, pp. 503–46.

Becker, G. M., DeGroot, M. H., and Marschak, J. (1964), 'Measuring Utility by a Single-Response Sequential Method', *Behavioral Science*, 9, pp. 226–32.

Brim, O. G., and Koenig, F. W. (1959), 'Two Aspects of Subjective Probability among College Students', *J. Communication*, 9, pp. 19–26.

Cohen, J., Dearnaley, E. J., and Hansel, C. E. M. (1956), 'The Addition of Subjective Probabilities : the Summation of Estimates of Success and Failure', *Acta Psychologia*, 12, pp. 371–80.

Crandall, V. J., Solomon, D., and Kellaway, R. (1955), 'Expectancy Statements and Decision Times as Functions of Objective Probabilities and Reinforcement Values', *J. Personality*, 23, pp. 192–203.

Davidson, D., McKinsey, J. C. C., and Suppes, P. (1955), 'Outline of a Formal Theory of Value', *Philosophy of Science*, 22, pp. 140–60.

— Suppes, P., and Siegel, S. (1957), *Decision-Making: An Experimental Approach*, Stanford, Calif. : Stanford Univ. Press.

— and Marschak, J. (1959), 'Experimental Tests of a Stochastic Decision Theory', in *Measurement: Definitions and Theories* (eds. Churchman, C. W., and Ratoosh, P.), New York : John Wiley & Sons.

Davis, J. M. (1958), 'The Transitivity of Preferences', *Behavioral Science*, 3, pp. 26–33.

Edwards, W. (1953), 'Probability Preferences in Gambling', *Amer. J. Psychol.* 66, pp. 349–64.

— (1955), 'The Prediction of Decisions among Bets', *J. Exptl. Psychol.* 50, pp. 201–14.

MacCrimmon — Implications of Decision-theory Postulates

Ellsberg, D. (1961), 'Risk, Ambiguity, and the Savage Axioms', *Quart. J. Econ.* 75, pp. 643–69.
— (1963), 'Risk, Ambiguity, and the Savage Axioms', *Quart. J. Econ.* 77, pp. 336–42.
Fellner, W. (1961), 'Distortion of Subjective Probabilities as a Reaction to Uncertainty', *Quart. J. Econ.* 75, pp. 670–89.
Herstein, I. N., and Milnor, J. (1953), 'An Axiomatic Approach to Measurable Utility', *Econometrica*, 21, pp. 291–7.
Irwin, F. W. (1953), 'Stated Expectations as Functions of Probability and Desirability of Outcomes', *J. Personality*, 21, pp. 329–35.
MacCrimmon, K. R. (1965), 'An Experimental Study of the Decision-Making Behavior of Business Executives', unpublished dissertation, University of California, Los Angeles.
McGlothlin, W. H. (1956), 'Stability of Choices among Uncertain Alternatives', *Amer. J. Psychol.* 69, pp. 56–67.
Marks, R. W. (1951), 'The Effect of Probability, Desirability, and "Privilege" on the Stated Expectations of Children', *J. Personality*, 19, pp. 332–351.
Marschak, J. (1950), 'Rational Behavior, Uncertain Prospects and Measurable Utility', *Econometrica*, 18, pp. 111–41.
— (1964), 'Actual Versus Consistent Decision Behavior', *Behavioral Science*, 9, pp. 103–10.
May, K. O. (1954), 'Transitivity, Utility and the Aggregation of Preference Patterns', *Econometrica*, 22, pp. 1–13.
Morlat, G. (1953), 'Comment on an Axiom of Savage', *Économétrie*, Paris : Centre National de la Recherche Scientifique, pp. 156–67.
Neumann, J. von, and Morgenstern, O. (1947), *Theory of Games and Economic Behavior*, 2nd ed., Princeton, N.J. : Princeton Univ. Press.
Papandreou, A. G. (1957), 'A Test of a Stochastic Theory of Choice', *Univ. Calif. Publs. Econ.* 16, pp. 1–18.
Pratt, J. W., Raiffa, H., and Schlaifer, R. (1964), 'The Foundations of Decision under Uncertainty: an Elementary Exposition', *J. Amer. Statist. Assoc.* 59, pp. 353–75.
Raiffa, H. (1961), 'Risk, Ambiguity, and the Savage Axioms : Comment', *Quart. J. Econ.* 75, pp. 690–4.
Ramsey, F. P. (1931), 'Truth and Probability', in *The Foundations of Mathematics*, London : Routledge & Kegan Paul.
Roberts, H. V. (1963) 'Risk, Ambiguity, and the Savage Axioms : Comments', *Quart. J. Econ.* 77, pp. 327–35.
Rose, A. M. (1957), 'A Study of Irrational Judgements', *J. Polit. Econ.* 65, pp. 394–403.
Savage, L. J. (1954), *The Foundations of Statistics*, New York : John Wiley & Sons.

DISCUSSION OF THE PAPER BY
DR. MacCRIMMON

Mr. Staël von Holstein: Dr. MacCrimmon's paper presents a test of the descriptive and normative values of certain decision-theory postulates, the latter mainly due to Savage. The point emphasized is that the theory is a normative theory and therefore should be tested with respect to its normative value. In some cases this was done by a second part of the experiments, in which arguments and counter-arguments were given for the postulate in question. This gave the subjects the possibility of thinking the matter over again and perhaps revising their answers. I agree with the author that this put the postulates to a very hard test.

A most important part of these experiments was the final interview, which took place some time after the last experiment. Here the subjects had inconsistencies pointed out and were given the possibility of explaining themselves and changing their answers if so desired. Here you find the normative implication of the theory. With few exceptions, mainly in connection with the second postulate, the subjects conformed with the postulates after having been given the postulates or rather the meanings of them. I think that by means of this interview and by the way in which it was performed the author has found a nice way to test the normative value of the theory.

The result of the experiments is that, although the descriptive value may not be as high as one would like it to be, the theory is very good as a norm. The reason that the answers given do not always conform with the postulates depends at times on the subjects really breaking the postulates, but much more often it depends on mistakes, which in turn are due either to laziness or to difficulties in answering the questions.

I shall now turn to the various postulates and take up some points for discussion. The first postulate is mainly concerned with intransitivities. In an experiment like this, with binary choices between two-dimensional alternatives, you have two possibilities of making errors. You may find intransitivities because of indifference between two alternatives. This is of course always a problem with binary choices. More important is the possibility that a subject may just focus his attention on one of the dimensions, and therefore no intransitivities may be detected, because he has a complete ordering in the one dimension he considers. In the experiments the subjects were first asked to rank the alternatives, and here you could see if the ranking had only been done with regard to one dimension. The final interview, however, took care of these two problems, and that is another reason for having an interview.

The second fault could very well happen with the experiment presented on paper. I should not be surprised if a business executive had difficulties with this one as he might find the problem not fully defined. He could ask, 'How much capital has to be invested on the various alternatives?' and 'How have these figures of expected return and expected market share been determined?' and similar questions.

It might be of interest normatively to perform this experiment with alternatives with more than two dimensions. This could make it more difficult for the subjects to conform with the postulate and create a more severe test, but it would also be more difficult to construct a suitable experiment.

The second postulate is treated in two versions and it is in my opinion the most interesting one. One interpretation is 'the irrelevance of identical outcomes' and I have not much to add to the presentation given in the paper. It is apparent from the interviews that the non-conforming answers to the greater part were due to the 'identical outcomes' being such a big part of the problem given. It was therefore difficult for some persons to just leave them aside.

The other interpretation of the second postulate concerns 'risk versus uncertainty'. In this kind of problem the subjects must be allowed to be indifferent between the two wagers, one associated with 'risk' and the other with 'uncertainty'. But this indifference problem was nicely solved by a slight reduction in the money outcome connected with the 'risk' situation, whereby indifference could be eliminated.

In these two experiments on the second postulate there were many violations of the postulate, even when the subjects were given arguments for and against the postulate. But this does not mean that the individuals must have been acting irrationally. They might have applied a maximum-procedure, by the use of which they could not conform with the postulate.

The third postulate in the paper deals with admissibility, and it is pretty obvious that people should conform with it. But the results of the experiments show that the theory fails to be a good descriptive one, as people are careless when stating their opinions. There are far too many 'wrong' answers in the written part of the exercise.

The fourth postulate about independence of beliefs and tastes should also be perfectly reasonable, but here also there are far too many answers that deviate from the theory. This, I believe, was mainly due to the complexity of the experiment. The subjects had to rank eight or twelve wagers and that proved to be far too many. Some violations could also be explained by the difficulties of comparing wagers where the subjective probabilities must have been very close, and where the order could well change from one choice to another.

The fifth postulate is a little rough as it does not aim at a very fine partition. There might have been more answers violating this postulate, had the steps between the values of the index been less than fifty — say ten or perhaps five. We should then perhaps have a zone of indifference which of course would in turn mean an inadmissible choice and a violation of the third postulate.

Economic Decisions under Uncertainty

As a conclusion I should like to say that I think the author has, by his well-designed and performed experiments, showed that the descriptive value of the theory is not so great but that the theory has a definite normative value. It could be noted that the normative value of the theory was recognized by some of the higher-level executives participating.

These experiments have in some respects no predecessors. As far as I know this is the first work dealing with all the relevant Savage postulates at one time and not just with one, which has earlier been the case. The design of the experiments has also stressed the importance of an interview after the experiments. These ideas have contributed to making this paper, and the dissertation behind it, a most stimulating reading, for which I should like to thank Dr. MacCrimmon.

Professor Siroyezhin : First of all I should like to stress the important practical implications which might be derived from investigations and experiments like those performed by Dr. MacCrimmon. Useful projections can be made from such experiments both for decision theory and for organization theory as well as for educational purposes.

But I feel that for such a use to be converted from a pure theoretical possibility into real practical results it is necessary to extend that part of the experiments which is concerned with the background of the experimental subjects. It would, for example, be useful to take into account the economic environment in which participants of such a game are regularly acting. Thus, I would expect that such experiments conducted with a group of executives in our country, or even with executives from another part of the U.S. (let us say from the East), would give different results. Because of different economic factors there could be different degrees of support for the postulates. I feel that a superficial remark about the position of the participants and their salary does not give us a chance to understand the conclusions of the paper deeply enough.

My second remark is connected with the result presented in the study of Postulate 2. As is pointed out in the paper, this postulate failed to be supported by the executives. The postulate was studied in two respects : firstly in terms of indifference between equal outcomes and secondly by a comparative analysis directed at discovering the attitude of participants to risk and uncertainty elements in decision-making.

The reason why the postulate is violated may be that in the theory which is used for comparison with the experimental results, there is no attention at all to some particular issues of decision-making in organizations. For each real economic problem there could be modelled two spaces : a space of conditions and a space of solutions. It is very reasonable to assume that a set of solutions in the latter space is concave and homogeneous. In the two-dimensional case (when there are only two possible criteria for determining a solution) this set has at least four points representing extreme solutions which the decision-maker could try to get to. These points, representing particular optimal solutions to be sought

26

by the decision-maker, represent two different types of solutions. One group (let us say points α_1 and α_2) represents *real economic solutions* which it is reasonable to look for, and the other group (let us say points β_1 and β_2) represents a set of solutions which are not real, in the sense that it is useless for a given decision-maker to seek for such solutions. The terms 'reasonable' and 'useless' are to be understood in relation to the fact that there is a difference between the real economic position of the decision-maker and the firm he represents (or any other partially separated system) and his own representation of this position. Given a sound materialistic decision theory you will have people (properly educated) who will select and group solutions properly. If this is not the case there could be a great deal of confusion and mixture in selecting the proper criteria and looking for appropriate solutions. I feel that with Postulate 2 there was a mixture of just such a form because participants were to distinguish solutions not only upon their formal representation but also on the basis of the nature of the situation itself.

I think in this connection (and this is my third remark) that some additional difficulty with Postulate 2 arose from the construction of the questions for the participants. The fact that they were to analyse such diverse problems as Goldwater's nomination, changes in stock prices, and the volume of GNP could only add uncertainty to a proper development of criteria to be used and to the problem of distinguishing between real and unreal solutions.

The fact that participants persisted in their instability towards Postulate 2 could also be considered as support for this idea. In my terminology, this would be because they had different groupings into real and unreal of the possible solutions to the problems given.

In conclusion I should like to point out once more my great interest in work like that performed by Dr. MacCrimmon and by Drs. Selten and Schuster. I hope that the IEA could organize a special session elsewhere to discuss in more detail research in decision-making and its implications for economic practice.

Dr. Leinfellner : If you want to have an order not only over the a's, b's, and c's, but over the alternatives

$$(a,\ z_i)\ ;\ (b,\ z_i)\ ;\ (c,\ z_i)$$

then it would be necessary to add a further postulate. I may for example suggest the following :

P_1' : If $\{(a,\ z_i)\geqslant(b,\ z_i)\}$ and $\{(b,\ z_i)\geqslant(c,\ z_i)\}$, then $\{(a,\ z_i)\geqslant(c,\ z_i)\}$.

This postulate together with Postulate 3 gives a quasi-order. If you add further :

$$P_2' :\ (a,\ z_i)(b,\leqslant z_i)\ \text{or}\ (b,\ z_i)\leqslant(a,\ z_i),$$

then you have a complete ordering of alternatives. I think that the decision-maker must have an order of preferences over alternatives to find out the best decision.

This type of event-matching theory needs — in my opinion — such a postulate. Luce's system has an analogous postulate. I do not think that P_1' and P_2' follow from your Postulates 1 and 3, simply because Postulate 3 has no *c*. I suggest adding P_1' and P_2' to your set of postulates.

Dr. Selten : I think that the experiment of Dr. MacCrimmon is a very valuable one. I should like to comment on that part of the experiment which is concerned with risk versus uncertainty. Maybe the stock-market events used here are not very good examples of uncertainty ; many subjects may think that they can make a very good estimate of these probabilities. Investment in developing countries seems to be a more suitable example of uncertainty in the sense of Knight. I do not understand why Dr. MacCrimmon puts less weight on this example because of its 'ambiguity'. I should think that ambiguity is the essence of uncertainty.

It has been said that the experiments of Dr. MacCrimmon show that the descriptive value of utility theory is low but that the normative value is high. I should like to raise some doubts about the normative value. There may be alternative normative theories which may be as convincing as utility theory if they are explained to the subjects. The concept which has been developed by Professor Sauermann and myself in our paper 'Ansprechsanpassungstheorie der Unternehmung' (*Zeitschrift für die gesamte Staatswissenschaft*, 1962) is only one of the available alternatives to utility theory. It is based on the ideas of H. A. Simon and makes use of aspiration levels and rules for the adaptation of aspiration levels. It would be interesting to make experiments which confront different types of normative theories.

Mr. Baret : I should like to stress one very interesting point in Dr. MacCrimmon's paper, because it has received too little attention. That is Postulate 2, which corresponds to a similar postulate in Savage's theory.

In 1952 Mr. Morlat made a test similar to Dr. MacCrimmon's, which was once more made by Mr. Allais in 1953. In this test and in Dr. MacCrimmon's experiment it seemed that the considered choice was a contradiction of the postulate.

Mr. Allais's conclusion is very simple. We have to reject the postulate. Mr. Savage's and Mr. Morlat's conclusions are no less simple : the individual made an error of judgement.

At first, bearing in mind these two logical conclusions, I tried to reconcile them by stating that in one of the possible decisions one was sure of the result, no matter what state would occur. Therefore, by attributing a value or price to certainty, it is possible to maintain Mr. Allais's conclusion while at the same time maintaining the theory with a slight modification.

As a matter of fact, this was only a reflection which led me to remark that nothing is certain in our world. No matter what decision an individual takes, he is never certain about the result he can expect from it. The whole set of the states of nature cannot be examined in a way which would exhaust everything : there are always states which cannot be understood and their consequences are not known after the decisions have been taken.

This is absolutely essential in every decision theory. We therefore cannot use such tests in order to reject Postulate 2. It is interesting to remark that some of the subjects who went through Dr. MacCrimmon's test justified their incoherent answers with respect to Postulate 2 by the fact that certainty does not exist in reality.

It is true that we can change this test a little so as to eliminate the certainty. The answers will remain contradictory to the postulate. The test is, however, not representative of reality as it includes objective or numerical probabilities. In reality the probabilities which we can associate with events (other than coin-tossing) are purely subjective and they are not quantifiable *a priori*. We can make a remark of the same nature about the consequences of decisions which have subjective utilities depending on the individual and on other factors.

It is also true that we shall always find cases in which an individual will decide in contradiction to a theory ; this, however, does not mean that we must reject that theory, but it means that man is not God and that he is not always capable of obeying the laws of a logic which he has made for himself, or which he has accepted.

Professor Menges : I am impressed by the ingeniously designed experiments and their concrete results. Although I am very much in favour of empirical research in the spirit of Dr. MacCrimmon's paper, I cannot accept the general conclusions wholly. This for two reasons :

(1) Even if many decision-makers make decisions consistent with one axiom at a time, nothing can be inferred about their conformity with the complete axiomatic system. I admit that the *ceteris paribus* argument employed extensively in the design and interpretation of Dr. MacCrimmon's work cannot be avoided. One should, however, make due allowance for its potential shortcomings in the formulation of the general result.

(2) Even if we could cope with the *ceteris paribus* difficulty, I doubt whether we can find out more than the degree of acceptance which the axiomatic system meets with in the social group under consideration. Any further implication, e.g. that adoption by business executives indicates a 'good' normative theory, is unwarranted. Such implications would presuppose that upper-middle executives 'are what they are' because they made 'qualified decisions'. This may be so — especially if they decided to have the right parents — but the paper produces no evidence to this effect.

Professor Marschak : (1) Perhaps alternative experiments concerning the acceptance of Postulate 5 could be based on a mechanical device for the generation of equiprobable events, for example a spinner attached to a circle that is divided into *n* equal parts. Presumably subjects will really concede the stopping of the spinner in each of the n parts to be equiprobable, thereby satisfying Postulate 5. One could then examine whether subjects are also willing to specify a value of n and a value of k (k an integer not greater than n) such that the following is true for some event E having a business setting : the subject is indifferent between a bet in which he receives a dollar if E occurs, nothing if it does not, and a bet in which he receives a dollar if the spinner falls in one of k specified parts out of the n equal ones, nothing otherwise. This would actually be a check on several postulates simultaneously.

(2) The acceptance of initially troublesome postulates like Postulate 2 may perhaps be easier once the subject comes to understand the implications of the postulates. The convenience of ranking actions according to expected utility may cause the subject to overcome his doubts about such postulates — he may regard this as a reasonable price to pay. We may perhaps come to expect such a change of view as a normal part of the training process in this field.

Dr. Winsten : I too must also emphasize the point that the environment in which this type of experiment takes place (and this includes the socioeconomic environment) may be important in influencing the results. I felt, for example, that there was a whiff of the schoolroom in many of the answers to Dr. MacCrimmon's papers. Perhaps this was because these questions were simple. I shall return to this point later. Consider people's attitudes to political events : the awful things that would have to happen if Goldwater had been elected is a case in point. People may have particular political attitudes which stop them betting on this event.

Another illustration could be from an event taking place today, on which, in fact, there is a lot of betting. This is the parliamentary election going on in Britain. Now some entrepreneurs may possibly stand to lose if there is a large Labour majority. They may therefore bet on Labour winning, as a form of insurance. On the other hand they may be reluctant to do this, for they would then stand to gain out of an event they do not want to happen. These two forces, quite different in kind, pull in opposite directions. One must understand their effects in a particular case before one can make generalizations from any particular case.

To return now to the particular tests on postulates. Consider the experiments on transitivity. These are very simple, so the subjects expectedly thought there was a 'correct' solution. But the following postulate is equivalent to transitivity in situations where more than pairwise comparisons are allowed. Suppose subjects are allowed to choose from triples (A, B, X). If A is chosen when B is present out of any triple, then B will never be chosen from any other triple in which A is present. This is supposed to be true for any pair.

Though these are logically equivalent, this equivalent postulate gives a more realistic situation. It is not necessarily true that people will obey this postulate in practice even if they obey the direct postulate of transitivity.

Record of Discussion

Dr. *MacCrimmon*: I wish to express my thanks to Mr. Staël von Holstein for his well-balanced summary of my paper and to express my appreciation to the various discussants for their stimulating comments. I am especially glad to see that the training possibilities of the postulates have come across.

Turning my attention first to the more general issues raised, I was intrigued by the question of cross-cultural differences — a point raised by both Professor Siroyezhin and Dr. Winsten. This is a very interesting subject area. Although differences with respect to the postulates between, say, executives in the U.S. and the Soviet Union would not surprise me, I note that researchers in many countries, including the U.S. and the U.S.S.R., have recognized the value of the postulates; in what ways would we expect practising decision-makers to be different? I should be interested to hear specific conjectures my colleagues would make about differences to be expected.

On Professor Siroyezhin's concern about using political, economic, and other elements in these experiments, let me note that these are the types of diverse things executives do have to consider in their regular decision-making. In addition to any verisimilitude provided, a more diverse mix puts the theory to a harder test, as Professor Siroyezhin implies, and is thus another desirable reason for using such elements.

Dr. Selten's general point about ambiguity is a good one. However, in experiments, ambiguity is only useful if you purposefully build it in. When it inadvertently crops up, as it did in the foreign investment decision referred to, it can lead to extraneous assumptions being introduced (as was the case there). This leads to a loss in uniformity and control, the reasons for which you run experiments. I should like to support Dr. Selten's other point about the desirability of studies comparing different types of normative decision theories.

I am in agreement with Mr. Baret's discussion about the pervasiveness of uncertainty. However, I do not accept his dismissal of the results when the certainty alternatives are removed as not representative because of numerical probabilities. The experiment to which he refers purposefully does *not* contain numerical probabilities, and in one of the other experiments of this type (alluded to briefly on p. 9) no numerical information was given at all, and there was no significant difference in the results. Mr. Baret's last paragraph seems to intermingle descriptive and normative theory, but I would follow up on his last statement to the effect that although man may not always be capable of obeying logical norms, we should try to teach him how to obey them more often and how to recognize and correct violations.

As Professor Menges observes, conformity with each axiom separately does not imply conformity with the complete axiomatic system, but I should like to point out that violation of particular axioms implies violation of inferences made from the complete system. It was in this latter sense

31

that the analysis was made in the paper.

As Dr. Winsten suggests, we should want to consider the various aspects — monetary and non-monetary (including psychological) — of an outcome such as a Labour victory. The 'equivalent postulate' discussed by Dr. Winsten, i.e. the usual notion of the irrelevance of accompanying alternatives, is implied in the paper not only for transitivity but for all the postulates, since it is the basis on which preference is defined (see p. 5).

Dr. Leinfellner's point is certainly appropriate to the postulates as presented in this summary paper. In the complete system (see Mac-Crimmon, 1965, p. 9, or Savage, 1954, p. 25) there is a definition relating preference among sure actions to preference among consequences. From this a complete ordering among consequences follows without introducing another postulate. In the present paper the matter could be resolved by adding the linking definitions, or by giving Postulate 3 an 'if and only if' form and noting that the labelling of alternatives is arbitrary.

Chapter 2

AN EMPIRICAL ANALYSIS OF RISK-TAKING BY FIRMS IN THE SAVINGS AND LOAN INDUSTRY[1]

BY

DONALD D. HESTER

RISK-TAKING by individual firms is difficult to evaluate empirically because risky actions and their outcomes are not reported in firms' financial statements. An exception exists in the case of financial institutions which are regulated and insured by Government agencies. These agencies collect detailed information about portfolios, earnings, foreclosures, losses, reserves, and write-offs from individual firms.

This paper reports preliminary results from a cross-section analysis of risk-taking by approximately 4,000 insured savings and loan associations in the United States. Different measures of risk-taking are considered in relation to location, corporate form, growth rates, and firm size. In Section I the activities and trends in the savings and loan industry are briefly described. A number of measures of risk-taking are examined in Section II. In Section III results of single-equation regressions and analyses of variance are reported. An experiment with a simultaneous-equation model of a savings and loan association is described in Section IV. Section V summarizes the analysis and suggests hypotheses for future work.

I. INTRODUCTION AND BACKGROUND

Savings and loan associations are financial institutions which acquire savings from the public and lend to the public primarily in the form of mortgages on residential real estate. At the end of 1962

[1] Research underlying this report was supported by a grant from the National Science Foundation. Data analysed in this report were made available to me by the Federal Home Loan Bank Board. The Federal Home Loan Bank Board does not necessarily share any of the views expressed below. I am indebted to John Jevons for research assistance connected with the preparation of tables and diagrams. I of course assume full responsibility for any errors remaining in this paper.

33

there were about 6,300 savings and loan associations in the United States with total assets of about $94 billion. Of these about 4,350 with total assets of $89 billion were insured by the Federal Savings and Loan Insurance Corporation. In the present study attention is restricted to insured institutions. If an institution is insured it must pay a regular insurance premium on its savings deposits and the first $10,000 in each of its savings accounts is fully insured by the Corporation in the event of the association failing.

Savings and loan associations represent an important part of the financial picture in the United States. By way of comparison, at the end of December 1962 American commercial banks had $118 billion of demand deposits and $97 billion of time and savings deposits, mutual savings banks had $38 billion of savings deposits, and life-insurance companies had total assets of $133 billion.[1]

Table 1.1 shows an aggregate balance-sheet for all insured savings and loan associations on 31 December 1962. These institutions,

TABLE 1.1 [2]

BALANCE-SHEET OF ALL INSURED SAVINGS AND LOAN ASSOCIATIONS
AS OF 31 DECEMBER 1962

Assets	($ million)	Liabilities	($ million)
Cash	3,741	Savings deposits	76,590
U.S. Govt. securities	5,323	FHLB advances	3,426
First mortgage loans	75,385	Other borrowed money	124
Other loans	931	Loans in process	1,983
Other investments	657	Other liabilities	691
Buildings, furniture,	1,370	Stock	137
and fixtures (net)		Deferred credits	209
FHLB stock	1,080	Reserves	5,501
Miscellaneous	844	Surplus	668
Total	89,330	Total	89,330

located in all fifty states, are chartered either by the Federal Government through the Federal Home Loan Bank Board or by individual state banking commissioners. At the end of 1962 there were 1,941 associations with Federal charters; by law these are all 'mutual institutions'. Mutual institutions are owned directly by savings depositors; depositors select trustees to manage the association.

[1] *Federal Reserve Bulletin*, June 1963, various pages.
[2] Federal Home Loan Bank Board, *Combined Financial Statements*, Part I, Assets and Liabilities, 1962, p. 14.

Their management is assumed to maximize depositors' welfare subject to legal and 'market' (interest rate or demand) constraints. In addition there were 2,391 insured state-chartered institutions, of which about 75 per cent were mutuals. The remaining 25 per cent were 'stock' institutions which were owned not by depositors but by a group of stockholders who exercised control over management. For stock institutions management is assumed to maximize stockholders' welfare subject to legal and market restrictions.

The distinction between stock and mutual organizations plays an important role in the following pages. We shall also consider whether Federal associations differ from state mutuals and whether associations operating in different states have different operating characteristics.

A remarkable feature of savings and loan associations is their rapid rate of growth in the post-war period. Thus between 1950 and 1960 time and savings deposits in commercial banks grew from \$35 billion to \$68 billion, savings deposits of mutual savings banks grew from \$20 billion to \$36 billion, and savings deposits of savings and loan associations rose from \$14 billion to \$62 billion.[1] At the end of 1965 savings deposits in savings and loan associations amounted to about \$110 billion and total assets were about \$129 billion.[2] The relation between growth and risk-taking is considered below.

A brief survey of institutional practice and regulations will provide a useful backdrop for the subsequent analysis. While regulations and practice vary slightly from state to state, the following statements broadly apply to the savings and loan industry. Mortgage loans are made only in an area within a radius of fifty miles from the association's office(s). Approximately 80–90 per cent of the firms' mortgages are conventional mortgages ; the remaining 10–20 per cent are Federally insured FHA and VA mortgages. Savings and loan associations' mortgages averaged about \$20,000 on new homes and \$16,000 on existing homes in 1962 ; these amounts were about 75 per cent of purchase price and both sums had grown about 15 per cent by the end of 1965.[3] The average term of contract of mortgages on new

---

[1] National Association of Mutual Savings Banks, *Mutual Savings Banking*, a monograph prepared for the Commission on Money and Credit (Englewood Cliffs, N.J. : Prentice-Hall Inc., 1962), p. 54.

[2] Federal Home Loan Bank Board, 'Savings and Mortgage Lending Activities', Dec. 1965, Table 1. This document is a regular monthly press release by the Federal Home Loan Bank Board.

[3] Federal Home Loan Bank Board, 'Home Mortgage Interest Rates and Terms', Mar. 1963 and Nov. 1965. This document is a regular monthly press release by the Federal Home Loan Bank Board.

homes is about 24 years and on existing homes about 20 years. Because people in the United States move about frequently, the average actual lifetime of a new mortgage is much shorter, perhaps of the order of 6 or 7 years. Interest rates on new mortgages were about 6·10 per cent at the end of 1962 and fell to about 5·85 per cent at the end of 1965. In addition, when first executing a mortgage, savings and loan associations charge closing fees of around 0·75 per cent of the face value of the mortgage.

Interest rates, fees, terms of contract, and purchase prices vary from area to area in the United States. Thus in December 1965 interest rates on new home mortgages were about 6·15 per cent in Los Angeles and 5·25 per cent in Boston. Fees were 2·10 per cent in Miami and 0·04 per cent in Boston, average term was 29 years in New York and 22 years in Miami, and average purchase price was $20,000 in Miami and about $32,000 in California. Why should such differentials exist at a point in time ?

There are really two quite distinct explanations. First, the housing market may not be in equilibrium at any point in time. Even though life-insurance companies, savings banks, and other national institutions are presumably buying mortgages where yields are highest, they may not be large enough to even out regional variations. Savings and loan associations, as noted above, are restricted to lending in their own immediate area. If this disequilibrium hypothesis is accepted, over time there should be widely different growth rates of savings flows and mortgage lending which are closely related to regional variations in interest rates. Evidence in support of this hypothesis is presented in Sections III and IV of this paper.

Second, financial contracts are multi-dimensional. If we assume that in all regions individuals have the same ' credit-worthiness', then variations in one of the terms of lending would be accompanied by variations in some other terms of lending if the multi-dimensional mortgage is to be equally acceptable to some group of investors.[1] In this view regional variations in terms of lending are quite compatible with the hypothesis that an economy is in equilibrium. To be sure, the reasons for the existence of regional variations need to be explained, but there is no reason why high-interest-rate areas need grow faster than other areas. This hypothesis is considered briefly in Section III.

---

[1] Donald Hester, 'An Empirical Examination of a Commercial Bank Loan Offer Function ', *Yale Economic Essays*, vol. 2, no. 1 (Spring 1962), pp. 1–57.

Finally, foreclosure rates are reported quarterly for different areas and types of mortgages by the Federal Home Loan Bank Board.[1] They vary widely across the country. The number of foreclosures divided by the outstanding number of mortgage loans averaged 0·57 per cent for the United States for the year ending 30 January 1965. On the west coast (California, Nevada, Arizona, Oregon, Washington, etc.) the foreclosure rate was 1·06 per cent; in the eastern and middle-western sections of the country the rate was about 0·41 per cent during the same period.

II. MEASURES OF RISK-TAKING

Before discussing measures of risk-taking, the nature of risk itself must be considered. A decision-maker typically exposes himself, subjectively at least, to possible losses when maximizing his objective function. Risk or uncertainty in this paper is assumed to be some unspecified functional of his distribution of possible losses; it could be a semi-variance, expected loss, or some other moment of this distribution of losses. Unfortunately, there is very little basis for preferring any single functional form. There is a further problem that we cannot observe what the decision-maker's subjective estimate of losses is at any point in time. Consequently, for purposes of empirical analysis a crude pragmatic approach must be used.

A basic condition necessary for the subsequent empirical analysis is that differences in risk-taking can be inferred from observable

FIG. 2.1

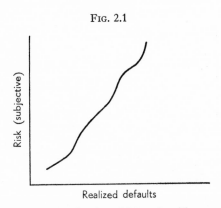

1 A foreclosure is simply a legal action which extinguishes a mortgagor's right to mortgaged property. Foreclosure and loss rates are likely to be closely related.

differences in either actual foreclosure experience or differences in balance-sheets and income statements. Specifically, the assumption is that risk is on average a monotonic function of foreclosures experienced and the values of certain balance-sheet ratios. Fig. 2.1 suggests what this means when mortgage foreclosures are analysed.

To be sure, an assumption of monotonicity is by no means empty ! It is embarrassingly easy to construct plausible examples where the assumption is not satisfied. For example, in the Markowitz quadratic programming portfolio selection model, the correlation between expected losses and risk need not be positive.[1] What is the justification for the assumption in this example ? In Fig. 2.2 all possible mortgage loans in some community have been ordered according to the expected probability that they will be foreclosed, conditional on a specific forecast about the future prosperity of the community. A savings and loan association probably attempts to rank prospective borrowers similarly. There are two reasons for believing that an institution's subjective evaluation of risks will be a monotonic function of observed average foreclosure rates. First, if associations are able to distinguish between good and poor mortgage loans, then a correspondence between subjectively expected and actual foreclosures will exist. Second, if the assumption about the community's economy proves faulty, the curve shifts more in absolute terms for loans with higher expected rates of default. The same factors which make certain individuals have high default rates, e.g. youthfulness, lack of education, poor previous credit experience, and

FIG. 2.2

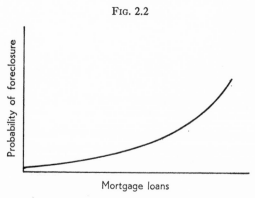

Probability of foreclosure

Mortgage loans

[1] Markowitz, H. M., *Portfolio Selection: Efficient Diversification of Investments*, New York : John Wiley & Sons, 1959.

discrimination, will also make them more vulnerable to cyclical fluctuations in employment.

Consequently, if different associations serve the same or similar markets, those institutions experiencing higher foreclosure rates are likely to be consciously taking more risks in mortgage lending. A similar defence can be constructed for other measures of risk considered below. These 'ordinal' measures of risk are convenient for empirical analysis, but they raise other serious problems of interpretation when comparing associations' willingness to take risks. First, precisely what objective function is an individual savings and loan association maximizing? Some measures of risk which will be proposed may not concern certain institutions. Other measures may relate monotonically to actual risk, but the relation may not be linear. In such cases, tests of hypotheses using the proposed measures will be very weak. Knowledge of the actual objective function would permit more powerful tests of risk-taking hypotheses.

Second, when two or more measures of risk are available and contradict each other when applied to two associations, it will not be possible to state unambiguously which association is more willing to accept risks. If all measures point in the same direction there is no problem. An attempt will be made to evaluate informally and qualitatively the significance of different measures at the end of this paper.

(a) *Measures*

(1) Foreclosure rate: concerns willingness to make marginal risky loans. This is the value of mortgages foreclosed in some period as a percentage of the value of mortgage loans outstanding. The foreclosure rate will be examined for all mortgage loans and for conventional mortgage loans. FHA and VA insured mortgage loans are not included in conventional loans. Because associations should not care about losses on these insured loans, it is expected that study of conventional loans will produce sharper evidence.

(2) Ratio of capital and reserves to assets: concerns willingness to protect the solvency of the association against a general collapse of the local mortgage market. This measure is very difficult to interpret because of existing tax laws in the United States which allow savings and loan institutions to pay no tax on retained earnings allocated to reserves so long as reserves do not exceed 12 per cent of savings deposits. Nevertheless, a low ratio is interpreted to imply a greater willingness to take risks.

(3) Ratio of foreclosures to capital and reserves: a measure combining (1) and (2) above. A high ratio implies greater willingness to take risks.

(4) Ratio of borrowing to total assets: concerns willingness to protect the solvency of the association against general collapse of the local mortgage market by avoiding excessive leverage. Borrowing may be from the Federal Home Loan Bank Board or other financial institutions. A high ratio implies a greater willingness to take risks.

(5) Ratio of real estate owned to assets: a measure concerning the amount of funds tied up in reacquired real estate. Such real estate may not be saleable and thus represents possible inflation of capital and reserves. Real estate owned does *not* include the value of the firm's office. A high ratio implies a greater willingness to take risks.

(6) Ratio of loans minus capital and reserves to savings deposits: a rough measure of illiquidity. This measure would be important in the event of a major loss of savings deposits. A high ratio implies a greater willingness to take risks.

These measures of risk-taking will be considered intensively in the next section. There are, of course, other measures of risk which could, in principle, be studied. Unfortunately data are not available for examining them in the present paper.

(b) *Data*

The Federal Home Loan Bank Board regularly collects income statements, balance-sheets, and foreclosure data from associations which belong to the Federal Home Loan Bank System. In this study income and balance-sheets for the years 1961–3 and foreclosure information for the years 1962–4 are studied. Only the 4,220 insured firms which reported income statements and balance-sheets for each of the three years and foreclosure information between the third quarter of 1962 and the first quarter of 1964 are included in the sample. At the end of 1962 there were 4,332 such institutions in existence. The 112 associations which were excluded either merged, collapsed, changed charters, closed, or came into existence some time during the years 1962–4. In addition 70 of the 4,220 firms had income or balance-sheets which were very untypical in some respects and were excluded. The majority did not have complete foreclosure reports. Other firms which grew at rates in excess of 500 per cent per annum were excluded because they often yielded estimated rates of return on either savings deposits or mortgages which were far out of line with actual interest rates and may have been the result of mergers. Interest rates on savings deposits were computed by dividing interest paid on savings deposits by the average value of successive year-end savings deposits. In addition a small number of other firms, typically with high growth rates, had computed interest rates which deviated from national averages by more than 2 per cent and were excluded from the sample on the grounds that they represented measurement errors.

Of the included banks, 518 have stock charters, 1,747 have state mutual charters, and 1,885 are Federally chartered mutual associations. The mean age of associations in the sample is forty-four years; their average annual rate of growth in 1962 was 19 per cent and in 1963, 16 per cent. Foreclosure rates on conventional loans were about 0·40 per cent per year in 1962 and 0·49 per cent in 1963. The average annual interest rate earned on mortgage loans was 5·81 per cent in both years; the average annual interest rate paid on savings deposits was 3·98 per cent in 1962 and 4·04 per cent in 1963. At the end of 1963, capital, reserves, and surplus averaged 6·8 per cent of total assets; real estate owned was 0·35 per cent of total assets; and borrowed money was 3·42 per cent of total assets.

In Table 2.1 variables concerning individual associations studied in this paper are defined and assigned symbolic equivalents. If a numerical subscript is associated with a symbol it refers to the last digit of the corresponding year, 1961, 1962, or 1963.

TABLE 2.1

Symbol	Definition
ST	Dummy variable having value of unity if association is stock-chartered, zero otherwise.
MU	Dummy variable having value of unity if association has state mutual charter, zero otherwise.
RM	Interest rate earned on mortgages, annual, in per cent.
RS	Interest rate paid on savings deposits, annual, in per cent.*
LA	Natural logarithm of an association's total assets at year-end; assets are measured in thousands of dollars.
YR	Length of time in years since date of incorporation.

* For stock associations the distinction between interest paid on deposits and cash dividends on capital is not observed. Hence estimates of *RS* are positively biased. Most stock firms paid no or small dividends; subsequent conclusions about *RS* are believed to be correct.

TABLE 2.1 — (*cont.*)

Symbol	Definition
SD	Average savings deposits, measured in thousands of dollars by averaging the value of successive year-end savings deposits.
GR	Annual rate of growth, in per cent, measured for year *t* by $(SD_t - SD_{t-1})/SD_{t-1}$.
CF	Quarterly foreclosure rate of conventional mortgages, the value of foreclosures of conventional mortgages as a percentage of the average value of an association's conventional mortgages. It is computed for year *t* by summing the values of foreclosures in the fourth quarter of year *t* and the first quarter of year $t+1$ and dividing by twice the year-end value of conventional mortgages.
TF	Quarterly foreclosure rate of all mortgages, the value of all foreclosures as a percentage of average value of an association's mortgages, computed in the same manner as *CF*.
FC	Quarterly value of all foreclosures as a percentage of year-end capital, reserves, surplus, and undistributed profits. Foreclosures are summed over the months October through March and divided by twice the year-end capital, reserves, etc.
LQ	Year-end loans minus capital, reserves, surplus, and undistributed profits in year *t* divided by average savings deposits at the end of year *t*.
CA	Year-end capital, reserves, surplus, and undistributed profits as a percentage of year-end total assets. It is computed by dividing the average value of the numerator in months October through March by the corresponding average value of the denominator.
OA	Year-end real estate owned as a percentage of total assets, computed in same manner as *CA*.
BA	Year-end borrowed money as a percentage of total assets, computed in same manner as *CA*.
ZI	Dummy variable having value of unity if firm is in state *I*, zero otherwise. All states having 28 or more institutions have an associated dummy variable. There are 34 such states.

III. SINGLE EQUATION RESULTS

In this section two aspects of risk-taking by savings and loan associations are examined. Part (a) is concerned with testing hypotheses about what characteristics of associations are related to risk-taking. Part (b) examines whether or not associations are compensated for bearing risks. This part also considers whether the industry has in some sense been in equilibrium in recent years.

(a) Characteristics of Risk-taking Institutions

At the end of Section I, it was observed that pronounced regional variations exist in statistics of the savings and loan industry. These variations may be associated with disequilibrium in the industry or with variations in asset quality in different areas of the nation. A neutral procedure is to allow for these variations among states with the 34 dummy variables, ZI, while studying the relationship between measures of risk-taking and association characteristics. Consequently, empirical results reported in this part should be understood always to have been estimated with individual state effects eliminated. Coefficients of the ZI are not reported in Part (a), but some are reported in Part (b) of this section.

Five hypotheses about characteristics of risk-taking firms are tested below. They are:

1. The form of charter of an association is related to its willingness to take risks; stock associations take more risks.
2. Large associations take more risks than smaller associations.
3. Associations earning high interest rates on mortgages will take more risks than associations earning lower rates.
4. Older institutions take fewer risks than young associations.
5. Rapidly growing associations take more risks than those which grow more slowly.

Hypothesis 1 is based on a view that stockholders are more effective in controlling managers in stock associations than are depositors in mutual associations. This greater influence derives from their smaller number and from the fact that managers are probably stockholders as well. Stockholders are assumed to value return more in relation to risk than is the case with depositors or managers of mutual associations. Common stock is held primarily for return in an investor's portfolio; insured savings deposits represent a desire for both return and safety. State and Federally chartered mutuals may also exhibit different degrees of risk-taking; state and Federal laws and examination practices may vary. However, one would expect these differences to be small in relation to those associated with the stock–mutual dichotomy.

Hypothesis 1 is tested with the two dummy variables, MU and

ST, which refer to state mutual and state stock associations. Co-efficients of these variables measure the deviation of measures of risk-taking from Federally chartered mutual organizations. For purposes of comparison, the intercept of a regression equation which included the unreported 34 dummy state variables, *ZI*, and the variables studied in the hypothesis is reported opposite the word 'Federal'. This procedure is repeated in tests of the other hypotheses.

In Table 3.1, Hypothesis 1 is accepted in seven of the eight tests performed. Stock companies experienced higher foreclosure rates, were less liquid, borrowed more money, and held more reacquired property. They also tended to have a lower capital/asset ratio, but this was not statistically significant. State mutual associations had about the same foreclosure pattern as the Federally chartered mutuals. They appear more conservative in their portfolio ratios; in three of the four ratios they were taking fewer risks than Federals. They did tend to have more reacquired property than Federals but much less than stock associations. Apparently organizational form is very critical in determining willingness to accept risks. Because of this result, *MU* and *ST* will be included in regressions which test the remaining hypotheses.

Hypothesis 2 is based on an application of the Law of Large Numbers. If firms are risk-averse, they should be less willing to expose themselves to risk when they are small; they unavoidably have less portfolio diversification. Specifically, although average mortgage size tends to increase with size of association, it does so less than proportionately. Therefore, if all firms are equally competent at judging mortgage quality and equally risk-averse, small firms should experience fewer foreclosures. Alternatively they should have more capital and less borrowing and reacquired property in relation to their total assets. They should have a more liquid port-folio.

In Table 3.1, tests of Hypothesis 2 are reported and are judged to be weakly favourable to the hypothesis. Large associations do experience more mortgage foreclosures, but comparison of CF_3 and TF_3 suggests that they are only in Federally insured FHA and VA mortgages. Large firms also have a higher ratio of capital and reserves to assets, contrary to the hypothesis. However, large associations do have more reacquired assets, more borrowed money, and less liquidity. The operation of the Law of Large Numbers apparently does not affect standards on individual mortgage loans; it does induce larger institutions to operate with more borrowed

TABLE 3.1

HYPOTHESIS 1

	CF_2	CF_3	TF_3	FC_3	CA_3	OA_3	BA_3	LQ_2
(a) Federal	0·0646	0·1303	0·1443	2·1847	6·5572	0·2609	4·3594	0·9268
(b) MU	0·0104	0·0212	0·0137	0·0469	0·1984*	0·0542*	-0·4195*	-0·0130*
	(0·0088)	(0·0128)	(0·0129)	(0·2361)	(0·0798)	(0·0266)	(0·1330)	(0·0030)
(c) ST	0·0730*	0·1262*	0·1189*	1·2481*	-0·1225	0·3090*	1·3715*	0·0118*
	(0·0143)	(0·0208)	(0·0210)	(0·3837)	(0·1296)	(0·0432)	(0·2161)	(0·0049)
R	0·268	0·293	0·283	0·238	0·274	0·339	0·339	0·332
F	8·841*	10·710*	9·929*	6·874*	9·290*	21·602*	14·834*	14·123*
Su	0·235	0·343	0·347	6·326	2·137	0·712	3·563	0·805

HYPOTHESIS 2

	CF_2	CF_3	TF_3	FC_3	CA_3	OA_3	BA_3	LQ_2
(a) Federal	0·0491	0·0949	0·0286	2·2395	5·4386	0·0509	2·1625	0·8265
(b) MU	0·0114	0·0235	0·0211	0·0434	0·2704*	0·0677*	-0·2782*	-0·0066*
	(0·0090)	(0·0132)	(0·0133)	(0·2431)	(0·0820)	(0·0273)	(0·1366)	(0·0031)
(c) ST	0·0735*	0·1274*	0·1226*	1·2463*	-0·0869	0·3157*	1·4413*	0·0150*
	(0·0143)	(0·0209)	(0·0211)	(0·3848)	(0·1298)	(0·0433)	(0·2162)	(0·0048)
(d) LA	0·0016	0·0036	0·0118*	-0·0056	0·1145*	0·0215*	0·2249*	0·0103*
	(0·0034)	(0·0050)	(0·0050)	(0·0916)	(0·0309)	(0·0103)	(0·0515)	(0·0012)
R	0·268	0·293	0·285	0·238	0·280	0·400	0·345	0·356
F	8·606*	10·434*	9·822*	6·686*	9·438*	21·153*	15·012*	16·138*
Su	0·235	0·343	0·346	6·327	2·134	0·711	3·555	0·797

* An asterisk indicates that the parameter is significantly different from zero with probability of error of 0·05.

TABLE 3.2

HYPOTHESIS 3

	CF_3	TF_3	FC_3	CA_3	OA_3	BA_3
(a) Federal	-0·0732	0·1672	1·3067	7·6707	-0·2353	2·1845
(b) MU	0·0193	0·0139	0·0386	0·2089*	0·0495	-0·4400*
	(0·0128)	(0·0130)	(0·2367)	(0·0799)	(0·0266)	(0·1333)
(c) ST	0·1203*	0·1196*	1·2224*	-0·0899	0·2945*	1·3078*
	(0·0210)	(0·0212)	(0·3871)	(0·1307)	(0·0435)	(0·2179)
(d) RM_2	0·0359*	0·0040	0·1585	-0·1964	0·0875*	0·3836*
	(0·0166)	(0·0168)	(0·3061)	(0·1034)	(0·0344)	(0·1723)
R	0·295	0·283	0·238	0·276	0·400	0·341
F	10·556*	9·660*	6·694*	9·142*	21·221*	14·581*
Su	0·343	0·347	6·326	2·136	0·711	3·561

HYPOTHESES 4 AND 5

	CF_3	TF_3	FC_3	CA_3	OA_3	BA_3
(a) Federal	0·1510	0·1798	2·0134	9·1766	0·5505	4·5309
(b) MU	0·0227	0·0164	0·1408	0·0927	0·0551*	-0·3324*
	(0·0130)	(0·0131)	(0·2355)	(0·0643)	(0·0270)	(0·1339)
(c) ST	0·0684*	0·0658*	-0·6502	1·3773*	0·2606*	0·5846*
	(0·0220)	(0·0222)	(0·3988)	(0·1089)	(0·0457)	(0·2268)
(d) YR	-0·00026	-0·00036	-0·0102*	0·0095*	-0·0007	-0·0111*
	(0·00022)	(0·00023)	(0·0040)	(0·0011)	(0·0005)	(0·0023)
(e) $GR^{<0}$	-0·0292	-0·0244	-0·1734	-0·2096	-0·0537	-0·1221
	(0·0226)	(0·0229)	(0·4102)	(0·1120)	(0·0471)	(0·2333)

* An asterisk indicates that the parameter is significantly different from zero with probability of error of 0·05.

	CF_3	TF_3	FC_3	CA_3	OA_3	BA_3
(f) $GR^{0,10}$	-0·0025	-0·0034	-0·0028	-0·2379*	-0·0293*	-0·0124
	(0·0029)	(0·0030)	(0·0533)	(0·0145)	(0·0061)	(0·0303)
(g) $GR^{10,20}$	-0·0009	-0·0012	0·0200	-0·1047*	-0·0013	0·0486*
	(0·0011)	(0·0011)	(0·0193)	(0·0053)	(0·0022)	(0·0109)
(h) $GR^{20,30}$	+0·0009	0·0007	0·0102	-0·0162*	0·0016	0·0214
	(0·0011)	(0·0011)	(0·0207)	(0·0057)	(0·0024)	(0·0118)
(i) $GR^{30,40}$	+0·0030*	0·0029*	0·0747*	-0·0188*	0·0024	0·0078
	(0·0010)	(0·0010)	(0·0174)	(0·0048)	(0·0020)	(0·0099)
(j) $GR^{>40}$	+0·0005*	0·0005*	0·0198*	-0·0019	0·0006	-0·0021
	(0·0002)	(0·0002)	(0·0036)	(0·0010)	(0·0004)	(0·0021)
R	0·321	0·309	0·323	0·653	0·412	0·378
F	10·996*	10·115*	11·093*	70·939*	19·514*	15·894*
Su	0·340	0·344	6·170	1·685	0·708	3·510

* An asterisk indicates that the parameter is significantly different from zero with probability of error of 0·05.

funds and to place a larger percentage of their funds in high-yielding, less liquid mortgage loans.

Hypothesis 3 argues that when mortgage interest rates are high, associations are more likely to be taking risks. First, associations can only be induced to absorb risky loans with higher loan rates. This argument implicitly recognizes the joint endogeneity of fore-closures, interest rates, and rate of growth. Second, when mortgage rates are high, associations will tend to borrow funds. This occurs because rates at which associations borrow funds are lower than average mortgage rates.

In Table 3.2 coefficients appear to support the hypothesis. Co-efficients of RM_2 suggest that conventional foreclosures, borrowing, and reacquired property are higher when mortgage interest rates are high. The evidence is not strong; high interest rates appear to induce associations to reach for debt and for more unsafe loans.

Hypothesis 4 suggests that older associations take fewer risks. This behaviour may be a consequence of the battle for survival experienced by most associations during the Depression. Older associations may simply be staffed by older and more conservative individuals who weigh safety more heavily in relation to return than is true of their adventurous younger counterparts. In Table 3.2 the hypothesis is not supported when examining foreclosure experience; conventional and total foreclosure rates are lower but not significantly so. However, the coefficients of YR in the FC_3, CA_3, and BA_3 regressions are significant in conformity with the hypothesis. On the basis of these results the hypothesis is tentatively accepted.

Hypothesis 5 argues that risk-taking is more likely to be observed when firms are growing rapidly. Firms which grow very rapidly have a young, less mature mortgage portfolio. If an individual has met monthly payments for some time on his mortgage, he has proved himself to be somewhat financially responsible. A large proportion of mortgage-holders have not passed this weak test and hence are probably on average more risky in the case of rapidly growing associations. Further, the relation between growth and foreclosures is not likely to be linear. High-growth associations are located in high-growth areas where job turnover is correspondingly high; risk is likely to rise more than proportionately with growth. Also, high-growth institutions will not conveniently be able to generate capital and reserves as fast as deposits and thus CA will tend to decline.

Hypothesis 5 will be tested by estimating a piecewise linear rela-tion between risk measures and growth rates. The relation is esti-

mated so that segments intersect at growth rates of 0, 10, 20, 30, and
40 per cent per annum. Slopes of these linear segments are reported
in Table 3.2, where superscripts on *GR* define the relevant range of
the growth rate. The growth rate is the average annual rate of growth
of an institution between 1961 and 1963. The relations between
measures of risk and foreclosures are drawn in Figs. 3.1 and 3.2.
For growth rates of 30 per cent or more, foreclosure rates are significantly related to growth as hypothesized. The ratio of reserves and
capital to assets is negatively related to *GR* and is significant for all
but the two open-ended intervals. On the basis of these results the
hypothesis is accepted.[1]

It should be noted that in foreclosure equations the highly significant coefficients of *ST*, the dummy variable for stock associations,
are reduced by about 50 per cent when growth is taken into account.

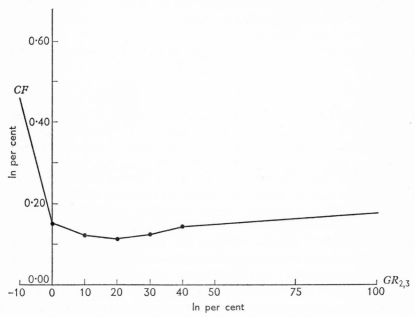

FIG. 3.1

QUARTERLY CONVENTIONAL FORECLOSURE RATE VERSUS AVERAGE ANNUAL
GROWTH RATE

(All Other Variables Valued at Zero)

[1] Extreme values for coefficients of *GR* are apparently a consequence of a small
number of associations which collapsed in 1963.

Fig. 3.2

VARIOUS RISK MEASURES VERSUS ANNUAL AVERAGE GROWTH RATE
(All Other Variables Valued at Zero)

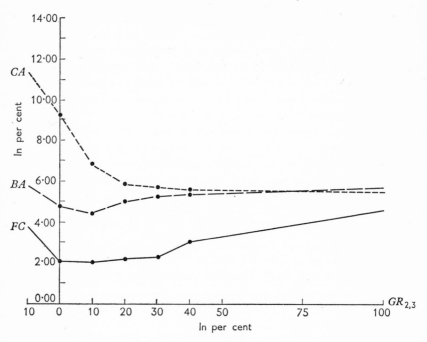

In Section III(b) it is seen that stock associations do indeed have very high rates of growth. Nevertheless, even after allowing for growth, stock companies appear more risky in the CF, TF, OA, and BA regressions. In the CA regression, where ST previously had an insignificant negative coefficient, stock associations now appear to have high ratios of capital and reserves to assets. This pattern is repeated in the FC regression where the coefficient of ST is insignificantly negative. Apparently risk-taking in stock associations does not extend to operating with little capital once growth is taken into account. Rather, stock associations exhibit relatively strong capital and reserve positions when compared to mutual associations.

One other experiment concludes this analysis of the characteristics of risk-taking associations. If an association has a large number of conventional foreclosures in 1962, will it tend to have an equally large number in 1963 ? Holding constant location and organization form, the coefficient of CF_3 on CF_2 was 0·3382 with a standard error of 0·0221. Thus high-foreclosure associations tend to remain high-foreclosure associations, although there is significant evidence of improvement. A bad foreclosure experience probably reduces an association's appetite for risk-taking.

(b) *Rewards for Risk-taking?*

In Section I large variations in rates of return, foreclosures, etc., were reported in different regions of the United States. Two competing hypotheses were suggested to account for this phenomenon. First, risks were different in various areas, and variations in terms of lending (including interest rates) were simply a consequence of regional variations in risk. In this view high interest rates should be related to different measures of risk, but the partial correlation between rates of return and growth should be negligible.

The second hypothesis argues that the industry is in disequilibrium. High interest rates will be associated with high growth rates, but the partial correlation between measures of risk-taking and interest rates should be negligible. Fig. 3.3 suggests that wide variations in both average rates of return to depositors and average growth rates do indeed exist in different states. RS_3 and GR_3 were regressed on ZI's, ST, and MU. Coefficients of the ZI, ST, and MU are plotted in the figure; the intercept has been added to each coefficient so that the axes show annual rates of growth and rates of return to savers, both measured in per cent.

There does appear to be a positive relation between RS_3 and GR_3, except in a group of states which are encircled, and stock associations grow much faster than mutuals. The encircled states are precisely those where stock associations are prominent. Apparently the presence of stock associations causes mutual associations to grow much more slowly in relation to their rate of interest paid on savings than they otherwise would. Alternatively, when stock and mutual associations are placed together, stock associations compete very effectively, causing mutual associations to have lower-than-expected rates of growth.

Why should this pattern obtain? Stock associations do have higher advertising outlays than mutuals and also earn higher rates of return on mortgages and pay higher rates on deposits. In the previous part of this section, a conclusion was that the stock form of organization was more willing to run risks; it may also aspire more

Fig. 3.3

AVERAGE 1963 GROWTH RATE VERSUS 1963 RATE PAID ON SAVINGS DEPOSITS
FOR 34 STATES AND 2 MEASURES OF ORGANIZATION FORM

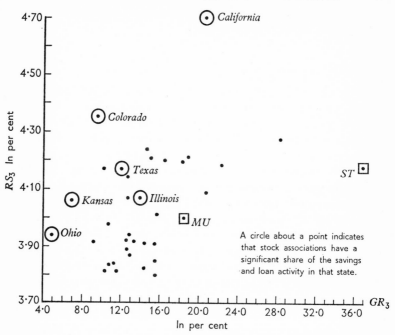

strongly for growth. It is possible, but most unlikely, that this result is a statistical artifact. There were a very small number of mergers, primarily among stock associations, during the years 1962–3. There was no way to exclude them from the sample; it is very implausible that this small number could account for the great observed difference in the growth of stock and mutual associations.[1]

To see which of these two hypotheses better characterizes the American savings and loan industry, three experiments were performed. First, mean values of CF_3, CA_3, BA_3, OA_3, LQ_3, GR_3, RM_3, and RS_3 were obtained for each of 35 geographical areas distinguished in this study, i.e. the 34 states having associated dummy variables and a 35th area consisting of the rest of the United States. Using these areas as observations, each of the two interest rates were

[1] About 15·0 per cent of all associations in the sample experienced growth rates of 30 per cent or more in either 1962 or 1963. Roughly 40 per cent of these were stock companies, even though only about 12·5 per cent of the total sample was stock-chartered.

regressed on (1) all the risk measures and growth variables, (2) only the risk measures, and (3) only the growth variables. Results of this experiment are reported in Table 3.3.

TABLE 3.3

EXPERIMENT 1

	RM_3	RS_3	RM_3	RS_3	RM_3	RS_3
Intercept	5·605	2·283	5·344	3·613	10·127	5·202
LQ_2	− 0·794	1·500	—	—	− 4·700*	− 1·021
	(2·080)	(1·590)	—	—	(2·168)	(1·576)
CF_3	0·626	0·920	—	—	2·498*	2·128*
	(0·873)	(0·667)	—	—	(0·862)	(0·627)
CA_3	0·073	0·014	—	—	− 0·056	− 0·070
	(0·062)	(0·047)	—	—	(0·062)	(0·045)
OA_3	− 0·273	− 0·086	—	—	− 0·454	− 0·203
	(0·238)	(0·182)	—	—	(0·280)	(0·204)
BA_3	− 0·041	− 0·029	—	—	0·037	0·021
	(0·047)	(0·036)	—	—	(0·051)	(0·037)
GR_3	0·036*	0·023*	0·030*	0·027*	—	—
	(0·010)	(0·007)	(0·006)	(0·005)		
R	0·745	0·779	0·648	0·720	0·577	0·683
F	5·834*	7·213*	23·869*	35·606*	2·890*	5·075*
Su	0·184	0·141	0·194	0·144	0·222	0·161
N	35	35	35	35	35	35

* An asterisk indicates that the parameter is significantly different from zero with probability of error of 0·05.

TABLE 3.4

EXPERIMENT 2

	12/65	12/64
Log_e of		
Per capita income	1·0	1·0
Correlation	0·699	0·329
$\text{Log}_e RM$	− 2·058	− 0·571
$\text{Log}_e FEE$	0·090	0·010
$\text{Log}_e MAT$	0·387	− 0·322
$\text{Log}_e L/P$	0·066	0·484
$\text{Log}_e PRICE$	0·535	0·475
N	18	18

The only consistently significant variable was GR_3, the rate of growth of savings deposits; the rate of growth of savings deposits is positively related to interest rates in conformity with the second hypothesis. The partial correlation between risk variables (considered individually or collectively) and interest rates, given the rate of growth, is not significantly different from zero. Hypothesis 2 is accepted and Hypothesis 1 is rejected. The significant correlation between CF_3 and interest rates in the last two columns of the table is a consequence of the previously noted correlation between GR and CF. This result means that if two associations with the same rate of growth have different foreclosure rates, the association with the higher foreclosure rate is not compensated for its additional risks. However, associations with high growth rates have high interest rates and high foreclosure rates; risk-taking related to growth is partly compensated for.

The second experiment consisted of looking at terms of lending which were observed in eighteen metropolitan areas of the United States. The first hypothesis implies that for individuals of a given credit-worthiness variations in rates of return should be matched by variations in other terms of lending. The model is a canonical correlation argument where only one variable, *per capita* gross income, is related to a set of loan terms. The terms are RM, the interest rate on new mortgages; FEE, the closing fees assessed by an association; MAT, the average term of contract on new loans; L/P, the average ratio of a mortgage loan to the purchase price of a new house; and $PRICE$, the average purchase price of a new house. The variables L/P, MAT, and perhaps $PRICE$ should measure risk and consequently have signs opposite to RM in the equation. FEE should have the same sign as RM. The expression, reported in Table 3.4, was estimated with a standard regression package in which the dependent variable was *per capita* gross income in the corresponding metropolitan area as recorded in 1959 income-tax returns.[1] Signs conform to *a priori* expectations in the case of $PRICE$, L/P, and RM, but coefficients are so erratic in 1964 and 1965 that the results are not interesting.

Given the results in Table 3.3, an attempt was made to measure the rewards for risk-taking using individual associations as observations and including the dummy variables, ZI, in the hope that it would be possible to find some compensation for bearing risks which

---

[1] United States Treasury Department, *Individual Income Tax Returns*, Washington: United States Government Printing Office, 1962, various pages.

are not related to growth. The results are reported in Table 3.5.

Coefficients of GR_3 in Table 3.5 reinforce the previous conclusion that high rates of growth and associated risks are compensated for by higher earnings on mortgage loans and savers are compensated for these risks with higher interest payments on savings deposits. The coefficient of LQ_2 suggests that savers are compensated for higher illiquidity of an association with higher interest payments on deposits.

TABLE 3.5

EXPERIMENT 3

	RS_3	RM_3
Federal	3·3960	5·7937
ST	0·0437*	0·0396*
	(0·0141)	(0·0200)
MU	0·0045	0·0547*
	(0·0081)	(0·0115)
LQ_2	0·5891*	− 0·2200*
	(0·0516)	(0·0731)
CF_3	0·0304*	0·0230
	(0·0116)	(0·0164)
CA_3	0·0074*	0·0058*
	(0·0019)	(0·0026)
OA_3	− 0·0030	0·0098
	(0·0056)	(0·0079)
BA_3	− 0·0037*	0·003*
	(0·0012)	(0·0016)
GR_3	0·0041*	0·0025*
	(0·0002)	(0·0004)
R	0·736	0·601
F	115·406	55·221
Su	0·217	0·308

* An asterisk indicates that the parameter is significantly different from zero with probability of error of 0·05.

Interestingly, associations which are less liquid appear to earn slightly lower rates on their mortgages; apparently associations attempt to compensate for lower local rates by assuming a less liquid position. Associations with high ratios of capital and reserves to assets reward savers with high interest payments. Highly capitalized associations tend to earn higher rates of interest on their mortgages.

55

That is, they may take advantage of their higher capitalization to acquire somewhat more risky, higher-yielding mortgages. Similarly, associations with large ratios of borrowed funds to assets earn higher rates on mortgages. They pay somewhat lower rates to savers; apparently some associations acquire marginal funds from other financial institutions rather than bid competitively for savings deposits.

Institutions with high foreclosure rates reward depositors by paying higher interest rates. Interestingly, they are not compensated for these risks by high mortgage interest rates. No explanation for this result is apparent. Stock associations earn high rates on mortgages and pass these earnings on to depositors. State mutual associations also earn higher rates on mortgages than Federal associations, but do not pass on these higher earnings to depositors.

To summarize this part, high interest rates are primarily related to high growth rates; because high growth rates are associated with risk, associations and their depositors are observed to be rewarded for bearing risks. However, high interest rates represent not only compensation for higher risks in growth associations but also the existence of excess demand in some areas of the country. Thus, results in Table 3.5 suggest that, even when allowance is made for higher values of risk measures studied here, high-growth associations reward depositors for moving funds to areas where excess demand for mortgages exists.

IV. A SIMULTANEOUS EQUATIONS MODEL

In an attempt to gain further insight into savings and loan associations' risk-taking behaviour, savings growth, foreclosures, and deposit interest rates are integrated in a system of simultaneous equations. A very simple three-equation model is considered in this section. It is estimated by two-stage least squares.

An important assumption necessary for the construction is that RM is exogenously given to a savings and loan association. Specifically, RM is assumed to be a function of dummy variables ZI, ST, and MU. If an association sets rates on mortgages too high it may lose customers to rival lenders; if it sets rates too low it forgoes income and will probably cause other lenders to lower rates to their mutual disadvantage. The personal relationship between association and borrower is very important; associations must deal with local borrowers because of the fifty-mile limit on lending. The relationship between savers and associations is less close. How does the association behave ? The first structural equation is :

$$RS_3 = \alpha_0 + \sum_{i=1}^{34} \alpha_i \, Zi + \alpha_{35} \, ST + \alpha_{36} \, MU + \alpha_{37} \, RM_3 + \alpha_{38} \, CF + u_1. \quad (4.1)$$

The argument is that associations, stock or mutual, always try to maximize the volume of mortgages made subject to the condition that $RM > RS + \epsilon$ where ϵ is the average rate of net income plus servicing costs associated with a dollar of mortgage lending. Because markets are broadly competitive, $RM - RS$ should not differ greatly across associations. If savers are rewarded for bearing foreclosure risks, α_{38} should be positive. However, if foreclosures are frequent, associations with a given rate on mortgages may pay less to depositors, the results in Table 3.5 notwithstanding.

How does the public respond to variations in RS_3 ? As suggested in the previous section, associations paying high interest rates on deposits grow much more rapidly than other associations. The second equation of the system is :

$$GR_3 = \beta_0 + \sum_{i=1}^{34} \beta_i \, Zi + \beta_{35} \, ST + \beta_{36} \, MU + \beta_{37} \, RS_3 + u_2. \quad (4.2)$$

Clearly, β_{37} is assumed to be positive. The third equation of the system concerns the foreclosure rate. In the preceding section we observed that foreclosure rates tended to be higher when RM was higher. This relation is assumed to be transmitted from RM to RS to GR to CF in this model.

$$CF_3 = \gamma_0 + \sum_{i=1}^{34} \gamma_i \, Zi + \gamma_{35} \, ST + \gamma_{36} \, MU + \gamma_{37} \, GR_3 + \gamma_{38} \, YR + u_3. \quad (4.3)$$

The assumptions underlying this equation are that γ_{37} should be positive and γ_{38} should be negative ; the arguments were presented in the previous section. Table 4.1 reports estimated coefficients for this system of equations. Again, coefficients of individual state dummy variables are not shown, in order to conserve space, although many are significant.

The coefficient of RM_3 in equation (4.1) is positive and significant as expected. However, the margin between RM_3 and RS_3 is not constant ; a difference in RM_3 of $1 \cdot 0$ is matched by only a $0 \cdot 086$

difference in RS_3. Thus when RM_3 is above its mean, gross receipts of the association are substantially higher; payments to savers appear to be only slightly higher. Further, the coefficient α_{38} concerning the effect of foreclosures on RS is positive although not significantly different from zero. The explanation for this peculiar result is not clear; perhaps the firms with negative growth rates which distorted relationships in Fig. 3.2 are the villains. Stock associations pay significantly higher rates on savings deposits than mutuals.

TABLE 4.1

ESTIMATE OF SIMULTANEOUS EQUATIONS MODEL [1]

	RS_3	GR_3	CF_3
ST	0·0801*	11·4376*	− 0·0707
	(0·0370)	(1·3055)	(0·0689)
MU	− 0·0087	0·4388	0·0082
	(0·0099)	(0·5635)	(0·0147)
RM_3	0·0862*	—	—
	(0·0190)	—	—
CF_3	0·3054	—	− 1 −
	(0·2840)	—	
GR_3	—	− 1 −	0·0107*
	—		(0·0037)
RS_3	− 1 −	61·5162*	—
		(7·3418)	—
YR	—	—	0·0006
	—	—	(0·0005)
R	0·708	0·463	0·298
F	108·739	30·333	10·577
Su	0·226	15·086	0·343
N	4150	4150	4150

[1] Coefficients of intercept and state dummy variables were estimated but are not reported in order to conserve space. An asterisk indicates that the parameter is significantly different from zero with probability of error of 0·05, assuming that estimates are normally distributed. Of course, the above estimates are only asymptotically normally distributed.

Equation (4.2) suggests again that the rate of interest paid on savings deposits is a principal determinant of the growth rate. The coefficient indicates that for every difference of 1 per cent in rate paid on savings capital there is an associated difference of 60 per cent in growth rates. Stock associations appear to grow faster than mutual associations.

In equation (4.3) the coefficient of YR, the average age of the association, is positive, contrary to hypothesis, and the coefficient of GR is significant in the expected direction. The latter coefficient suggests that for each 10 per cent increase in GR, the annual foreclosure rate on conventional mortgages will rise by 0·4 per cent.

The system superficially seems quite plausible; yet it seems to shed no new light on the behaviour of savings and loan associations. Perhaps the telling failure is that coefficients of the dummy state variables ZI retained their significance in all equations. Presumably a correct structural model would account for interregional variations among associations.

V. SUMMARY

Risk-taking by savings and loan associations has been measured by seven indices constructed from foreclosures and balance-sheet ratios. In single-equation tests, five characteristics of associations were found to be related to risk measures. The characteristics are organizational form, size, age, growth rate, and mortgage interest rate. In addition, individual risk measures of savings and loan associations vary significantly among states in the United States. No stress was given to the last point because the explanation for observed regional variations would require a very extensive discussion of local housing markets and examination standards which are of limited interest to the present Conference.

The second phase of the empirical analysis concerns measurement of the rewards for bearing risks.[1] The savings and loan industry has been growing very rapidly, especially in the south-western and western parts of the United States. Interest rates in local mortgage markets and interest rates paid on savings deposits exhibit correspondingly great variations. In Section III empirical evidence that high-growth associations earn high interest rates on mortgages and pay high interest rates on deposits was introduced. In part these high rates represent compensation to savers and associations for the risks which they bear. However, even after allowing for the risks examined in this paper, high-growth associations earn significantly higher rates of return on their mortgages and pay correspondingly

[1] For another study in which rewards for bearing risks are estimated, see Hester, Donald, and Zoellner, John F., 'The Relation between Bank Portfolios and Earnings: an Econometric Analysis', *Review of Economics and Statistics*, vol. xlviii (1966), pp. 372–86.

higher rates to depositors. The conclusion is that high interest rates in part reflect greater risks associated with growth, but primarily are evidence that the industry is out of equilibrium. Of course, one reason for this disequilibrium may be that potential depositors thought risks were present; we do not observe their subjective beliefs. A simple simultaneous equations model was examined in Section IV, but did not add appreciably to our understanding of savings and loan associations.

A number of results in this paper suggest directions for future research. First, what precisely is the relation between organizational form and decision-making ? There are two important aspects of this question : (*a*) Are there differences in the objective function for different organizational forms ? (*b*) Is the implementation of decisions different ? In the present study markedly different behaviour is observed when stock and mutual associations are compared, but determinants of these differences cannot be inferred.

Second, large associations are found to take more risks than small associations, apparently as a result of the operation of the Law of Large Numbers. However, large organizations may also be characterized by very rigid organizational forms. In one study of Indian commercial banks, I found evidence of excessive centralization of decision-making which was partly a result of fear of experiencing losses.[1] To be sure about the observed relation between risk-taking and size, further analysis of the relation between decision-making structure and size is desirable.

Third, the questions of what are risks in the minds of individuals and what the firm maximizes have been troublesome throughout this paper. This has been especially serious when growth enters the picture. A clear theoretical understanding of what a firm or a firm's management knows or believes, what it attempts to achieve, and what it attempts to avoid are essential if empirical analysis is to prove more successful.

Finally, a related question is how important are the various measures of risk ? Of the measures considered above, illiquidity seems to be of very limited interest given the high rate of growth in the industry. Similarly, reacquired real estate is very small in relation to total assets or capital and is probably a symptom of risk-taking behaviour, but not itself a cause for concern about the safety of an association. Conventional foreclosures, high borrowing, and low

[1] Hester, Donald, *Indian Banks: Their Portfolios, Profits, and Policy*, Bombay : Bombay Univ. Press, 1964.

capitalization are probably the most significant. A useful statistical study would be an analysis of how extreme values of these measures on a particular date are related to subsequent bankruptcies and the subsequent operations of an association.

What do the results of this paper suggest for regulatory policies involving savings and loan associations ? Very significant regional variations exist in rates of growth of savings deposits, mortgage interest rates, and rates of return paid on savings deposits. The market appears to cause the flow of funds into capital-deficit areas. Stock associations appear to be causing funds to flow even faster than mutual associations; they also have higher values of most risk measures. Policies which discourage the formation of stock associations represent a choice of low risk over fast growth. Estimates of the relation between organizational form and growth and various measures of risk indicate that a little less risk costs a lot of growth at the association level.

————

DISCUSSION OF THE PAPER BY PROFESSOR HESTER

Dr. Koerts : Before I give my comments on Professor Hester's paper I want to mention explicitly that I found his paper very interesting and stimulating. I want to make the following comments :

(1) In testing Hypothesis 1 Professor Hester uses the following regression :

$$R = \alpha_0 + \alpha_1 MU + \alpha_2 ST + \sum_{i=1}^{34} \beta = {}_i Z I_2 + u_i$$

where u_i is a random variable with zero mean and constant variance σ^2. This last assumption, although not explicitly mentioned in the paper, is made in every regression. Because Dr. Hester bases all his arguments on point estimates he must try to estimate his coefficients as well as possible. In this respect I am not so happy with his assumption of homoscedasticity. I have the feeling that the variance in risk measures among stock associations is larger than among mutual associations. It must be easy to verify this assumption. I would suggest that Professor Hester should do this and, if my assumption is correct, use a weighted least-squares estimation procedure.

(2) In econometric work it becomes standard practice to assume normality. I am afraid that people do not think about this assumption any more. Yet I have never met a normal distribution in economics in

my life. The only reason for this assumption is, I think, mathematical convenience. The normality assumption is, however, very important in Professor Hester's work because he bases his reasoning on it. (He uses an F-test, and to decide whether a coefficient is significant or not he uses the rule of taking twice the standard deviation.) Unfortunately, in many cases we cannot verify this assumption. Professor Hester, however, is in a very good position, because he can verify the assumption fairly easily. I would ask him whether he has done it and if not I would strongly suggest that he does.

(3) I would suggest that Professor Hester tests whether there exists autocorrelation among his disturbances. I realize that the idea of possible autocorrelation leads to another model, but it is worth thinking about this possibility.

I would suggest the use of a Best linear unbiased disturbance estimate with a scalar covariance matrix (BLUS).

(4) I am not very happy with Hypothesis 4 for the following reasons :

(*a*) The economic theory behind this hypothesis is not very convincing and not in accordance with my own experience.

(*b*) As pointed out by Professor Hester himself, the empirical results are not very convincing. My doubts about Hypothesis 4 become even stronger when I see that the coefficient of YR in the simultaneous equation system is not significant.

(*c*) I have the idea that the risk measures 2 and 4 are interdependent. If this is correct, then only two instead of three coefficients in Table 3.2 must be taken into account.

I suggest therefore that Hypothesis 4 is not accepted at this moment but that one should look for further evidence.

(5) Professor Hester has estimated his simultaneous equation system with two-stage least squares. Why not for instance three-stage least squares or full-information maximum likelihood, because we nowadays know that these methods are more efficient. Estimating this system with different methods gives at the same time a sort of sensitivity analysis, which is important in this case.

(6) I regard Professor Hester's interesting paper as a first step ; further investigation is necessary. For instance, the important fact that stock associations grow faster, are more efficient, and take more risk than mutual organizations needs further explanation. Why is this the case, what sort of a function are they maximizing ? To answer this sort of question one has to look inside the firm to see how decisions are really made. I would ask Professor Hester whether he has done this ; if not, I suggest that he does.

Dr. Walter : The study by Professor Hester is declared as an empirical one. I welcome such studies very much, since I think they are necessary as tests of different theories and proposed models.

My remarks will be concentrated on the methodological issues. I am very interested in the testing methods used in the study because I am sure they may stimulate similar research in other countries as well.

I am curious whether similar studies are possible for other industries : I know there will be lack of official statistics, but there could be a possibility of getting some information through special inquiries.

Professor Hester speaks about sampling data. But there was no real sample, because all units were included in the statistics (perhaps with some exceptions which were not acceptable for further analysis). There exists a possibility, however, of sampling from some time-interval, which is not mentioned in the paper. This is connected with the possibility of introducing time-lags in the regression equations. They can play a certain role as regressors when estimating the strength of some of the relations under study. In the hypothesis testing, which is the first task of the author, they may not be of so great interest, however.

Different firms are treated in the sample : I am not sure if a test should be made to determine whether or not it is plausible to introduce some weights for different firms, which, as can be assumed, perform transactions of different volumes.

Dr. Thore : What disturbs me in this paper is the absence of a systematic specification of the underlying theory. I would not complain about this if the nature of these theoretical structures were a matter of course, or well known. But they are not.

Let me begin with the *stock* associations. I would suggest that the theory of commercial-bank portfolio management can be drawn upon as a general framework for formulating some of the underlying theoretical relationships here. What I have in mind in particular is the theoretical analysis of a financial institution aiming at an optimization of net earnings in the face of uncertainty. Let me call this the 'net earnings model'. Reference can be made for instance to the work by Porter (*Yale Economic Essays*, 1961). Forming net earnings before dividends of a stock association, and calculating the mathematical expectation E and the standard deviation σ of this uncertainty variable, we can depict relations between E and σ in a diagram such as the figure below.

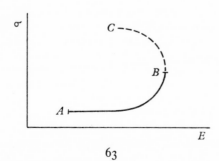

ABC is the budget curve (possibility curve) of feasible points which the association can attain. As the association becomes more and more 'loaned up', the association would follow the path from *A* to *B*. (If lending is expanded beyond a certain limit, corresponding to the point *B*, the association will typically become so illiquid that the curve becomes backwards-sloping from *B* to *C*.) The association then chooses the point on *ABC* where it attains the highest utility level. Optimum points of different associations having different utility structures would then trace the locus of efficient portfolios *AB*.[1]

The natural thing, then, on this theory, would be to measure net earnings before dividends and to use it as a proxy for *E*. But Professor Hester does not provide any data at all on this variable.

Turning to mutual associations, Professor Hester obviously flatly rejects the net earnings model as a guideline for theory, and instead assumes that such associations 'maximize depositors' welfare', i.e. are primarily concerned with the rate of interest paid on deposits rather than net earnings (before dividends). There are two difficulties here. For one thing I think that the net earnings model cannot be dismissed simply on the formal ground that mutuals are owned directly by the savers. I should like to see a test of which theoretical model serves best for the explanation of mutual association portfolio management.

Secondly, assuming for a moment that the net earnings model won't do, the question then arises : what is the form of the alternative theory that is to be used ? It seems that we are here completely in the dark, and it is rather difficult to interpret Professor Hester's many regression equations in the absence of such a pinning-down of the underlying model. It seems that Professor Hester is somehow subsuming some kind of theory *where the savers* are balancing risk against interest on deposits (rather than balancing risk against net earnings), but the nature of this relationship is not specified. One would have wished for clearer language on this point.

Professor Rosett : Is it possible that a high foreclosure rate is associated with risk aversion rather than risk preference ? One bank might foreclose quickly in order to avoid the risk of a larger loss, while another might wait and give the mortgagee an opportunity to recover, meanwhile running a greater risk of loss.

Professor Hester : I want to thank the four discussants for their interesting and diverse observations about my paper.

Professor Rosett raised an ingenious question concerning my interpretation of high foreclosure rates as evidence of willingness to accept risks. My interpretation conforms to the conventional view that foreclosure is an expensive action in terms of both measurable costs and goodwill.

---

[1] An alternative theoretical approach, which seems to have wide scope, is to formulate an earnings maximization model, subject to chance-constraints. See A. Charnes and S. Thore, 'Planning for Liquidity in Financial Institutions : the Chance-Constrained Method', *Journal of Finance*, Sept. 1966.

Foreclosure proceedings will commence when the probability of realizing a loss on a mortgage loan passes some threshold value. Consequently, if an association is more willing to take risks, we should observe a higher foreclosure rate.

Professor Rosett's argument is that a foreclosure represents an action to stop possible losses and is thus a device for eliminating risk. An association with a high foreclosure rate has on average reacted more quickly to avoid possible losses and is thus less willing to take risks. I believe that both foreclosure and holding reacquired real estate are very risky activities and thus will not be preferred by risk-averting associations. One empirical test of which of these two hypotheses is valid would be to study the correlation between realized losses on mortgage loans and foreclosures. I shall perform this test in response to his suggestion. A negative correlation would tend to support Professor Rosett's argument. Usually, realized losses on real estate occur after a foreclosed property has been resold ; I should be very surprised if this correlation were not strongly positive.

Dr. Walter asked whether this kind of empirical analysis can be extended to other industries. I think it can, but only with some further sacrifices in the precision of risk measurement and in the quality of available data. For example, retail stores have inventory losses and losses on trade credit which probably appear in the income statement measure, non-recurring expenses. A large number of other events may also influence this measure ; consequently tests of hypotheses will be weak. He also suggested special inquiries to firms about their losses and risks. The risk and loss experience of a firm is usually very confidential information in Western economies and I do not think that this is a promising approach. It might be feasible to apply this method in Socialist countries. Dr. Walter suggested the possibility of pooling cross-section data for firms in different years with the idea of introducing lagged variables. I have plans for studying such pooled data and agree that interesting models exist which have lagged variables as regressors.

Both Dr. Walter and Dr. Koerts suggested that weighting of observations might serve to reduce heteroscedasticity in the empirical analysis. Weighting of observations to obtain more efficient estimators is convenient, but very dangerous when the weights are not known *a priori* from theory.[1] When the number of observations is large, the importance of heteroscedasticity is diminished. Therefore, with 4,000 observations, it seems prudent to avoid weights and suffer some inefficiency in the present instance.

Dr. Koerts made three other suggestions for improving the estimation and reporting of empirical relationships. First, I did not test for normality

---

[1] Cf. Meyer, J. R., and Kuh, E., *The Investment Decision*, Cambridge, Mass. : Harvard Univ. Press, 1957, Appendix C.

of residuals; with 4,000 observations the central limit theorem can be applied with some justification. Computing residuals for this number of observations is costly even on modern computers. Second, two-stage least-squares estimators were reported because convenient computer programmes were available. I concur with Dr. Koerts that three-stage least squares is a preferable procedure.

Third, I understand Dr. Koerts's reference to autocorrelation to mean instead that some residuals are not independent. This lack of independence is a consequence of the existence of competition between associations serving a given community. The action of one association will elicit a response from its rivals. I agree that this argument applies, but think that it is not very important. Lack of independence will not lead to inconsistent estimates; it will adversely affect efficiency.

Dr. Koerts did not accept Hypothesis 4 (concerning the relation between age of firm and risk-taking) in Section III (*a*) because (1) a corresponding hypothesis about a parameter in the simultaneous equations model was rejected, (2) he found the theory implausible, and (3) some of the dependent variables in Table 3.2 are related. His first reason is not convincing; in neither Table 3.2 nor Table 4.1 is age of firm significantly related to foreclosure rate. His third reason is valid and raises indirectly the point that pooled tests of coefficients across risk measures in Table 3.2 should have been performed. Apparently Dr. Koerts would not accept pooled tests either because he believes the endogenous variables are measuring the same thing. I do not feel strongly about this hypothesis but would still accept it on the basis of available evidence.

Dr. Koerts and Dr. Thore have addressed themselves to the more general question of evaluating the relation of this study to other possible research on savings and loan associations. I concur with Dr. Koerts that this study constitutes a very elementary first step towards understanding risk-taking by these institutions. Much more careful analysis at the firm level (including interviews of association managers) will be required before satisfactory models of stock and mutual associations are established. As noted in my paper's second paragraph, I intend the paper to be a preliminary report; more will follow.

Dr. Thore on the other hand apparently believes that it is not an acceptable research strategy to test whether meaningful differences exist between different firms without completely describing their behaviour; induction or empirical reasoning may not be applied before a complete deductive specification of a model is reported. He does not deny that I have carefully defended my hypotheses; he simply objects that the Porter model applies to savings and loan associations; banks and savings and loan associations differ markedly in (1) their legal setting, (2) the properties of their assets and liabilities, and (3) their objective function. These differences are well known in the American literature on financial institutions. Finally, it is impossible to develop two complete *dynamic* theories of financial institutions and report extensive econometric results in a short paper. I have reported one tentative simultaneous equations model of an association.

Dr. Thore does not discuss what I have done. Rather he vaguely suggests an alternative research strategy that I should have followed. I most assuredly desire and intend to construct interesting and complete models of savings and loan associations. I submit that Dr. Thore misinterprets the purpose and contents of this paper. His suggested research strategy does not seem to me to be efficient or appropriate, but he is welcome to try it!

Chapter 3

MEASURING THE PERCEPTION OF RISK

BY

RICHARD N. ROSETT

I. THE FRIEDMAN–SAVAGE HYPOTHESIS

IF you are a Friedman–Savage gambler,[1] who is willing to buy an Irish Sweepstake ticket, it follows immediately that your willingness to share the ticket equally with partners will decline with increases in the number of partners until you finally refuse to buy your share, and it also follows that you will then be unwilling to buy any smaller share. This is illustrated in Fig. 1.

The levels of wealth associated with losing and winning some gamble are given by w_1 and w_2, w_0 is initial wealth, w_E is the mathematical expectation of the gamble, and U_E is the expected utility of the gamble. Let $\lambda(w_0 - w_1)$ be the amount risked in the gamble and let $\lambda(w_2 - w_0)$ be the possible gain. For values of λ between 1 and 0 the curve ab gives the relationship between the expected value of the gamble and the expected utility of the gamble. Fig. 1 depicts a gambler who would be unwilling to risk less than $w_0 - w_l$ in the gamble under consideration. Notice that the odds, given by $(w_2 - w_0)/(w_0 - w_1)$, are the same for all values of λ and that λ merely represents the proportion of the lottery ticket.

This result seems odd, since it is not merely a possible consequence of the Friedman–Savage hypothesis, but an inescapable implication. Casual empiricism is frequently invoked in this realm and in this case the results are, as usual, divided. I feel that I should be willing to buy even an infinitesimal share of an Irish Sweepstake ticket, abstracting of course from the transaction the cost of drawing

[1] The Friedman–Savage hypothesis is that over some range of wealth the marginal utility of wealth increases. If von Neuman–Morgenstern expected utility is maximized, some unfair gambles will be accepted. Fig. 1 emphasizes the range of increasing marginal utility and illustrates a gamble for which the expected utility of an unfair gamble exceeds the utility of the pre-gamble level of wealth. For a full exposition of the Friedman–Savage hypothesis, see Friedman, M., and Savage, L. J., 'The Utility Analysis of Choices Involving Risk', *Journal of Political Economy*, Aug. 1948.

68

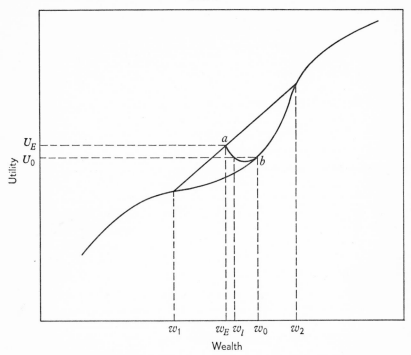

the infinitesimal amount of money from my purse and of depositing
my infinitesimal winnings, should they materialize. Not all of my
friends agree with me.

Another way of depicting this phenomenon is given in Fig. 2.

Fig. 2 is an indifference map of gambles on some event, E, that
will occur with probability p. If E occurs the gambler will receive
an amount x, and if E does not occur he will receive an amount y.
Thus every bet on E is represented by a point (x, y). Bets in favour
of the occurrence of the event lie in the fourth quadrant where x is
positive and y is negative. All bets against the occurrence of E lie
in the second quadrant. The line

$$y = -\frac{p}{(1-p)}\, x \tag{1}$$

is the locus of all fair bets on E. All bets above the line are favourable and all bets below it are unfavourable. The curves are indifference curves. Along an indifference curve we find all gambles on E

Fɪɢ. 2

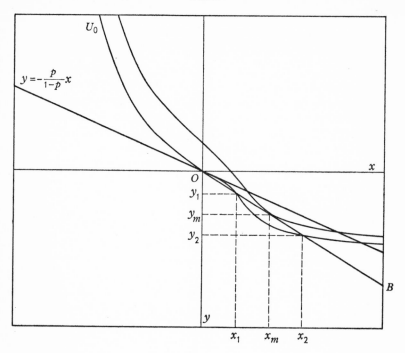

that have the same expected utility. The indifference curve containing the origin divides the plane into acceptable and unacceptable gambles. The gambles that lie above this curve are in the acceptance set. Although there are indifference curves below this one, they have not been drawn since they are of no interest. It is an implication of the Friedman–Savage hypothesis that the frontier of the acceptance set (the indifference curve labelled U_0) is tangent to the line given by (1) at the origin. From this it follows that if some acceptable point lies below the fair-bet line, the acceptance set must be non-convex as shown. The line OB represents gambles in favour of E at unfair odds. The gambler whose indifference curves are as shown in Fig. 2 will refuse to bet less than $|y_1|$ or more than $|y_2|$ and would most like to bet $|y_m|$ at the odds given. The existence of some $|y_1| > 0$ is implied by the Friedman–Savage hypothesis. It also happens that if paradoxes are to be avoided there must also be some $|y_2| > 0$, but that need not concern us here. In order to draw Fig. 2 we need to know an individual's wealth, his utility function, and the event on which he is betting. For other levels of wealth we might find that no point in the acceptance set lies below the fair-bet line. The frontier of the acceptance set would still be tangent to the fair-bet line at the origin, but the acceptance set would be convex. For other events we might find that the non-convexity arises because there are acceptable bets below the fair-bet line in the second quadrant or possibly in both the second and fourth quadrants.

Experiments have been carried out, most notably by Mosteller and Nogee,[1] to test the Friedman–Savage hypothesis. The method of measuring utility is to offer a subject a number of gambles on some event with a known probability of occurring, p. The gambles all involve the possible loss of a fixed sum but the prizes are varied. Each prize is offered a number of times and it is found that sometimes a subject prefers not to gamble for a given prize and that sometimes he will gamble. It is assumed that if a subject regards a particular gamble as equivalent to not gambling he will accept that gamble half the time. If $|x_1|$ is in the fixed amount risked and $|x_2|$ is the prize for which the subject will agree to gamble half the times it is offered, we can calculate $U(x_2)$ by assuming that $U(x_0) = 0$ (where x_0 is initial wealth) and that $U(x_1) = -1$, and by solving the equation

$$pU(x_2) + (1-p)U(x_1) = U(x_0),$$

which reduces to

$$U(x_2) = \frac{1-p}{p}.$$

Since p is known we can determine the utility of x_2. This experiment is repeated with varying values of p until the utility of several values of x_2 is determined. The resulting estimated utility function can then be examined for the non-convexity hypothesized by Friedman and Savage.

II. THE YAARI HYPOTHESIS

There are many objections to the Mosteller–Nogee experiment. Most of them flow from the unwarranted assumption that x_0 was constant for each subject throughout the entire experiment. Yaari[2] has pointed out that the experiment is open to an even deeper objection. In order to calculate $U(x_2)$ it is necessary to assume that

[1] Mosteller, F., and Nogee, P., 'An Experimental Measurement of Utility', *Journal of Political Economy*, vol. 65, pp. 371–404, 1951.
[2] Yaari, M., 'Convexity in the Theory of Choice under Risk', *Quarterly Journal of Economics*, vol. 79, pp. 278–90, 1965.

p is known. If the Friedman–Savage hypothesis is correct, p for any event can be calculated from the slope of the frontier of the acceptance set (I shall call this curve U_0 for brevity) at the origin. We might examine the Mosteller–Nogee data from that point of view and find that the p thus calculated from the data diverged from the value for p that the experimenter assumed in solving for $U(x_2)$.

Subjects in the Mosteller–Nogee experiment played a very simple form of poker. The experimenter displayed a poker hand and a prize to the subject. The subject had to decide whether or not to risk 5c. on a chance of drawing a better poker hand. It is known that in this game the probability of drawing a better poker hand than $(2, 2, 2, 6, 3)$ is about $1/6$. The slope of U_0 at the origin should be $-p : (1 - p) = -\dfrac{1}{5}$. Suppose we performed an experiment exactly like the Mosteller–Nogee experiment except that instead of fixing x_1 at $x_0 - 5c$. we allowed it to vary and that we thus were able to determine the curve U_0. We measure the slope of U_0 at the origin and find that it is $-\dfrac{1}{3}$.

We might now find that some points in the acceptance set lay below the line $y = -\dfrac{1}{3}x$ and this non-convexity of the acceptance set would imply that the marginal utility of wealth was increasing over some range of wealth. But it would no longer be necessary to hypothesize increasing marginal utility in order to explain acceptance of unfair bets, since some points in a convex acceptance set could lie below the line, $y = \dfrac{1}{5}x$, that actually divides favourable from unfavourable bets. Yaari hypothesized that acceptances are all convex and that it would be found that the curve U_0 is not tangent to $y = -\dfrac{p}{1-p}x$ at the origin where p is the probability Mosteller and Nogee assumed they knew through knowing the mechanics of the game they were playing.

Having found the slope of U_0 at the origin to be $-\dfrac{1}{3}$ we could adopt Yaari's definition of subjective probability, p_s, as a number that can be determined from the slope of U_0 at the origin. Solving

$$-\frac{p_s}{1 - p_s} = -\frac{1}{3},$$

we get

$$p_s = \frac{1}{4}.$$

Yaari attempted to determine whether acceptance sets were convex in order to test the Friedman–Savage hypothesis. Finding that acceptance sets do seem to be convex, he hypothesized a

FIG. 3

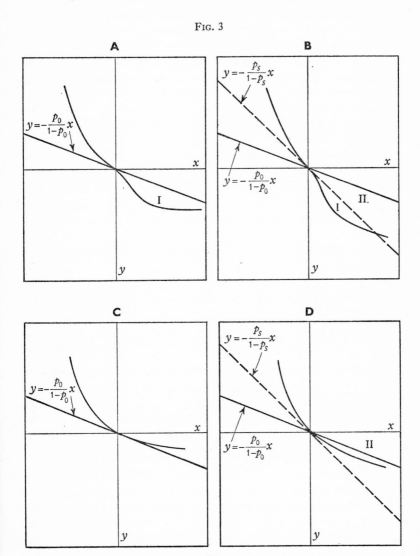

divergence between subjective probability, p_s, and objective probability, p_0. He hypothesized that for high values of p_0, $p_s < p_0$, and that for low values of p_0, $p_s > p_0$. This would explain all the phenomena (simultaneous purchase of lottery tickets and of insurance) explained by the Friedman–Savage hypothesis without requiring increasing marginal utility or the implied non-convex acceptance sets. Fig. 3 represents the four possible cases that could be observed.

Fig. 3A represents the usual Friedman–Savage gambler. He accepts bets in the region labelled I because of increasing marginal utility of wealth. In Fig. 3B we have a Friedman–Savage–Yaari gambler. Gambles in region I are accepted, despite being unfavourable, because of increasing marginal utility. Gambles in region II are accepted because the subject treats them as though they were favourable despite the fact that they are not. In Fig. 3C we have a risk-averse subject who will not accept unfair gambles, and Fig. 3D represents a risk-averse Yaari gambler who accepts unfavourable gambles in region II because he treats them as though they are favourable. It is in principle possible to distinguish, experimentally, among all four possibilities.

III. EXPERIMENTAL DETERMINATION OF THE ACCEPTANCE SET

In order to determine a subject's acceptance set for a particular gamble it is necessary that three conditions be satisfied in the design of the experiment:

(1) The subject must know that with probability $p > 0$ he will engage in exactly one gamble after answering the questions that are put to him during the experiment, and that with probability $(1 - p)$ he will not gamble at all.

(2) The probability that any gamble will be conducted is independent of all his answers during the experiment and the probability that he will engage in a gamble is affected only by answers to questions put to him about that gamble.

(3) He must be provided an incentive to make a bid on the curve, U_0.

These requirements are necessary to ensure that his responses with respect to gambles offered to him are not part of an overall gambling strategy involving more than one gamble offered to him in the experiment. As an illustration of how one might fail to determine the acceptance set, consider an experiment in which an event is described to the subject, he is told that a prize, x, will be paid if the event occurs, and the subject is asked to submit a sealed bid of the amount, $|y|$ (the amount is referred to as $|y|$ since it is assumed that $y<0$), that he is willing to risk in order to have a chance to win x. Naturally we hope that in this auction he will name an amount such that the point (x, y) is on the frontier of the acceptance set. But what incentive does the subject have to oblige us in this way? The expected utility of such a bid is a convex sum of the utility of the gamble and the utility of not gambling (being at the origin). Since both of these points are on the same indifference curve, the utility of the bid is the same as the utility of being at the origin. But consider some bid $|y^*|$ such that $|y^*|<|y|$. The utility of the gamble (x, y^*), is at least as great as the utility of the gamble (x, y). If p_1 is the probability that the subject will be allowed to gamble when he bids $|y^*|$ and p_2 is the probability that he will be allowed to gamble when he bids $|y|$, it is immediate that

$$p_1 U(x, y^*) + (1-p_1)U(0, 0) \geqslant p_2 U(x, y) + (1-p_2)U(0, 0)$$

regardless of the values of p_1 and p_2. These two convex sums are equal only if $p_1=0$. The sense of this is that if a bid, $|y^*|$, that is less than $|y|$ has any chance of winning the privilege of gambling, the utility of bidding $|y^*|$ is greater than the utility of bidding $|y|$.

Suppose p_1, p_2, and p_3 are the probabilities that bids of $|y_0|$, $|y_2|$, and $|y_3|$ will be sufficient to win an auction for the right to gamble for the prize x_1. The utility of these bids are,

$$\text{(I)} \quad p_1 U_0 + (1-p_1)U_0,$$
$$\text{(II)} \quad p_2 U_2 + (1-p_2)U_0,$$

and

$$\text{(III)} \quad p_3 U_3 + (1-p_3)U_0.$$

Since $U_2>U_0$ and $U_3>U_0$, it follows that both II and III are greater than I. The subject who maximizes expected utility should not be expected, therefore, to bid $|y_0|$. He should choose the maximum of I, II, and III and make the bid associated with that maximum. Even if p_2 and p_3 are both zero the subject is indifferent among I, II, and III and therefore has no incentive to bid $|y_0|$.

Suppose that in order to ensure that every subject will engage in exactly one gamble, the subject is told that from among the auctions in which he is the high bidder, one will be selected at random and that he will be required to engage in the implied gamble. The probability that he will engage in any gamble depends on the outcome of all auctions. Thus in calculating the utility of a bid he will need to account for the effects of that bid on the utility of all other bids. In general it will not be optimum for the subject to make offers that lie on U_0.

The difficulty here comes from the failure to make the probability that any gamble will be engaged in independent of the bids on all gambles. The difficulties that will be encountered when subjects know that they may be asked to engage in more than one gamble or when they know that they will not be asked to gamble at all are obvious and will not be illustrated.

The following scheme satisfies all three requirements for determining a point on the curve U_0:

For a specified event, auction a number of different prizes in an open auction. After all auctions are complete, select only one auction at random and the winner of that auction will gamble his winning bid against the associated prize. A record must be kept of the highest bid by each subject in each auction. This, together with the prize for which the bid is made, gives a point on the curve U_0, except for the winner of the auction who may not have been driven to his reservation price. One method for conducting the auction might be to describe the event on which the bet will be made and to quote a low starting bid. Every subject who is willing to make the starting bid indicates his willingness by pressing a button that causes a record to be made of his willingness. The number of bids is announced and a higher price is named. Again all willing bidders record their intentions and all those who are unwilling to bid the new price are required to press a second button that causes their withdrawal from the auction to be recorded. After each price announcement the number of bidders who remain is announced. Once a bidder has withdrawn he cannot re-enter the auction. When only one bidder remains, the auction is terminated. If the number of bidders drops from more than one to zero, the auction is awarded to all the tied high bidders.

This procedure is complicated and probably expensive. The number of participants in the auction must be large enough to make collusion unlikely. Determination of the curve U_0 will require a large number of auctions, especially in the region of the origin if the slope of U_0 at the origin is to be well determined.

Fortunately, if we are only interested in measuring subjective probability a much simpler experiment will reveal the slope of U_0 at the origin in the case where the acceptance set is convex. Instead of attempting to discover the frontier of the acceptance set we discover an offer curve which, at the origin, has the same slope as U_0 provided the acceptance set is convex. We obtain the offer curve by quoting, for a given event, various odds at which bets can be made. Each subject is asked to state the amount he would like to bet at the quoted odds, and to state whether he wants to bet in favour of or against the occurrence of the event. Subjects are told that after all responses have been recorded, one gamble will be selected at random and every subject will be required to engage in the gamble, betting for or against the occurrence of the event the amount he indicated. If the acceptance set is convex, the subject will refuse to bet either way at odds he regards as fair. From the odds at which the subject chooses to bet nothing we can infer his subjective probability. If the acceptance set is non-convex, we shall find that the offer curve is non-continuous around the origin and we shall need to resort to the more difficult experiment in order to discover the desired slope. Fig. 4 illustrates these two possibilities. In Fig. 4A, the lines O_1, O_2, and O_3 represent three different odds quotations. The subject should select a point at which the odds line is tangent to an indifference curve. Offers of various odds will trace out the offer curve represented by the dotted line. The acceptance set here is convex, so that at odds represented by O_2 the subject should choose to bet nothing. These are taken as odds he regards as fair, and from them his subjective probability can be inferred. Fig. 4B illustrates the case of a non-convex acceptance set. The same procedure yields the dotted line that does not include the origin. At odds O_2 this subject is indifferent between the points a and b and prefers them both to all points in between. It is not possible to determine the slope of U_0 at the origin for this subject except by determining U_0 itself.

IV. CAN WE REALLY MEASURE SUBJECTIVE PROBABILITY?

The title of this section is intended to provoke a particular doubt, not all possible doubts, about the experiments described in Section III. Suppose that a subject chooses among gambles as Friedman and Savage or Yaari or all three hypothesize. The subject comes to our experiment already committed to a collection of gambles. A

Fig. 4

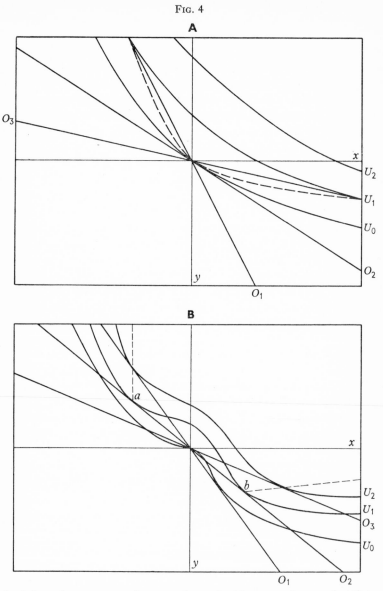

physician who wants to photograph our insides can ask us to fast for a suitable period and to drink a substance that will increase the precision with which the photograph can be interpreted. It is more difficult to ask an experimental subject to refrain from contracting for gambles for a suitable period before engaging in our experiment.

Does the fact that a subject enters the experiment already engaged in various gambles affect the possibility of determining (1) his utility function, or (2) his subjective probability? The answers are that we cannot determine the utility function that led him to engage in the gambles in which he is already engaged, but we can measure his subjective probability. Suppose that the subject selects from among a menu of gambles by choosing the set that maximizes his expected utility. Let

$$U(\sum_{i=1}^{n} x_i)$$

be the utility of having n gambles result in increases or decreases in his wealth of x_i ($i = 1, \ldots, n$). Then the expected utility of the gambles is

$$E(U) = \int \ldots \int U(\sum_{i=1}^{n} x_i) f(x_1, \ldots, x_n) dx_1 \ldots dx_n,$$

where f is the joint density of the n random variables, x_i. The x_i are chosen so as to maximize $E(U)$. If we offer the subject an opportunity to engage in a gamble that is statistically independent of all those he is already engaged in he will maximize the function

$$E(U^*) = \int \left[\int \ldots \int U(\sum_{i=1}^{n+1} x_i) f(x_1, \ldots, x_n) dx_1, \ldots, dx_n \right] g(x_{n+1}) dx_{n+1}.$$

But the part of this function that is enclosed in brackets is an increasing function of x_{n+1} that satisfies whatever requirements U itself satisfies in order to qualify as a utility function. It is this bracketed function, U^*, that can be experimentally determined.

I believe that the following conjecture about U^* must be correct: If a subject has maximized his expected utility and if in doing so he was able to select the gambles in which he engages from among a wide variety of odds (as at the race-track where the odds may vary from less than 1 : 1 to more than 100 : 1), then experiments will reveal that acceptance sets derived from functions like U^* are all convex. This is illustrated in Fig. 5. The solid curve is a Friedman–Savage utility function. This subject is engaged in a gamble that will leave him with either w_1 or w_2 and that has a mathematical expectation w_E. Assume that this gamble was selected so as to maximize his expected utility. If we were to increase or reduce his present wealth, we should trace out points (w_E, U_E) lying along the dotted curve. The new curve would be the function, U^*, described above. Since the slopes at w_1 and w_2 are equal, and since the points around w_E on the dotted curve are of the form $(p(w_1+x), (1-p)(w_2+x))$, the slope of the dotted curve would be the same as the slope of the utility function at w_1 and w_2. The function U^* might have regions to the left or right of w_E, where the second derivative is positive, but they would never be such as to lead this subject to accept unfair gambles given his present wealth. They would imply that if he were richer or

Fig. 5

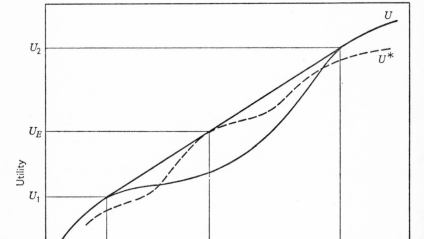

poorer and if the consistency axiom holds, he could then be induced to accept unfair gambles.

This conjecture would explain why Yaari might observe only convex acceptance sets even though the Friedman–Savage hypothesis is a correct explanation of why people accept unfair gambles.

What is the effect of all this on our ability to measure subjective probability ? There is no effect. The tangency of the curve U_0 to the line regarded by the subject as separating the space of gambles into those that are fair and those that are unfair is unaffected by the fact that the subject is maximizing the expected value of U^* instead of U. The tangency depends only on the assumption that the subject maximizes the expected value of a function that is an increasing function of w, that is continuous, and is continuous in its first derivative. The form of U^* implies that if U satisfies these requirements, U^* does also, and that subjective probability can be determined even in the case of subjects who are already engaged in gambles, provided

FIG. 6

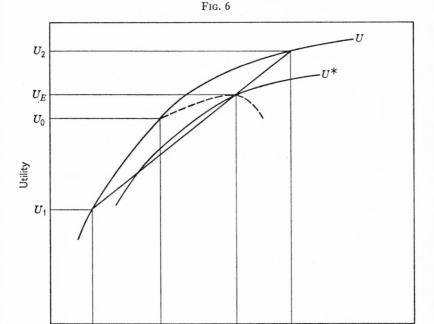

that subjective probability could have been determined had they not been engaged in gambles, and provided they are offered gambles that are statistically independent of those they are already engaged in.

Suppose we imagine that a subject is already engaged in a gamble characterized by w_1, his wealth if he loses; w_2 his wealth if he wins; and p, the probability that he will win. Assume that he was presented with an opportunity to gamble at some odds and selected $(w_0 - w_1)$, the amount he is willing to risk, so as to maximize his expected utility. If w_0 was his initial wealth, the odds offered were $(w_2 - w_0)$: $(w_0 - w_1)$. Suppose he was risk-averse to begin with and that the expected value of this gamble is positive. Fig. 6 illustrates the basis of his choice.

The dotted curve gives the expected value of wealth and of utility for various amounts, $w_0 - w_1$, that could be risked. It is from this curve that a maximum is selected. Having selected this gamble the subject generates a new utility function, U^*. Now it can be shown that for every favourable gamble there is some amount $(w_0 - w_1) > 0$ for which $E(U) > U(w_0)$. This implies that a bet of some size will always be accepted at favourable odds. This is as true for U^* as it was for U. Suppose we now offer the subject another opportunity to gamble at the same odds and probability as before. He will maximize the expected value of U^* by accepting a bet of some size greater than zero. But he had already maximized the expected value of his utility and had bet the optimum amount at these odds. It seems as though we can always induce the subject to increase the size of his bet even though he has just chosen the size that maximizes his expected utility. This odd result is an illusion. If the new gamble is statistically independent of the old one, it is correct that he will accept a bet even though he has previously chosen the optimum amount to bet on a similar gamble. On the other hand, if we are offering him an opportunity to change the size of his original bet so that the outcome of the new gamble is perfectly correlated with the old one, he will refer to U and not to U^* and will refuse to alter the size of the bet.

V. THE YAARI PARADOX AND THE RESOLUTION

In performing his experiments Yaari seems in most cases to have offered gambles on which the objective probability was not known, even to him. Yaari inferred that objective and subjective probability must differ from the following line of argument:

(1) People do accept unfair gambles.
(2) The Friedman–Savage explanation for this behaviour implies that acceptance sets are non-convex.
(3) Experimental evidence is that acceptance sets are convex, contradicting the Friedman–Savage hypothesis.

If we accept the principles of expected utility maximization, the alternative to non-convex acceptance sets as an explanation of lottery-ticket buying is that the subjective probability used in the calculation of the expected utility of a lottery ticket is different from the objective probability used in the ordinary calculation of the ticket's expected value. Yaari's hypothesis is that these subjective probabilities are related to objective probabilities and that they tend to be lower than high probabilities and higher than low probabilities. We have seen that Yaari's experimental evidence need not contradict the Friedman–Savage hypothesis at all. Nevertheless, Yaari's hypothesis raises some interesting questions and should be carefully examined. Fig. 7 illustrates a possible relationship between p_0 and p_s.

If we ask the subject to gamble on an event for which $p = p_0^*$, he will behave as though $p = p_s^*$, which is less than p_0^*. Suppose we now ask him to gamble on the occurrence of a sequence of n independent occurrences of this same event. If he applies the probability calculus he will behave as though the probability of the sequence is $(p_s^*)^n$, but if he merely follows the rule that $p_s = a + b p_0$ he will behave as though the probability is $(p_s^*)_n$. If the subject understands the probability calculus he is faced with a paradox. Which probability should he apply?

This paradox is easily resolved if we assume that the subject is a Bayesian who attaches probability values to prior states of the world. In the case illustrated in Fig. 7, suppose the subject imagines three prior states of the world: (1) The event is certain not to occur; (2) the event is certain to occur; (3) the event will occur with probability p_0^*. He assigns probabilities p_1, p_2, and p_3 to these states of the world. Now the probability that a sequence of n independent events of this sort will occur is

$$p_n = p_2 + p_3 (p_0^*)^n.$$

Thus in the equation relating objective to subjective probability, the constant term a is equivalent to p_2 and the coefficient b is p_3.

It is likely that if this is to be a reasonable model, it must take account of many more than three prior states, but it may be that in simple experimental situations the assumption of three states will be sufficient to explain a subject's behaviour. Since it is possible to measure subjective probability, it is in principle possible to determine the relationship between p_0 and p_s, where p_0 is varied by taking event sequences of various lengths, and where the probability of a single event is known. It is also possible to measure the prior probabilities in the simple case illustrated in Fig. 7. This suggests that it might be

Fig. 7

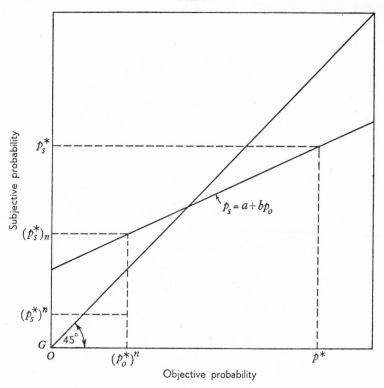

possible to investigate changes in prior probabilities as the subject becomes experienced in gambling.

The experiments suggested in this section involve measuring the slopes of the frontiers of acceptance sets at the origin. It has been shown earlier that this can be done and that these slopes are unambiguously related to subjective probability provided only that the subject maximizes expected utility. Money has been granted by the National Institute of Health for the purpose of carrying out experiments to measure subjective probability and the prior probabilities hypothesized here. The results of these experiments will be reported in a subsequent paper.

Record of Discussion

DISCUSSION OF THE PAPER BY
PROFESSOR ROSETT

Dr. Selten : Although this paper does not contain experimental results, it should be very interesting to experimenters in the field of utility measurement. Professor Rosett's paper contains useful suggestions for future experimentation and stimulating theoretical arguments about the consequences of Friedman–Savage gambling and possible interpretations of experimental results.

Let me first say that Professor Rosett is a master of the diagrammatic method, but the subject-matter of the paper is so complicated that the almost exclusive use of graphical methods seems to be inadequate. Mathematical proofs are needed in order to avoid the pitfalls of graphical reasoning.

I must confess that I do not understand the graphical argument behind Fig. 5.

In the beginning of the paper Professor Rosett shows that a Friedman–Savage gambler should not buy very small shares in an Irish Sweepstake ticket. I should like to point out that the same is true for any utility function which is differentiable at present wealth, because for very small bets utility is approximately a linear function of expected money value.

If the author wants to buy infinitesimally small shares in Irish Sweepstake tickets he must have a 'kinky' utility function which is not differentiable at present wealth.

Professor Rosett discusses the Mosteller–Nogee procedure and the objections raised by Yaari. I wonder why he does not consider the arguments of other experimenters and utility theoreticians. I think that he should pay attention to the possibility that subjective probabilities may not sum up to 1. If he wants to measure subjective probability by the slope of the acceptance set he has to assume that the subjective probability $\tilde{p}$ of the event on which the bets are taken and the subjective probability $\tilde{q}$ of the complement of that event sum up to 1 ; otherwise he would not measure $\tilde{p}$ but only $\tilde{p}\,\tilde{q}$.

Professor Rosett proposes experiments which take the form of an auction game. This interesting idea may solve some problems but it introduces new ones. In such games one has to take into account the possibility of social interaction. In our experimental oligopoly games, imitation has been an important mode of behaviour. Imitation of others is an easy substitute for the development of new behaviour patterns and goal structures in uncertain situations. The imitator does not need a utility function. Imitation is only one example of many kinds of social interaction which would have to be expected in auction situations.

In order to defend the Friedman–Savage hypothesis, Professor Rosett makes use of the very interesting idea that the influence of betting opportunities outside the experiment must be taken into account in the interpretation of experimental results. If this idea is taken seriously it follows that a subject having a choice not to bet at all can accept only bets which are subjectively more favourable than those available on the outside market. Therefore the acceptance set as measured by Professor Rosett's auction scheme may not only reflect U^* but also expected future betting opportunities.

I think that Professor Rosett's argument about the outside betting market is not quite as strong as it seems to be at first glance. An experimental subject must somehow limit his field of attention. We cannot assume that human beings are subconscious geniuses, who, without knowing how they are able to do this, solve the incredibly complicated problem of maximizing the expected utility of their lives. This assumption of unlimited rationality may have some merit for normative theories, but if we try to explain experiments we have to take into account psychological facts. It is highly dubious whether there is a unique utility function guiding all economic decisions of a given subject. There may be different utility functions for different purposes and it is also possible that subjective probabilities and utility functions do not constitute an adequate description of human behaviour under uncertainty.

In Section V Professor Rosett investigates what he calls the Yaari paradox. This paradox occurs if objective probabilities are misjudged in a systematic way such that small probabilities are overestimated and high probabilities are underestimated by subjective probabilities. Then the mapping of objective probabilities into subjective ones will not conserve the laws of probability calculus. I think that Professor Rosett's attempt to overcome this difficulty by the assumption of Bayesian experimental subjects is not wholly successful. If each of n mutually exclusive events occurs with probability $\frac{1}{n}$ where n is sufficiently great, the mapping $\tilde{p} = f(p)$ from objective probabilities p to subjective probabilities $\tilde{p}$ will take $p = \frac{1}{n}$ to $\tilde{p} = f(\frac{1}{n}) > \frac{1}{n}$. Therefore the sum of the subjective probabilities for the n events, which is $nf(\frac{1}{n})$, will be greater than 1.

In my opinion it is not necessary to reconcile subjective probability phenomena with probability calculus. In descriptive theory we cannot assume that subjective probabilities will follow the rules of probability calculus.

Finally, I should like to point out a problem connected with the interpretation of the Friedman–Savage hypothesis. If somebody wants to insure some valuable property he has to pay a premium. If 'present wealth' is interpreted as the sum total of the market values of all liquidable assets — this seems to be the only definition in harmony with the Friedman–

Savage hypothesis — the actual payment of the premium will reduce present wealth ; thereby the utility function will be shifted into a new position. Should the utility of the insurance contract be calculated according to the old utility function or should it be calculated according to the new one ? How do we proceed if several such transactions are to be made one after the other ? I think that this problem arises from the fact that the Friedman–Savage theory tries to formalize the dynamic influence of present wealth within the static framework of a von Neumann–Morgenstern utility function.

Professor Gordon : It is fairly common for an individual to buy both insurance and lottery tickets. This behaviour is considered a paradox, since a lottery ticket involves buying a gamble at a price in excess of its fair value and insurance involves selling a gamble at a price below its fair value. The former can be explained by risk preference or increasing marginal utility of wealth, the latter by risk aversion or diminishing marginal utility of wealth. How do we explain the coexistence of both in one person ? The primary purpose of Professor Rosett's paper is to propose experiments designed to test two explanations of the paradox.

Yaari suggested that the subjective probability an individual assigns to an event with a small objective probability will be larger than the objective probability. If people behave this way, risk aversion, the attitude towards risk considered common, is consistent with buying unfair lottery tickets as well as insurance and the paradox is resolved.

Friedman and Savage have suggested that the utility of wealth function in Fig. 1 of Professor Rosett's paper is a representation of the behaviour in question. It is true that if a person's utility increases with his wealth in this way he will buy lottery tickets and insurance. However, no reason is given why an individual should have such a utility function.

In Fig. 2, Professor Rosett provides an ingenious and effective representation of the problem. If x is a prize with probability p and y is the price of the prize, the line $y = -px/(1-p)$ provides the fair value of y as a function of x. As the line is drawn $p < 0.5$, and in the fourth quadrant the gamble resembles a fair lottery. In the second quadrant the individual gives up x in return for y, and gambles in this quadrant are analogous to a fair insurance policy. An indifference curve is the value of y as a function of x at which an individual is indifferent between not gambling and buying (selling) a chance on the indicated value of x.

It is no coincidence that in a small interval about the origin this indifference curve is tangent to the fair-gamble line. It can be shown that at $x = 0$ an individual is indifferent between a gamble and its expected value regardless of whether utility increases by increasing or decreasing amounts with wealth. This property of a utility function is essential to Rosett's experiments.

The objective of experimental gambling with subjects is to establish indifference curves such as the one in Fig. 2. Rosett points out quite correctly that previous experiments did not really establish a subject's indifference curve, because the structure of the experiments employed encouraged a subject to decide whether or not to accept a gamble with the objective of influencing the terms of the next gamble he is offered. The auctions Rosett describes are very clever instruments both for avoiding this and other pitfalls and for obtaining a great deal of information at a comparatively small cost in time and money.

Let us pass over the mechanics of the experiments and speculate on the data they will produce. The data for a subject will be a set of points in the x, y space, and a curve fit to these points is an estimate of a subject's indifference curve. The slope of the curve in a small interval around $x = 0$ provides a test of the Yaari hypothesis. Recall that at $x = 0$ an individual is indifferent between a fair gamble and not gambling regardless of how his utility increases with wealth. Hence the subjective probability a subject assigns to the event x may be inferred from the indifference curve's slope in this interval. If the subjective is greater than the objective probability of the event, Yaari's hypothesis is confirmed.

The Friedman–Savage hypothesis requires that at some value of x shortly after it becomes positive the slope of the indifference curve becomes positive and remains so over an interval of x as in Fig. 2. The four alternative possible results, both Yaari and Friedman–Savage true, both false, and each true with the other false, are represented in Fig. 3.

However, I am afraid that the experiment may not produce one of the above four results. In spite of what the calculus tells us, Professor Rosett does not believe that in a small interval about x an individual is indifferent between a fair gamble and no gamble regardless of how his utility varies with wealth. I doubt it also. Furthermore, for x very small other considerations than the terms of the gamble will have a large influence on the subject's behaviour.

I cannot be sure that my fears will be realized, and my hope is that they will not be realized. The experiment Professor Rosett proposes is the most effective device I have seen for testing these hypotheses, and it will be most interesting to see what happens.

In closing, perhaps I may be allowed a brief comment on the insurance/lottery paradox unrelated to Professor Rosett's paper. The people who buy unfair lottery tickets and similar gambles may be put in three classes : (1) people of means who gamble on a large scale ; (2) people of means who gamble on a negligible scale ; and (3) poor people who gamble a small but significant fraction of their income. Those in the first class soon go broke, and they need not be considered. In so far as the behaviour of the people in the second category is paradoxical, it is one instance of a larger class of paradoxes. For a more glaring case consider the individual who spends a small fortune to go to the Canadian Rockies to catch a trout with some probability when he can buy the fish at a nominal price per pound in a neighbourhood store. On the third class, if I were supporting a family on say \$3,000 a year and could see no practical way of escaping this drab and financially harried existence, I should gladly exchange some of the marginal 'luxuries' my income provides for a chance, for the illusion of a chance, of striking it rich. Of course there is a big gap between statements such as the above and theories that may be tested and employed to tackle other economic problems. While I share the interest in finding an effective resolution of the paradox, my judgement is that it is likely to be of marginal value in the analysis of important economic decisions under uncertainty such as investment decisions.

Professor Borch : In his paper Professor Rosett discusses the shape of the utility function which governs the decisions made by a rational person. This question has been discussed by several other speakers at the Conference. It may therefore be useful to recall some classical results.

Let us begin by considering the 'St. Petersburg game'. In this game a coin is tossed until it falls heads. If heads occurs for the first time at the nth toss, the player gains 2^n ducats. His expected gain is obviously infinite, since the series

$$\sum_{n=1}^{\infty} \frac{1}{2^n} 2^n$$

diverges. Hence a person who seeks the greatest possible expected gain should be willing to pay any infinite amount for a chance to play the St. Petersburg game.

This is obviously nonsense, and D. Bernoulli proposed to solve the paradox by assuming that a rational person would seek to maximize expected utility (moral expectation). He assumed a utility function of the form $u(x) = \log x$. This leads to the sum

$$\sum_{n=1}^{\infty} \frac{1}{2^n} \log(2^n) = \log 2 \sum_{n=1}^{\infty} \frac{n}{2^n},$$

which converges.

Bernoulli's clever device will, however, break down if we construct another game, where the prize is e^{2^n} if heads occurs for the first time at the nth toss.

In order to avoid paradoxes of this kind we must assume that the utility function is *bounded from above*. This seems reasonable on intuitive grounds and has been proved rigorously by Menger (*Zeitschrift für Nationalökonomie*, 1934, pp. 459–85).

By the same argument it follows that the utility function must also be *bounded from below*. If somebody offers me one million dollars if I will play a St. Petersburg game with him, I shall accept.

A bounded function which is continous and differentiable over the whole domain $(-\infty, \infty)$ must have at least one inflexion point.

Professor Rosett makes a very important point in Section IV, and I should like to express it with more force — and possibly with more clarity.

Several speakers have referred to the 'utility of wealth' without really defining wealth. It may be convenient to avoid this difficult problem, but sooner or later we must face it. It is clear that 'wealth' is not just cash in hand. It must include all the 'gambles' we have to play in the future — or all the 'prospects' we own. This means, however, that we have to bring a *time element* into the model.

Let us assume that we are offered a gamble which will be decided in a second — by tossing coins or spinning a roulette wheel. It is then natural to assume that the decision should depend only on our cash S, and the utility function $u(x)$ which represents our preferences. If the gamble will give a gain x, which is a variate with distribution $F(x)$, we will accept the gamble if and only if

$$\int_{-\infty}^{\infty} U(S+x)dF(x) > U(S).$$

Let us next consider a 'serious' problem concerning investment or insurance. The decision must then depend on our 'wealth' at some future date, and that is necessarily a variate. To illustrate the point, let us assume that a number of uncertain elements, represented by the variates $x_1, x_2, \ldots, x_n$, can affect our cash holding at the relevant future date. If $G(z)$ is the distribution of the variate $z = x_1 + x_2 + \ldots + x_n$, the utility of our actual situation is

$$V(S) = \int_{-\infty}^{\infty} U(S+z)dG(z).$$

If the serious investment-insurance proposal gives a gain x, which is a variate with distribution $F(x)$, we will accept the proposal only if

$$\int_{-\infty}^{\infty} V(S+x)dF(x) > V(S).$$

This may give an explanation of the Friedman–Savage paradox. The von Neumann–Morgenstern utility theory is time-less. The utility function which governs decisions in this theory has a well-defined meaning, but it is not the utility function which determines decisions in 'serious' situations where the time element inevitably plays an important part.

Friedman and Savage *observed* that people at the same time would buy both insurance and lottery tickets at unfavourable odds. This observation can be reconciled with the von Neumann–Morgenstern theory only if the underlying utility function has a peculiar shape. However, why should we try to reconcile actual decisions, where the time element has played an important part, with a theory which does not consider this element at all?

Dr. MacCrimmon : I should like to see the term 'subjective probability' used in a more careful manner. This applies somewhat to Professor Rosett's paper, but most particularly to the comments of Dr. Selten. Dr. Selten's assertion that subjective probabilities may not sum to unity (or some other positive constant) is, to me, meaningless. Although this statement has been made in the psychology literature, I would not like to see it propagated in the proceedings of this Conference without at least a single objection.

Let us remember that 'subjective probabilities' stem from a theory of *consistent* behaviour. We should reserve the term 'subjective (or personal) probability' for those degrees of belief that do obey the rules of the usual probability calculus. (Although other probability calculi might be suggested, the fruitfulness of these different formulations should first be shown before we widen or change our terminology.)

These comments are not meant to deny that we do observe inconsistent beliefs in a decision-maker's *actual* behaviour (see, for example, the experiments and results discussed in Section IV of my paper). In such cases, however, let us not refer to 'subjective probabilities' but rather let us recognize these beliefs for what they are — illogical. Such situations suggest the need for training people to develop consistent beliefs (and tastes) !

Dr. Winsten : A remark on subjective probabilities : In choosing between courses of action, the absolute probabilities need not be used, only the relative probabilities of the states involving these actions. These probabilities need not add up to unity. Professor Rényi axiomatized probabilities with (or rather without) this property more than ten years ago.

Professor Siroyezhin : My remark is connected with the idea that a set of subjective probabilities may have the property of not summing to one. From a gnoseological point of view, I cannot agree with this statement. I feel that if we want to represent the real world in terms of subjective probability, then this representation must reflect the order of things in this world. Practical experience has shown us that there exist in the real world laws of dependency capable of being described by a set of probabilities that sum to one. In the case of a set of events whose objective probabilities *cannot* be determined by experimentation, we have no other way out than to assign to the elements of this set the same properties that were experienced with other objects of that world. This is why I do not see any reasonable points for rejecting the requirement that subjective probabilities should sum to one.

Dr. Leinfellner : I shall add only some remarks concerning subjective probability and utility. Professor Rosett puts the question : Can we really measure subjective probability ? The von Neumann–Morgenstern theory assumes subjective values, but not subjective probabilities. Work since von Neumann and Morgenstern has proceeded in two directions : (1) probabilistic theories based upon probabilistic transitivity ; (2) theories incorporating subjective probabilities. W. Edwards discovered several results concerning subjective probabilities. We define subjective expected utility as

$$\sum_{i=1}^{n} \phi_i \, u_i,$$

where u_1 is the utility and ϕ_i the subjective probability corresponding to the event i. Can both scales admit linear transformations :

$$\phi_i' = \alpha \phi_i + \beta \; ; \; u_i' = a u_i + b \, ?$$

(In the von Neumann–Morgenstern theory, probabilities admit no transformations.) Edwards has shown that if subjective and objective measures differ, then it is always possible to find a pair of events, one with a given objective probability, such that the inequality of subjective probability is in the opposite direction from the inequality of objective probability. Under these conditions a subjective probability measure must be monotonic. There are difficulties in the subjective approach of Edwards. Two ways of avoiding these difficulties are known. Savage assumes that there is no 'objective probability' but only the subjective variety. Luce, Davidson, Suppes, and Siegel assume a sparser set of events. In an earlier publication I have discussed this second approach and have given an experimental approach to measurement of utility given a subjective probability of 1/2. I was using the choice situation represented by the payoff matrix :

$$\begin{array}{cc} & X \qquad Y \\ \begin{array}{c} \alpha \\ 1-\alpha \end{array} & \left(\begin{array}{cc} a_1 & a_2 \\ b_1 & b_2 \end{array} \right), \end{array}$$

where the subject X chooses the column and a chance event α chooses the row. Fixing α by a particular event whose subjective probability is 1/2, one can observe how subjects' choices depend on the payoffs. A particular event α^* is chosen by using the following choice situation :

$$\begin{array}{c} \alpha^* \\ 1-\alpha^* \end{array} \left(\begin{array}{cc} a_1 & a_2 \\ b_1 & b_2 \end{array} \right)$$

to find an event for which the probability that the subject chooses column 1 is 1/2. This event is defined to have subjective probability 1/2. We get

$$u(\alpha^* a_1, \, (1-\alpha^*) \, b_1) > u(\alpha^* a_2, \, (1-\alpha^*) \, b_2)$$

if the expected utility hypothesis is correct, then

$$u(a_1) \, \phi \, (\alpha^*) + u(b_1) \, \phi \, (1-\alpha^*) > u(a_2) \, \phi \, (\alpha^*) + u(b_2) \, \phi \, (1-\alpha^*).$$

Since $\phi = 1/2$, we get

$$u(a_1) + u(b_1) > u(a_2) + u(b_2).$$

We are interested only in cases where equality holds. By assigning zero and unit utilities to two outcomes, utilities can be assigned to a set of outcomes. By an axiom system it is possible to justify the method and further to determine whether the relevant experiment can be effectively performed.

Professor Rosett : I believe that Professor Borch has already answered Dr. Selten's question about Fig. 5. Taking Dr. Selten's other questions in order :

(1) Regarding the possibility that the subjective probabilities may not sum to one. I realize that if an individual regards all improbable events as more probable than they are, it is possible to partition states of nature so as to make all events improbable and that subjective probability adds to more than one. I assume that my subject, engaged in calculating expected values, will do that correctly. He will use the formula

$$\frac{\sum p_i x_i}{\sum p_i},$$

so that for the purposes of ordering his preferences among these two valued lottery tickets he will behave as though his subjective probabilities sum to one.

(2) I agree that the auction procedure will introduce problems, as will the offer-curve method which I prefer. If I have anything to contribute to this discussion it is an experiment that will *in principle* give the subject an incentive to reveal what we want to know about him. This is a condition that has been unsatisfied by other experiments, which were also plagued by the difficulties Dr. Selten raises.

(3) I agree that human beings probably treat a limited number of problems at any given time. The common sense of my defence of Friedman and Savage is that a subject who has availed himself of opportunities to gamble outside the experimental situation may be disinclined to accept what he regards as an unfair gamble even if the utility function that led him to accept the outside gambles was of the Friedman–Savage type.

Chapter 4

INVESTMENT BEHAVIOUR WITH UTILITY
A CONCAVE FUNCTION OF WEALTH

BY

MARSHALL FREIMER

AND

MYRON J. GORDON

I

In its simplest terms this paper is concerned with the following problem. An individual is confronted with two assets : (1) a bond for which the payoff at time $t+1$ per dollar invested at time t is certain and equal to or greater than one ; and (2) a share of stock for which the payoff at $t+1$ per dollar invested at t is a random variable with a known distribution and an expected value greater than the bond's payoff. The individual's wealth less his investment in the share is invested in the bond. Investment in the bond may be negative, that is, he may go in debt. How will the individual allocate his wealth between the two assets if his utility is a concave function of his wealth and his objective is the maximization of the expected value of his utility one period hence ?

What we have to say on the above problem falls under two headings. First, we shall explore the conditions under which the problem is a useful model for research on optimal portfolio policy, the structure of security yields, and investment in real assets under uncertainty and aversion to risk. Second, we shall establish and evaluate the properties of the solutions to the problem provided by a number of alternative utility functions.

The following section will begin with a review of the theory of portfolios.

II

The first significant contribution to the theory of portfolio policy was made by Markowitz (1959). Let x_i be the fraction of an indivi-

94

dual's wealth invested in the ith share, $i = 1, 2, \ldots, n$. A portfolio drawn from n shares is any assignment of values to the x_i that satisfies

$$\sum_{i=1}^{n} x_i = 1 ; \quad 0 \leqslant x_i \leqslant 1. \tag{1}$$

Let $\bar{r}_i$ and v_{ii} be the mean and variance of the rate of return on the ith security. r_i is the dividend plus the change in price of the ith security divided by its current price. The covariance of the rate of return on the ith and jth securities is v_{ij}. The mean of a portfolio's rate of return is

$$\bar{e} = \sum_{i=1}^{n} x_i \bar{r}_i \tag{2}$$

and its variance is

$$\sigma^2 = \sum_i \sum_j x_i x_j v_{ij}. \tag{3}$$

It is clear that the smaller the covariance in r among the securities in a portfolio, the smaller the variance of the portfolio's rate of return.

Markowitz assumed that of two portfolios with the same $\bar{e}$, an investor prefers the portfolio with the lower standard deviation, and of two portfolios with the same standard deviation he prefers the portfolio with the higher $\bar{e}$. Accordingly, he defined a portfolio as efficient if:

(1) No other portfolio with the same return has a lower standard deviation.

(2) No other portfolio with the same standard deviation has a higher rate of return.

In Fig. 1 the curve EE' represents the set of efficient portfolios that may be drawn from the n shares. Any point in the space to the left of the curve is a feasible but inefficient portfolio, while any point to the right of the curve is not a feasible portfolio given the parameters of the n securities from which portfolios may be drawn. Markowitz demonstrated that non-linear programming could be employed to establish the efficient set of portfolios that may be drawn from a set of securities.

The Markowitz model is not only a computational device for finding efficient portfolios. It is also a demonstration that with few if any exceptions investors have aversion to risk. An investor who is indifferent to or prefers risk will put all his wealth in one security. If

Fig. 1

Portfolio Rate of Return and Standard Deviation

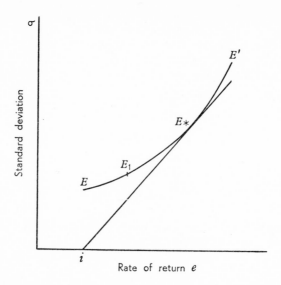

he is indifferent, it will be the one with the highest rate of return regardless of its risk. A portfolio consisting of one security is very rare for an individual whose primary source of income is a portfolio of securities.

A significant extension of the Markowitz model was recognized by Tobin (1958) and Sharpe (1963). Assume that an investor can lend or borrow freely without risk at an interest rate i. That is, there is some security with a rate of return i, zero variance, and zero co-variances with all other securities. Then, by putting the fraction of his wealth m in a Markowitz or pure portfolio of shares and lending or borrowing the fraction $(1 - m)$, an investor can obtain a mixed portfolio with a rate of return

$$\bar{e}_m = m\bar{e} + (1 - m)i = i + m(\bar{e} - i) \tag{4}$$

and standard deviation

$$\sigma_m = m\sigma \tag{5}$$

where $\bar{e}$ and σ are the expected value and standard deviation of the rate of return on a pure (share) portfolio.

For any pure portfolio such as E_1 on EE' in Fig. 1, the alternative mixed portfolios the investor can have are obtained by drawing a line from the point i on the return axis through the point E_1.[1] The important conclusion to be drawn from this analysis is that a line from i tangent to the EE' curve supersedes EE' as the efficient set of portfolios. If E_* is the point of tangency, the only efficient pure portfolio is E_*.

However, the outstanding shares not held in the pure portfolio E_* are held in other portfolios. These other portfolios must, therefore, also be efficient, and from (4) the condition under which a pure portfolio is efficient is that it falls on the line iE_* in Fig. 1. As Sharpe (1964) and Lintner (1965) have shown, stock prices adjust so that the outstanding shares of all stocks are held in pure portfolios that fall on iE_*. It follows that if $E_\alpha = (\bar{e}_\alpha, \sigma_\alpha)$ and $E_\beta = (\bar{e}_\beta, \sigma_\beta)$ are two efficient portfolios, then

$$(\bar{e}_\beta - i)/(\bar{e}_\alpha - i) = \sigma_\beta/\sigma_\alpha,$$

or (6)

$$\bar{e}_\beta = i + \frac{\bar{e}_\alpha - i}{\sigma_\alpha}\sigma_\beta$$

to parallel (4). Given a mixed portfolio on E_α there is some mixed portfolio on E_β that will provide a return with the same expected value and risk (i.e. standard deviation).

We have just established that the return on a portfolio is a linear function of its risk. The parameters of the function are the interest rate and the return and risk on the 'standard' portfolio. However, this analysis tells us nothing about the yields on shares. A share's rate of return will depend on its variance and its covariances with the returns on other shares. If the returns on all shares are perfectly correlated, (6) describes how return varies among shares as well as portfolios. The relation between the mean and standard deviation of a share's return is the same as that of a portfolio. This, of course, is too drastic an assumption, but it is possible that one need not go that far. The simplified model of portfolio analysis elaborated by Sharpe (1963) rests on plausible assumptions, and under these

---

[1] Points on the line joining i and E_1 to the right of E_1 represent borrowing at the interest rate i and investing all one's wealth plus the amount borrowed in the pure portfolio E_1. If the individual borrows at a higher rate than he lends, the slope of the line changes at E_1 (see Sharpe, 1963). If there is a limit on the amount the individual can borrow without risk to the lender, iE_1 can be extended only to this limit (see Freimer and Gordon, 1965).

assumptions the expected value of the return on a share is a linear function of one variable.[1]

At the start of this paper we stated that the bond–stock problem presented there is a useful model for research on optimal portfolio policy and the role of portfolio policy in the determination of security yields and investment in real assets. We are now in a position to evaluate this statement. First, on the basis of the argument leading to (4), the determination of how an individual does or should allocate his wealth between a bond and a share determines how he does or should allocate his wealth between a bond and a pure portfolio with the same parameters as the share. Second, on the basis of (6), the actual or optimal mixed portfolio on the basis of one pure portfolio provides the actual or optimal mixed portfolio on the basis of every other pure portfolio. Third, under Sharpe's assumptions with respect to the decomposition of a share's variance, the relation between the mean and relevant standard deviation of a share's return is the same as that of a portfolio. Therefore, the determination of how an individual does or should allocate his wealth between a stock and a bond provides all we want to know as to how he does or should allocate his wealth between a bond and any efficient pure portfolio.

III

(a) *Bernoulli's Choice Model*

Daniel Bernoulli began his remarkable paper by observing that there had been general agreement that the value of a gamble is its mathematical expectation. In arriving at this quantity, 'no characteristic of the individual ought to be taken into consideration' (1954, p. 23). Bernoulli questioned the truth of this proposition by asking should a poor man who had been given a lottery ticket that pays 20,000 ducats or nothing, both with equal probability, be willing to sell the ticket for 9,000 ducats? Should a rich man be willing to

---

[1] Sharpe assumed and found consistent with the data the assumption that the return on a share is $r = a + \beta I + \varepsilon$, where I is an index of economic activity with zero mean and positive variance, and ε is a random variable with zero mean, positive variance, and zero covariance with I and with ε for every other share. The variance of a portfolio containing such shares is

$$\sigma^2 = \sum_i x_i^2 \, \varepsilon_i^2 + \sum_i \sum_j x_i \, x_j \, \beta_i \, \beta_j \, \varepsilon^2_{n+1},$$

where ε^2_{n+1} is the variance of I. As the number of shares in the portfolio becomes large, the first term on the right side approaches zero. It can be shown that when portfolio risk is independent of the ε_i, $i = 1, 2, \ldots, n$, the expected value of r for each share, a, is a linear function of the share's β.

pay 9,000 ducats for the ticket? An affirmative answer to both of these questions seemed plausible to Bernoulli. To explain this behaviour, he advanced two interrelated propositions: (1) an individual maximizes the expected value of his utility and not his wealth, and (2) his utility increases by diminishing marginal amounts with his wealth. Then with a boldness that is a model for a modern operations-research worker, he took the reciprocal of an individual's wealth as the marginal utility per unit increment in wealth. That is, letting U = utility and φ = wealth,

$$dU/d\varphi = 1/\Phi, \tag{7}$$

from which it follows that

$$U = \log \varphi. \tag{8}$$

The utility of wealth Φ is its logarithm.

With this utility function and with the assumption that when his wealth is uncertain, an individual's utility is the expected value of the various possible utilities, Bernoulli could arrive at the price at which a poor man would sell a gamble and the price at which a rich man would buy the gamble. Let the poor man's *initial wealth* be W and p_j be the probability the lottery ticket will pay y_j. His utility with the lottery ticket is

$$U = \sum_{j=1}^{n} p_j \log (W + y_j). \tag{9}$$

If the poor man's wealth is $W = 1,000$ ducats, and the lottery ticket is the one described above, the poor man's utility with the ticket is

$$U = 0\cdot5 \log (1,000 + 20,000) + 0\cdot5 \log (1,000 + 0)$$
$$= 3\cdot6611.$$

Since the antilog of $3\cdot6611$ is 4,582, he is indifferent between keeping the ticket and selling it for $4,582 - 1,000$ or 3,582 ducats.

The price a rich man would be willing to pay for the ticket is the value of Q that satisfies

$$\log W = \sum_{j} p_j \log (W - Q + y_j). \tag{10}$$

The solution of (10) for Q involves a trial-and-error calculation. However, if the price of the ticket is given, whether or not the rich man would buy it involves a simple calculation. If, for example, $Q = 5,000$ and the rich man's initial wealth is 100,000 ducats, his utility after buying the ticket is

$$U_g = 0 \cdot 5 \ \log \ (100,000 - 5,000 + 20,000) + 0 \cdot 5 \ \log \ (100,000 - 5,000)$$
$$= 5 \cdot 0285.$$

His utility with the ticket at a price of 5,000 ducats is equal to that of 104,500 ducats with certainty. The rich man would find the ticket a bargain at 5,000 ducats. In fact, he would be willing to pay anything up to 9,500 ducats for the ticket.

(b) *A Bernoulli Investment Model*

In the previous section we assumed that the individual was confronted with a gamble for which the payoff on each event was fixed. His decision problem was whether or not to play given the price, or at what price he would be willing to buy or sell the gamble. We now assume that the gamble may be played on any scale the individual desires, and his decision problem is the scale of play. Specifically, an individual with wealth W has the alternative of investing it in any combination of two securities. One of the securities, called a bond, will pay L per dollar invested with certainty. $L = 1 + i$, where i is the rate of interest on the bond. The payoff on the other security, called a stock, is $\tilde{R} = 1 + \tilde{r}$ per dollar invested, and $\tilde{r}$ is the rate of return on the investment. $\tilde{R}$ is a random variable with p_j the probability of $\tilde{R} = R_j$ and $\bar{R}$ its mean. The expected value of $\tilde{R}$ is greater than L.

Using Bernoulli's utility function, the utility of an individual who invests X in the stock and $W - X$ in the bond is

$$U = \sum_j p_j \ \log \ ((W - X) \ L + X R_j). \tag{11}$$

To examine the implications of this utility function let us assume that the stock can have one of two possible outcomes, R_1 with probability p_1 and R_2 with probability p_2. We may without loss of generality and with some simplification in the mathematics let $i = 0$. The requirement that $\bar{R} > L$ is now satisfied if $p_1 R_1 + p_2 R_2 > 1$. For the stock to involve some chance of loss, one of the payoffs, say R_2, must be less than one. (11) then becomes

$$U = p_1 \ \log \ (W + X(R_1 - 1)) + p_2 \ \log \ (W + X(R_2 - 1)). \tag{12}$$

Taking the derivative with respect to X, setting it equal to zero and solving for X, we find that U is maximized at

$$X = \frac{W(p_1(R_1 - 1) + p_2(R_2 - 1))}{-(R_1 - 1)(R_2 - 1)} = \frac{W\tilde{r}}{-(R_1 - 1)(R_2 - 1)}. \tag{13}$$

Since $R_2 < 1$, the denominator of (13) and X are positive.

The first point to note about (13) is that X/W, the fraction of wealth invested in the stock, is independent of W. Second, X and X/W increase with $\bar{r}$ the expected rate of return on the stock. Third, X and X/W fall as the uncertainty of the stock's payoff increases, since the denominator of (13), $-(R_1 - 1)(R_2 - 1)$, increases with the spread between R_1 and R_2. That is, if we vary R_1 and R_2 so as to keep $\bar{r}$ constant but increase the standard deviation of R, the investment in the stock falls.

It is interesting to note that as the size of the unfavourable outcome (and its probability) falls, the fraction of wealth invested in the share falls. The conclusion is that an investor with Bernoulli utility is not concerned solely with the mean and standard deviation of the payoff. With these two parameters held constant, the attractiveness of a gamble increases with its right skewness. In less precise language, lottery-type shares are preferred to symmetrical shares, and they in turn are preferred to shares with payoffs similar to insurable-type risks.

(c) *Plausibility of Bernoulli's Function*

Bernoulli's utility function has not won general acceptance, comment on it being devoted largely to its validity as an explanation of the St. Petersburg paradox. The paradox is a gamble with an infinite expected value, and the gamble is a paradox because no one will pay more than a finite, a comparatively small finite, price for it.[1] Bernoulli's utility function provides a rationalization for this behaviour. However, his utility function is only one among the set of concave functions that result in a finite price for the gamble. Furthermore, alternative rationalizations than concave utility have been advanced.[2] In support of these alternatives it has been argued that a person whose expected utility is a concave function of his wealth will not accept a fair gamble, while people do in fact engage in fair gambles — they even buy lottery tickets with the expected value of the payoff less than the price of the ticket.

Friedman and Savage (1948) have established a utility function under which it is rational for a person simultaneously to buy lottery

---

[1] The gamble pays 2^n dollars with n the first time that a fair coin lands heads. The probabilities that a heads will turn up first on toss number $1, 2, \ldots, n$ are 0.5, 0.25, 0.125, $\ldots$, $1/2^n$. Hence each possible outcome has an expected value of one dollar, and the fair value of the gamble is infinite.

[2] See Durand (1957).

tickets and insurance against large losses that have a small probability. In one case the expected value of the ticket obtained is less than the price paid, while in the other the expected value of the loss avoided is less than the price paid. A utility function that rationalizes an individual's decision simultaneously to pay (on an expected value basis) to incur one risk and to avoid another risk is highly desirable in view of the fact this behaviour is common. However, the inability of a concave utility function to do both is not in our judgement grounds for rejection. Our objective is to explain the relation between an individual's wealth and his investment in risk assets. Few people of wealth invest more than negligible amounts in risk assets with zero or negative net expected values. Therefore, an investment model that cannot explain gambling as the term is ordinarily used is not critically impaired by this failure. To compensate, the assumption that utility is a strictly concave function of wealth allows us to go much further in the analysis of investment as the term is ordinarily used than is possible with the Friedman–Savage approach.

We feel that the preoccupation with the inability of Bernoulli's utility function to explain ordinary gambling may well have impeded its profitable employment for the explanation of investment behaviour. Passing over this limitation, we find that the statements about behaviour which follow from it are eminently reasonable. The price an individual will pay for a gamble with scale fixed increases with his wealth, and the amount he will invest in a gamble with the price fixed and scale variable also increases with his wealth. Both of these theorems are particularly worth noting because much of the recent literature on gamble decisions has not explicitly recognized the individual's wealth as a relevant variable. A Bernoulli function also responds in a plausible way to variation in the parameters of the investment opportunity available to the individual. We have seen that the amount and share of his wealth that an individual allocates to the risk asset increase with the asset's rate of return, fall with the standard deviation or risk of the investment, and vary with the skewness of the investment in a manner that appears to reflect observed preferences.[1]

One possible objection to a Bernoulli function is that X/W, the share of wealth invested in the risk asset, is independent of wealth. However, if it is believed that X/W rises or falls with W, the function

[1] An interesting rationalization of Bernoulli's utility function is provided by Latane (1960).

can be modified accordingly. We need only rewrite (11) as follows:

$$U = \sum_j p_j \log ((W-X) L + XR_j + C). \tag{14}$$

If C is positive X/W falls as W increases, and X/W rises if C is negative. Which of the three alternative types of behaviour is most likely is a matter of considerable interest and significance.

Perhaps the most severe limitation of Bernoulli utility is that under it, all persons with the same investment opportunity and the same wealth will make the same investment decision regardless of the differences in personality among them. In what follows we shall examine alternative functions which do not have this limitation.

IV

(a) *Quadratic Utility of Wealth*

Bernoulli demonstrated that an individual will show aversion to risk on the assumptions that utility is a concave function of wealth, and expected utility is maximized when wealth is uncertain. Bernoulli's utility function is logarithmic, while quadratic utility functions are now commonly employed to represent these assumptions. With utility a quadratic function of wealth and wealth the random variable $\tilde{W}$, an individual's expected utility is

$$U = \sum_{j=1}^{n} p_j W_j + \frac{\alpha}{2} \sum_{j=1}^{n} p_j W_j^2; \quad \alpha < 0. \tag{15}$$

Perhaps the chief advantage of a quadratic utility function and the reason for its popularity is that carrying out the summation in (15) results in a simple expression

$$U = \bar{W} + \frac{\alpha}{2}(\bar{W}^2 + V), \tag{16}$$

where $\bar{W}$ is the expected value of $\tilde{W}$, and V is the variance of $\tilde{W}$. Utility is a function of only two parameters of wealth, its mean and variance. Another possible advantage is that alternative hypotheses with respect to the relation between utility and wealth may be represented by alternative values of α.[1]

However, quadratic utility functions have certain undesirable

---

[1] With $\alpha = 0$, utility is proportional to wealth and the individual is indifferent to risk, and with $\alpha > 0$, utility is a convex function of wealth and the individual prefers risk.

properties. A widely recognized one is that utility is maximized at $\bar{W} = -1\alpha$, and falls as wealth increases beyond this value. (It is possible, however, to avoid having utility decrease as $\bar{W}$ rises by setting α so that $-1/\alpha$ is larger than the largest possible value of $\bar{W}$.)

To evaluate the implications of a quadratic utility function further, let us consider its solution to the bond–stock portfolio problem stated earlier. Once again, the investor's *initial wealth* is W, X is the amount invested in the stock, and the payoff per dollar invested in the stock is the random variable $\tilde{R}$ with p_j the probability of R_j and $\bar{R}$ and V the mean and variance of $\tilde{R}$. Also, for simplicity, let the interest rate $i = 0$. If utility is a quadratic function of wealth

$$U = \sum_j p_j(W + X(R_j - 1)) + \frac{\alpha}{2}\sum_j p_j(W + X(R_j - 1))^2$$

$$= (W + X(\bar{R} - 1)) + \frac{\alpha}{2}(W^2 + 2\ W\ X(\bar{R} - 1) + X^2 V). \quad (17)$$

Taking the derivative dU/dX, setting it equal to zero and solving for X, we find that the investment in the share that maximizes the investor's utility is

$$X = \frac{(\bar{R} - 1)(1 + \alpha W)}{-\alpha V}. \quad (18)$$

Since $-\alpha V$ and $\bar{R} - 1$ are positive, X is positive if $W < -1/\alpha$.

As with Bernoulli utility, the investment in the share increases with $\bar{R}$ and it falls as V increases. The similarity ends there. In favour of quadratic utility, X increases with α, the parameter of the utility function, which may vary among investors with their personality. Bernoulli's function does not recognize variation in risk aversion among investors. The major objection to quadratic utility is that the investment in the stock decreases as W increases, while X increases with W under Bernoulli utility. *A fortiori*, the ratio X/W falls as W increases under quadratic utility. It appears questionable that aversion to risk on the part of investors is so great and universal that X is a decreasing function of W as well as X/W. Another disadvantage of quadratic utility is connected with its computational advantage. Only the mean and variance of the distribution of $\tilde{R}$ enters into the determination of the investment decision, and the influence, if any, of the skewness of the distribution of $\tilde{R}$ on the investment decision cannot be recognized with this utility function.

(b) *Quadratic Rate of Return Utility Function*

In developing his model of portfolio policy, Markowitz made no assumptions about the relation between utility and wealth. Instead, he assumed merely that an investor's utility increases with the *rate of return on his wealth* and decreases with some measure of dispersion such as the standard deviation of the rate of return. That is, if $\bar{e}$ and σ are the mean and standard deviation of rate of return on wealth,

$$U = f(\bar{e}, \sigma), \tag{19}$$

with $\partial U/\partial \bar{e} > 0$ and $\partial U/\partial \sigma < 0$.

Tobin (1958) went further and assumed that an investor's utility is a quadratic function of the rate of return on his wealth, say $e + (\alpha/2)e^2$, which, like the above quadratic wealth function, is only defined for $e \leqslant 1/-\alpha$. If the investor's rate of return on his wealth is the random variable e with p_j the probability of e_j

$$U = \sum_j p_j e_j + \frac{\alpha}{2} \sum_j p_j e_j^2. \tag{20}$$

Let the rate of return on a share be the random variable r, with p_j the probability of r_j and $\bar{r}$ and σ^2 the mean and variance of r. With i the rate of interest at which the investor may lend or borrow with certainty and x the fraction of his wealth invested in the share, (20) then becomes

$$U = \sum_j p_j(xr_j + (1-x)i) + \frac{\alpha}{2} \sum_j p_j(xr_j + (1-x)i)^2 \tag{21}$$

$$= (x\bar{r} + (1-x)i) + \frac{\alpha}{2}(x^2(\sigma^2 + \bar{r}^2) + 2x(1-x)i\bar{r} + (1-x)^2 i^2).$$

The value of x that maximizes utility is

$$x = \frac{(\bar{r}-i) + \alpha(i\bar{r} - i^2)}{-\alpha(\sigma^2 + \bar{r}^2 - 2i\bar{r} + i^2)}. \tag{22}$$

How is the investment decision determined in this model?

Since W does not enter the right side of (22), $x = X/W$ is independent of W, and X increases with W. In this respect, (21) differs from and is superior to the quadratic wealth function, where X varies inversely with W. On the relation between x and $\bar{r} = \bar{R} - i$, with $i = 0$ for simplicity,

$$\frac{dx}{d\bar{r}} = \frac{(\sigma^2 - \bar{r}^2)}{-\alpha(\sigma^2 + \bar{r}^2)^2}. \tag{23}$$

The change in x with $\bar{r}$ is positive if $\sigma > \bar{r}$. Tobin has shown that given the requirements $\bar{r} > 0$ and that some value of $r < 0$, then if r is symmetrically distributed, and the optimal x given by (22) $\leqslant 1$ for at least one individual, then $\sigma > \bar{r}$ must be true. Under any plausible distribution of r, $\sigma < \bar{r}$ is unlikely. Therefore, x and X increase with the profitability of the share. They also vary with α and inversely with σ.

Therefore, a quadratic rate of return function has all the desirable properties of a quadratic wealth function and avoids a major difficulty. X no longer varies inversely with W. However, x and X/W remain independent of the skewness of the distribution of r. Perhaps more important is the fact that this function precludes the possibility of $x = X/W$ rising or falling with W, since W does not appear on the right side of (23).

V

In this section we establish and evaluate the properties of utility functions in which utility is a power function of wealth. These are, in fact, just a generalization of the logarithmic utility function of Bernoulli, with individuals allowed to differ in aversion to risk. Let us begin, however, on a more general level. We assume that utility is an increasing function of wealth, but that marginal utility is a decreasing function. Thus, if $U(\varphi)$ is the utility function, we have $U'(\varphi) > 0$ and $U''(\varphi) < 0$. We shall also assume that $U(\varphi)$ is only defined for $\varphi \geqslant -Q$, where Q is some lower bound to the individual's wealth. For the utility functions we consider $U'(-Q) = \infty$, so that it is in fact impossible to define utility for $\varphi < -Q$.

In terms of our two-asset portfolio problem with $W = $ initial wealth

$$E(U) = E\{U((W-X)(1+i) + XR)\}$$

$$= \int_{-\infty}^{\infty} U(W(1+i+x(r-i)))f(r)dr. \tag{24}$$

The change in utility with the fraction of wealth invested in the share is

$$\frac{d}{dx}E(U) = W\int_{-\infty}^{\infty} U'(W(1+i+x(r-i)))(r-i)f(r)dr. \tag{25}$$

At $x = 0$

$$\frac{d}{dx}E(U) = WU'(W(1+i))(\bar{r} - i), \tag{26}$$

so that a positive investment in the share is desirable if $\bar{r} > i$. Next,

$$\frac{d^2}{dx^2}E(U) = W^2\int_{-\infty}^{\infty} U''(W(1+i+x(r-i)))(r-i)^2 f(r)dr < 0, \tag{27}$$

so that expected utility is a concave function of the proportionate investment decision.

Because the utility function is defined only for wealth $\geqslant -Q$, the integrals can only make sense if $\bar{r} \geqslant r_{\min}$ for some constant $r_{\min}$. Then

$$W(1+i+x(r_{\min}-i)) \geqslant -Q$$

or

$$x(r_{\min} - i \geqslant) -\frac{Q}{W} - (1+i). \tag{28}$$

If $r_{\min} - i > 0$, then an infinite investment is desirable. Therefore, assuming that $r_{\min} - i < 0$,

$$x \leqslant \frac{(Q/W)+(1+i)}{i-r_{\min}} = x_{\max}. \tag{29}$$

It would be desirable to be able to show that the value of x which makes $dE(U)/dx = 0$ lies between 0 and $x_{\max}$. Unfortunately, that is not true, since we can construct examples for which $dE(U)/dx > 0$ throughout the interval $0 \leqslant x \leqslant x_{\max}$ so that utility is maximized at the end-point $x = x_{\max}$.

Suppose now that $U(\varphi) = g(\varphi + Q)$ with $g'(\varphi + Q) = (\varphi + Q)^{\alpha-1}$ and $0 \leqslant \alpha < 1$.[1] Then, with $\varphi \geqslant -Q$,

$$\frac{d}{dx}E(U) = W\int_{-\infty}^{\infty} (W(1+i+x(r-i))+Q)^{\alpha-1}(r-i)f(r)dr$$

$$= W(W(1+i)+Q)^{\alpha-1}\int_{-\infty}^{\infty} \left(1+\frac{Wx(r-i)}{W(1+i)+Q}\right)^{\alpha-1}(r-i)f(r)dr. \tag{30}$$

---

[1] The limiting values correspond to Bernoulli utility and indifference to risk respectively.

If x_0 satisfies this equation with $Q = 0$, i.e. if

$$0 = \int_{-\infty}^{\infty} \left(1 + \frac{x_0(r-i)}{1+i}\right)^{\alpha-1}(r-i)f(r)dr, \tag{31}$$

then in general

$$\frac{Wx}{W(1+i)+Q} = \frac{x_0}{1+i};$$

or

$$x = x_0\left(1 + \frac{Q}{W(1+i)}\right). \tag{32}$$

Thus, if $Q > 0(<0)$, then x is a decreasing (increasing) function of wealth, approaching x_0 in the limit as $W \to \infty$. Note that $X = xW$ is always an increasing function of wealth. It can also be shown that x is an increasing function of $\bar{r}$, and an increasing function of its right skewness.

We can conveniently find an explicit expression for x only for very special distributions of $\tilde{R}$. One of these is when there are only two values for $\tilde{R}$. In this case utility is maximized at

$$X = \frac{(W(1+i)+Q)\left\{1 - \left(\dfrac{-p_2(R_2-1-i)}{p_1(R_1-1-i)}\right)^{\frac{1}{1-\alpha}}\right\}}{(1+i-R_2)+\left(\dfrac{-p_2(R_2-1-i)}{p_1(R_1-1-i)}\right)^{\frac{1}{1-\alpha}}(R_1-1-i)}. \tag{33}$$

If we set $\alpha = 0$, $i = 0$, and $Q = 0$, this reduces to (13).

Power utility functions satisfy all the qualitative criteria raised in the previous pages. X increases with wealth and with the mean and right skewness of the share's payoff, and it falls as the standard deviation of the share's payoff increases. The presence of α as a parameter allows X and X/W to vary with the individual's personality, and the presence of Q as a parameter allows X/W to vary with the individual's wealth. Since utility is a function of wealth, (24) may be substituted for W in the above expressions, and X responds to autonomous changes in the elements of W. The only objection we can find to the use of a power function to represent investor portfolio decisions is one of mathematical convenience. For some problems, even (33) may be too cumbersome, and it is based on a very simple payoff function for a share.

REFERENCES

Bernoulli, Daniel (1954), 'Exposition of a New Theory on the Measurement of Risk', *Papers of the Imperial Academy of Science*, v. St. Petersburg, 1738, reprinted in *Econometrica*, 22, pp. 23–36.

Durand, David (1957), 'Growth Stocks and the Petersburg Paradox', *J. Finance*, vol. xii, no. 3 (Sept.), pp. 348–63.

Freimer, Marshall, and Gordon, Myron J. (1965), 'Why Bankers Ration Credit', *Quart. J. Econ.* vol. lxxix, no. 3 (Aug.), pp. 397–416.

Friedman, Milton, and Savage, L. J. (1948), 'The Utility Analysis of Choices Involving Risk', *J. Polit. Econ.*, vol. lvi, no. 4 (Aug.), pp. 279–304.

Latane, Henry (1960), 'Individual Risk Preference in Portfolio Selection', *J. Finance*, vol. xv, no. 1 (Mar.), pp. 45–53.

Lintner, John (1965), 'The Valuation of Risk Assets and the Selection of Risky Investments in Stock Portfolios and Capital Budgets', *Rev. Econ. and Statistics*, vol. xlvii, no. 1 (Feb.), pp. 13–37.

Markowitz, Harry M. (1959), *Portfolio Selection*, Monograph 16, Cowles Foundation for Research in Economics at Yale University. New York: John Wiley Inc.

Sharpe, William F. (1963), 'A Simplified Model for Portfolio Analysis', *Management Science*, vol. ix, no. 2 (Jan.), pp. 277–93.

— (1964), 'Capital Asset Prices: a Theory of Market Equilibrium under Conditions of Risk', *J. Finance*, vol. xix, no. 3 (Sept.), pp. 425–42.

Tobin, James (1958), 'Liquidity Preference as Behavior Toward Risk', *Rev. Econ. Studies*, vol. xxvi (Feb.), pp. 65–86.

DISCUSSION OF THE PAPER BY PROFESSORS FREIMER AND GORDON

Professor Bühlmann : I am going through the paper following the authors' order of presentation and I shall, under each section, (i) first present the authors' main ideas, and (ii) add my personal comments.

SECTION I

(i) In this section the authors state the basic problem which they propose to solve : 'An individual has the choice of investing his money in one stock and/or one bond. How does he allocate his money if he aims at maximizing expected utility, the utility function being concave from below.' It is pointed out that maximizing expected utility may not be the only goal which the investor wants to achieve and that for instance a realistic investor may be looked on as seeking to maximize the expected utility of his lifetime consumption. The paper does not intend to go into the analysis of this more diversified goal, but the authors promise to do so in their forthcoming researches.

SECTION II

(i) This section is devoted to a review of the theory of the investment of the individual and the firm under certainty and uncertainty. This review is mainly intended to indicate the validity of the problem as stated under Section I for more complex situations as they are actually occurring in real life. The reasoning to support this thesis is as follows :

In a world of uncertainties and risks, corporations provide for an additional decision to be made by the individual investor who in the case of certainty essentially only can decide how much of his income to consume and how much to reinvest ('savings decision', in Keynesian terminology). The additional decision provided for concerns the element of risk. In other words in a world of uncertainty the individual decides upon the allocation of his wealth in such a way as to achieve an optimal mixture of expected return and risk. In particular, because of the risk element and given his risk aversion, an investor will invest his money in *stocks of different companies*. To save the practical importance of the basic problem treated in the paper, it has hence to be shown that the basic problem of how to allocate money in a one stock–one bond situation leads to useful solutions also for the actions to be taken in the real-life situation where allocation is possible to a portfolio of stocks — or to one (or several) bonds.

'Bond' is here always used as an investment with certain return equal to a universal interest and no risk element; any bond is hence as good an investment as any other one. To show that for stocks the whole portfolio can be considered as if it were one single stock, the theory of Markowitz on optimal portfolio policy is used. Within the framework of this theory it is shown that for optimal portfolios the expected return is a linear function of the standard deviation of the return. The same relation does not hold for the individual share unless very drastic assumptions are made.

(ii) I may add two remarks of my own : It might be possible that I am missing a point and that is why I am inviting the discussant to elucidate it to me. To my way of thinking the model case treated is one of a choice between two situations :

(*a*) an investment at return i and no risk ;
(*b*) another investment at return $E(r) > i$, where r is a random variable with essential infimum of $r < i$.

The situation (*b*) can stand for *one stock* or a *portfolio of stocks*, and I believe that the authors of the paper call it *one stock* just for reasons of simplified language. Why then this discussion whether the model also applies to portfolios ?

It would also seem to me that in the whole paper the expressions 'risk' and 'uncertainty' are used in an interchangeable way. Defining 'risk' as a situation where outcomes are associated with probabilities whereas for 'uncertainty' this would no longer be the case (except possibly for subjective probabilities), I would say that all the situations treated in the paper are risk situations.

SECTION III

(i) In this section the basic problem how to split investments between one stock and one bond is treated for the case of the *utility function* as introduced by Daniel Bernoulli, namely $U(x) = \log x$, where x stands for the wealth measured in money units. If, further, i is the interest rate on the bond and r the random yield on the stock, then the authors find for the case of only two possible outcomes, R_1 (with probability p_1) and R_2 (with probability p_2),

$$X_{opt} = W \frac{\bar{r} - i}{(R_1 - (1+i)) (R_2 - (1+i))},$$

where W = total wealth, X = investment in stock, and $W - X$ = investment in bond. X_{opt} stands for the choice which maximizes expected utility.

Under a Bernoulli utility function the following behaviour is therefore derived :

(1) $\dfrac{X}{W}$ independent of W.

(2) $\dfrac{X}{W}$ increases linearly with $\bar{r}$.

(3) $\dfrac{X}{W}$ decreases in inverse proportion to $(R_1 - (1+i)) (R_2 - (1+i))$ and hence decreases with the standard deviation of R.

(4) $\dfrac{X}{W}$ increases with the right skewness of the distribution of R,

which can also be expressed as follows : leaving mean and standard deviation of R unchanged, the part invested in stock is biggest if it offers a small chance of a very large gain as against a big chance of a very small loss (lottery-type situation,) whereas the investment in stock is smallest if it offers a big chance of a very small gain as against a small chance of a very big loss (abstention from insurance situation).

The authors then discuss the possible attacks against the use of a logarithmic utility curve :

(1) It only offers situations of risk aversion.

(2) No subjective parameter.

(3) It is unrealistic that $\dfrac{X}{W}$ should be independent of W.

These objections are met by the arguments that :

(1) Risk aversion is the normal attitude of any investor.

(2) And (3) can be overcome by slightly changing the utility function from $U(x)$ into $U(x+C)$. Then if $C>O$, $\dfrac{W}{X}$ decreases with increasing W, and vice versa.

SECTION IV

(i) In this section the basic problem is attacked for the case where the utility is a *quadratic function of wealth*. If $\bar{R}$ is the mean payoff of an investment of 1 in the stock and V its variance, then (working in the case where $i=0$) one finds

$$X_{\text{opt}} = \frac{(\bar{R}-1)(1-\beta W)}{\beta V},$$

where β is some measure of risk aversion. Here X increases with $\bar{R}$, and decreases with both V and β. These are reasonable properties, an attribute that cannot be claimed for the fact that X also decreases with W. This seems to convey that 'the more you have the more cautious you become'. But even accepting this thesis, one might not be willing to permit that with increasing wealth the investment in stock has to be taken gradually back into a bond investment.

The authors also feel that mean and standard deviation alone might not be sufficient information on the distribution of returns and that therefore any optimization based on these two parameters alone is reproachful.

The first objection (although not the second) can be overcome by assuming that utility is still a quadratic function *not of the wealth directly but of the rate of return obtained from investment*. Writing $x=\dfrac{X}{W}$, one obtains

$$x_{\text{opt}} = \frac{\bar{r}}{\beta(\bar{r}^2 + \sigma^2)},$$

where $\bar{r}$ is the expected rate of return, σ^2 the variance of rate of return, and $\beta>0$ a risk-aversion parameter. Here x is independent of W by construction, and

$$\frac{dx}{d\bar{r}} = \frac{\sigma^2 - \bar{r}^2}{\beta(\bar{r}^2 + \sigma^2)} > 0,$$

if $\sigma > \bar{r}$, which is usually true for 'practical cases'. Only minor objections can be raised against this risk behaviour, namely that

(1) x is independent of W;
(2) x is not dependent upon the skewness of the distribution of return rate;

which would indicate that a quadratic utility on the rate of return is quite reasonable.

(ii) It might be worth while to add that for practical purposes it is quite difficult to establish the exact distribution of return rates. That is certainly the major reason for the fact that procedures based upon mean and standard deviations alone are very popular. Markowitz has shown that the only utility function that leads to a mean-standard deviation procedure for all distributions must be quadratic.

SECTION V

(i) Although this section aims at treating the basic problem for the case of a power utility function, the authors start the discussion by considering the utility function in a very general form; U is only assumed to be defined in the interval $(-Q, \infty)$ and $U' > 0$ (in particular $U'(-Q) = +\infty$), and $U'' < 0$.

Let x be again the percentage of investment in stock. Then under these very general assumptions

$$\frac{d}{dx} E(U) > 0,$$

for $x = 0$ and $\bar{r} - i > 0$, which indicates that in any case some investment in stock has to be made. Further,

$$\frac{d^2}{dx^2} E(U) < 0,$$

hence expected utility is always a concave function of the percentage of wealth invested in stock.

The optimal percentage — so one concludes — lies between 0 and some x_{max}, the latter being determined by the essential infimum of r and the lower bound $-Q$ for the possible situations of wealth. It is possible that the optimal percentage is equal to x_{max}.

From here on the authors then use the special power-function form for the first derivative of the utility function

$$U'(x) = (x + Q)^{\alpha - 1} \qquad 0 < \alpha < 1.$$

Observe the limiting cases $\alpha = 0$ for Bernoulli utility and $\alpha = 1$ for linear utility.

Let x_0 be such that

$$\left(1+\frac{x_0(r-i)}{1+i}\right)^{\alpha-1} \qquad (r-i)\,f\,(r)\,dr = 0.$$

Then the maximum expected utility under the above form of utility function is reached at

$$x_1 = x_0\,\left(1+\frac{Q}{W(1+i)}\right),$$

with the following properties :

(1) If $Q>0$, then x_1 decreases with increasing W, and vice versa, and $x_1 W$ is always increasing with W.

(2) x_0 and hence x_1 is increasing with $\bar{r}$, decreasing with $\sigma(r)$, and increasing with the right skewness of the distribution of r.

x_1 is explicitly worked out in the special case where r can take on only two values. The formula is quite complicated from a computational point of view.

The authors conclude the paper by observing that utility power functions lead to all the properties of investment behaviour which one would expect intuitively. The only reproach against this type of function is its computational complications.

(ii) I should like to say that the discussions at the beginning of this section are most interesting, particularly as no special assumptions regarding the shape of utility function are made. I have tried to expound the authors' calculations for this general utility function in the case of only two possible outcomes for the stock investment yield. One then finds that the optimal choice for x must be such that $(r_2<i<r_1)$

$$\frac{U'\,(1+i+x(r_2-i))}{U'\,(1+i+x(r_1-i))} = \frac{(r_1-i)p_1,}{-(r_2-i)p_2}$$

or in words :

'The ratio of possible marginal utilities must be equal to the inverse ratio of expected deviations from pure interest return rate.'

Finally, I want to add that I find the whole paper most valuable and that I am impressed by the light which the basic simple problem treated in the paper throws on the rather complex decisions to be made by any investor.

Mr. Baudier : (1) My first remark concerns the paper as a whole. It possesses a characteristic which is common to a great part of economic literature. We could say that if economists often speak of an economy without money, Freimer and Gordon's paper submits money without any economy. Nowhere in the paper is there a question of exchanging the acquired incomes for goods. This method, it seems to me, is not only unrealistic, but it also complicates the already arduous problems which economists are facing.

(2) The reading of the first part of Section II inspired me with an idea. I am asking myself whether it may not be true that the difficulties arising from the introduction of risk into economic models are due to our incapacity to imagine a situation where all risk would be eliminated ? It seems to me that models of uncertainty have some characteristics which in reality are those of uncertainty. The paper describes a random mechanism in which there is a random variable D_t at every date. What justifies such a classification of the variables, however, is that date t is the one on which the originally random variable D_t attains a certain value. If the uncertainty disappears, the classification loses its sense. Nevertheless, in reality it is maintained. When risk is introduced in its most simple form, it implies a time of two periods (in the first period the variables are unknown, in the second period they take on certain values). We therefore have to allow one time measure with an infinite number of periods and another with two periods to coexist in the same model.

The difficulty is such that the authors later completely abandoned their reference to the certainty model which they had submitted.

(3) My third remark concerns Markowitz's criterion. Despite the fact that it is being considerably used, it does not seem to be fully satisfactory.

In 1952 Massé and Morlat proposed another criterion which seems to be more satisfactory (the domination criterion). If two prospects of making a profit are offered to a person, and if these two prospects are represented by probability laws like $f_i(a) = Pr(X_i \geqslant a)$, $i = 1$, 2, and if we have, for all a, $f_1(a) \geqslant f_2(a)$, then the first prospect is always preferred to the second.

Therefore, if we offer lottery tickets free of charge to a person who acts according to this principle, he will take as many tickets as possible — which is natural — since the situation in which the number of tickets is the highest dominates all other situations.

According to the Markowitz criterion, this is not the case. The increase in the number of tickets increases the average profit but also the variance, so that no situation dominates the other and all situations are efficient (in the Markowitz sense).

It therefore seems to be exaggeratedly rich in efficient situations.

Mr. Selten : When I received this paper my colleague Otwin Becker at Frankfurt University had just submitted his doctoral dissertation 'Die wirtschaftlichen Entscheidungen des Haushalts'. Chapter 4 of his dissertation contains some results which are similar to those of Professors Freimer and Gordon. Mr. Becker and I have prepared a short statement of his results which may be interesting to the Conference.

Mr. Becker has investigated the same two-security model as Freimer and Gordon have. The amount X is invested in risky shares, where the payoff per dollar invested is a random variable R, and $W - X$ is invested in bonds, where payoff per dollar invested equals a constant $L \geqslant 1$ (W stands for total wealth).

The investor wants to maximize his expected utility :

$$U = E(u(L(W - X) + RX)).$$ (1)

Let us consider utility functions $u(Y)$ with

$$u'(Y) = AY^{\alpha-1}; \quad A > 0; \quad \alpha < 1.$$ (2)

For $\alpha = 0$ we get Bernoulli's utility function and for $\alpha \neq 0$ we get concave power functions. In order to get a utility maximum we must have

$$\frac{dU}{dX} = E(u'(L(W - X) + RX)(R - L)) = 0.$$ (3)

From (2) and (3) we get

$$E((L(W - X) + RX)^{\alpha-1}(R - L)) = 0.$$ (4)

Define

$$x = \frac{X}{W}$$ (5)

and

$$\phi(x) = (R - L)((R - L)x + L)^{\alpha-1}.$$ (6)

Then (3) may be written as follows :

$$E(\phi(x)) = 0.$$ (7)

The Taylor expansion of $\phi(x)$ at $x = 0$ yields

$$\phi(x) = (R - L)L^{\alpha-1} + (\alpha - 1)(R - L)^2 L^{\alpha-2}x +$$
$$\frac{(\alpha - 1)(\alpha - 2)}{1 \cdot 2}(R - L)^3 L^{\alpha-3}x^2 + \ldots.$$ (8)

This converges for

$$\left| \frac{xL - R}{L} \right| < 1.$$ (9)

(9) is satisfied if R is near L and x is not much greater than 1, which is economically plausible. Define

$$M_k = E((R - L)^k) \qquad \text{for } k = 1, 2, 3, \ldots.$$ (10)

The M_k are the moments of R about L. A first approximation of (7) is given by

$$M_1 L^{\alpha-1} + (\alpha - 1)M_2 L^{\alpha-2}x = 0.$$ (11)

This yields

$$x = \frac{1}{1 - \alpha} \cdot \frac{M_1 L}{M_2 L} = \frac{1}{1 - \alpha} \cdot \frac{\bar{R} - L}{\sigma^2 + (\bar{R} - L)^2}L,$$ (12)

where $\bar{R}$ is the mean and σ^2 is the variance of R. This formula corresponds to formulae (13) and (33) of Freimer and Gordon ; their results are exact but only valid for two-point distributions. Mr. Becker's formula (12) is far more general ; it may be applied if the distribution of R is symmetric or nearly symmetric. If the distribution is more than moderately skew, the following second approximation of (7) will yield better results :

$$M_1 L^{\alpha-1} + (\alpha-1) M_2 L^{\alpha-2} x + \frac{(\alpha-1)(\alpha-2)}{2} M_3 L^{\alpha-3} x^2 = 0. \tag{13}$$

Instead of (2), a quadratic utility function may be used, say

$$u'(Y) = 1 - \frac{Y}{S}, \tag{14}$$

where S is the saturation level. Then we get the exact formula

$$x = \frac{S - LW}{LW} \cdot \frac{\bar{R} - L}{\phi^2 + (\bar{R} - L)^2} L. \tag{15}$$

Formula (15) is very similar to formula (12).

Mr. Becker has shown that formula (12) is also valid for a many-period model where total utility can be written as the sum of discounted utilities of period consumption amounts and where the payoff rates R_t for the periods are stochastically independent. This can be proved by induction, but formula (15) is not generalizable in this way.

Mr. Baret : After having applied Bernoulli's utility function, which is not very satisfactory, to his model, Professor Gordon studied other, more realistic utility functions.

It seems that two cases must be considered here :

  (i) the individual who administers his personal patrimony and who therefore acts as the 'father of a family'.

 (ii) the individual who manages an enterprise and must therefore make decisions in its name.

The first individual tries to avoid risks and associates subjective utilities to possible gains or losses. His utility function is very undetermined. It is not only a function of these profits and losses but also of such personal factors as wealth, taste for risk, pursuit of the surest possible profit, etc. Two individuals may, in the same conditions, have very different utility functions. A given individual may have different utility functions under the same conditions at two different moments.

In such a case, therefore, it may be illusive to try to give a representation of his utility in the form of an algebraic function.

As far as the second individual is concerned, however, it seems that things are clearer and simpler. If we eliminate such questions as the improvement of market position, reactions to competitors' behaviour, non-quantifiable policies, etc., it seems that the aim of the manager of the enterprise is to maximize his benefit. In that case the simplest and most realistic utility indicator would be the monetary system. The utility function is then linear, i.e. $n = m$ (m being the estimated profit or loss). The goal is then maximization of the mathematical expectation of profits. It may be necessary to make a restriction as to losses, however. The enterprise may not be able to face certain losses which are too high in relation to its size. In that case the utility function would have a convex form in its negative part.

Professor Gordon : First, let me thank Professor Bühlmann for his excellent review of our paper. He asks why we go to so much effort to establish that the model applies to portfolios. What we have tried to show was that under certain assumptions the return on a portfolio is a linear function of its risk, and under certain additional assumptions the return on a share is the *same* linear function of its risk. If these assumptions are in fact true, the recognition of risk and aversion to risk in macroeconomic models of investment is greatly simplified. For instance, we can study the interaction of the rate of profit (on risk assets) and the rate of interest with the supply of risk and non-risk assets and other economic variables.

Professor Bühlmann is quite right in noting that estimating the mean and variance of a random economic variable is quite difficult, and we shall rarely be able to get higher moments of a distribution. However, on certain assets such as share warrants and convertible bonds the skewness is so great that it can be estimated. Our model and some empirical observation show that it should not be ignored.

Mr. Baudier complains that our model deals with money without an economy. It would be more correct to say that we have wealth without consumption. This limitation of our model is acknowledged. Perhaps he means that we take the returns on risk and non-risk assets as given. In fact these variables will be determined by the supply and demand of each type of asset. However, solving this type of problem takes us to the macro-level and is beyond the scope of our paper.

I do not understand Mr. Baudier's comments on our treatment of time. I also am not sure I understand his comparison of the Markowitz and Massé–Morlat utility functions. It seems to me, however, that the latter provides no basis for choice in most investment situations.

Mr. Baret is correct in noting that in a proprietorship other characteristics of an asset than its possible payoffs enter an individual's utility function. Our model is valid only when the investor is concerned exclusively with the possible monetary payoffs. Mr. Baret also suggests that if the utility function is approximately linear, we may greatly simplify matters by assuming it is linear in the relevant range. However, the implications of this assumption are inconsistent with observed behaviour both of individuals in making portfolio decisions and of firms in making investment decisions.

I am delighted to learn from Dr. Selten that his colleague, Mr. Becker, has tackled the same problem in a somewhat different way and that he has come up with more general results. More important, it is interesting to learn that he has investigated a multi-period model with utility a sum of discounted utilities of future consumption. We have looked at that problem with little success and we look forward to seeing what he has accomplished.

On the comparison between his results and ours, his contribution is the approximation of a power utility function with a Taylor expansion. Whereas we were able to get an explicit solution only if the gamble has a two-valued payoff, he obtains one under the condition that the gamble's payoff is symmetrical.

My colleague, Professor Freimer, thought it might be worth noting that Becker's equation (12) is more appropriately compared with our quadratic rate of return model than our equations (13) or (33). The expression

$$L(W - X) + RX = W(1 + xr + (1 - x)i)$$

and for the utility functions in question (logarithmic or fractional power) the constant factor W does not affect the maximization process ; hence we can consider

$$E\{u(1 + xr + (1 - x)i)\}.$$

Expanding around 1 we obtain

$$E\{u(1) + u'(1)(xr + (1 - x)i) + \frac{u''(1)}{2}(xr + (1 - x)i)^2 + \ldots\}.$$

Without loss of generality we can let

u (1) $= 0$
u' (1) $= 1$
u'' (1) $= \alpha$ (not the same α as in the power functions),

which results in our formula (22). The value of x which maximizes expected utility is given by our formula (23), which differs from Dr. Selten's formula (12) in minor detail.

It can be argued that expanding about $1 + i$ is superior to expanding about 1, and that going as far as the cubic term permits consideration of skewness. However, a cubic utility function need not be concave, while the quadratic, logarithmic and fractional power utilities are.

PART II

GENERAL DECISION THEORY

Chapter 5

UNCERTAINTY AND THE
COMMUNICATION OF INFORMATION

BY

C. B. WINSTEN

I. STATISTICAL INFERENCE

THIS paper is concerned with problems of statistical inference in economic work where there is some random variation and therefore some uncertainty.

Attitudes to statistical inference have changed in the last two or three decades. There have been several schools of thought. Firstly, there have been the proponents of 'statistical decision theory'. It is fair to say that most statistical work in economics at the moment is based, at least implicitly, on the concepts of decision theory, or at any rate on the way statistical decision theory has been used to under-prop and support the traditional statistical notions of significance testing and estimation theory. Decision theory must nearly always assume a cost and (sometimes or) a utility function.

Secondly, there have been the proponents of various types of Bayesian inference (there are some important subdivisions here). Harold Jeffreys and L. J. Savage are leading members of this school. And G. A. Barnard and R. A. Fisher have developed what is in effect a third school, which has laid especial emphasis on the likelihood function. The present author has been especially influenced by this last school, for it has clarified for him many of the issues of, and resolved some of the difficulties arising in, the analysis of economic and other non-experimental research, especially in time series (see Fisher, 1956) and also in problems of sampling theory. In this paper I want to discuss some of these problems further from a rather Bayesian point of view and show how the likelihood function is especially important from the point of view of communicating research results where there is an element of uncertainty.

The Bayesian bases his reasoning on the following theorem. Suppose there is a set of hypotheses $\{\theta_i\}$. On the hypothesis θ_i

the probability of getting an observed result X is $Pr(X \mid \theta_i)$. The probabilities of the θ_i when the results of X are not known are $Pr(\theta_i)$ and are called the 'prior probabilities'.

The probabilities of the hypotheses θ_i when the X are known are the posterior probabilities $Pr(\theta_i \mid X)$. Bayes's theorem states that

$$Pr(\theta_i \mid X) \propto Pr(X \mid \theta_i) \quad Pr(\theta_i).$$

posterior   likelihood   prior
probability   function   probability

Since the results X of the observations are supposed known, each of these terms is being considered as a function of θ_i, the variable indicating the hypothesis. Both the X and the θ_i can be considered as continuous without any important modification of the result.

Now Bayes's theorem has been used in three ways. Firstly, in a thoroughly objective way, in cases where, as in some situations in sampling inspection, there is a stable situation with a routine. The θ_i may be the proportions defective in batches, the X the results of taking a sample from these batches. The $Pr(\theta_i)$ may be known from long experience of batches in this supposedly stable set. This is the type of problem to which Professor Hald has made important contributions.

Secondly, the $Pr(\theta_i)$, the prior probabilities, may be considered as subjective probabilities, as representing a state of mind of a research worker before examining the evidence X. Then the $Pr(\theta_i \mid X)$ sum up his state of mind *after* examining the evidence X. This point of view has been expounded (and, of course, exemplified and modified) in the work of L. J. Savage (1954), and is now very familiar.

Thirdly, there is the attempt to make the Bayes mode of inference more objective, by having some rules for determining the prior probabilities, rules which it is hoped that scientific investigators will find convincing. These either invoke Occam's razor, that hypotheses should be simple, and involve as few parameters as possible, or they involve an appeal to principles of invariance. Harold Jeffreys especially has adopted this approach, though his work has influenced most others also.

The above précis must necessarily parody some of the views, but is necessary to define the argument below. This will not be concerned wtih the first use of Bayes's theorem, but will mainly be concerned with the second, together with some reference to the third. It is the second view which is most relevant to the procedures of applied research considered as a continuing activity.

II. THE LIKELIHOOD FUNCTION

I am going to assume in all that follows that for each value of θ_i, the probability $Pr(X \mid \theta_i)$ is known. This is, admittedly, a drastic assumption, and it is rarely true in fact. But it does enable us to divide our problem into parts, and to make some progress with one side of it. The nature of the likelihood function is discussed in Barnard, Jenkins, and Winsten (1962). After the observations have been made, or the study has been carried out, the X is known. Thus the likelihood is then a function of θ, and is *not* considered a function of X. We shall write it as $L(\theta)$ to emphasize this fact.

Bayes's theorem can now be written in the form

$$Pr(\theta \mid X) = \frac{L(\theta)Pr(\theta)}{\sum_{\theta} L(\theta)Pr(\theta)}.$$

The formula for $Pr(\theta \mid X)$ is unchanged if we multiply $L(\theta)$ by some constant k for each θ. Thus $kL(\theta)$, considered as a function of θ, tells us as much about the posterior probability of any value of θ as does $L(\theta)$. We can therefore consider $L(\theta)$ as determined only as far as a multiplicative constant.

If, for example, we take a sample x from a normal distribution with mean θ, and variance known to be unity, then the likelihood function $L(\theta)$ is $\dfrac{1}{\sqrt{2\pi}} \exp\{ -\frac{1}{2}(\theta - x)^2 \}$. x is known after we have carried out our experiment, so this is considered as a function of θ. But the function $\exp\{ -\frac{1}{2}(\theta - x)^2 \} = \sqrt{2\pi}\, L(\theta)$ contains just as much information as $L(\theta)$.

The same is true if the constant is a function of x. For example, if we are interested in the parameter θ of a binomial distribution, from which we have taken a sample of n and have found an observation x (defectives, for example), then for a given x,

$$L(\theta) = \binom{\eta}{x} \theta^x (1 - \theta)\eta - x.$$

But, as x is a known constant, the function $\theta^x(1 - \theta)\eta - x$ contains just as much information about θ, so far as the calculation of the posterior probability is concerned.

One further example : suppose we take a sample of size n from the normal distribution $N(\theta, 1)$ mentioned above. Then $L(\theta) \propto$

$$\exp -\tfrac{1}{2}\sum(X_i - \theta)^2 = \exp -\tfrac{1}{2}\sum(X_i - \overline{X})^2 \exp -\tfrac{\eta}{2}(\overline{X} - \theta)^2.$$

The first of these factors is independent of θ. Thus $L(\theta) \propto$ $\exp - \frac{\eta}{2}(\overline{X} - \theta)^2$, where $\overline{X}$ is the sample mean. The sample values X_i only enter into this version of the likelihood function in the form of the single constant $\overline{X}$. Since this form of the likelihood function is all that is needed, $\overline{X}$ contains all the information in the sample result, and, following R. A. Fisher, is called *sufficient*.

Often the function $l(\theta) = \log L(\theta)$ is calculated. Then we only have to know $l(\theta)$ as far as an additive arbitrary constant.

The research worker has two points of view which he can take after doing an experiment or after studying some non-experimental data. If he is interested in the research purely from his own point of view, he can calculate a prior distribution, based on his opinions before he has carried out the experiment, calculate the likelihood function, and then calculate the posterior distribution which sums up, so to speak, the present state of his beliefs. This may be a valuable guide to his own further research, for he can pursue only those ranges of hypotheses with a quite high posterior probability.

But if he is to *publish* his research, or communicate it to other people, then his situation is rather different. He then has to pass on to other people the objective part of his findings, for different people may well have very different subjective probabilities; but the results of his own investigations may be very helpful to them. This suggests that he publishes the likelihood function, and this is the thesis of this paper.

There are two rejoinders which immediately arise. The first is that the type of investigation that was done may well have been suggested by the investigator's subjective probabilities in the first place. This is true, but the *results* may be very useful to other workers all the same even if they have very different views. The point will be taken up again below, when the 'extension' property of the likelihood function is discussed. The second rejoinder is that he can publish a posterior probability distribution, provided that the prior distribution used is itself objective.

III. 'OBJECTIVE' PRIOR DISTRIBUTIONS

This latter point needs more discussion. 'Objective' prior distributions can arise from attempts to codify scientific method of the Jeffreys sort. For example, one can suppose that, in fitting a polynomial, one should, by an Occam principle, give much higher probabilities to lower-power coefficients than higher powers. Such a principle may arouse confidence in people working in the natural sciences, either from past experience or from optimism about the simplicity of the universe (an optimism which seems less appropriate at the moment than it did a few decades ago). It does not seem so appropriate to people working in the human sciences, where reactions are rarely simple, and where different factors are likely to operate at different levels of, say, income.

But there can be another sort of 'objective' prior distribution function. Our investigator is not likely to be the first in his field. Much information may have been collected previously which turns out to be relevant to the hypothesis. This material may be incorporated in the prior distribution.

In this situation, it is still important to distinguish what can be learnt from the particular investigation discussed and what has been learnt from other investigations. The distinction is really similar in kind to two different sorts of papers. Survey papers attempt to collect, and, even more relevant here, to collate information from a wide variety of sources. Other papers present particular research results. Of course, there are papers which combine these two aims; they do distinguish them though. So papers should also distinguish the prior probability distribution from the likelihood function, and should publish the two separately.

Strictly speaking, no prior distribution can ever be quite free from the subjective element. Thus what should be published in the idealized model of information presentation which is being presented here is a product of likelihood functions collected from previous investigations of data from independent sources. In practice, however, provided each set of data provides some relevant information about the range of hypotheses being considered, then the posterior probability distribution becomes relatively independent of all but the most 'extreme' prior distributions, so the point becomes less relevant.

Prior distributions obtained in this way from quantitative evidence can also be very helpful in suggesting which part of likelihood surface is worth closer examination.

Unless much previous work has been done on the hypotheses being considered, it is often, in fact, quite implausible to think of any investigator reflecting *before* he has collected the new evidence on what his subjective views on the various hypotheses might be. To put the matter another way, the word 'prior' in the phrase 'prior distribution' is a misnomer. Usually it is too much work to go through all possible hypotheses and give them a weight. What is more likely to happen, and there is nothing wrong with it as a method, is that the research worker goes through the hypotheses *after* he has done his investigation. He may then consider the hypotheses with a high likelihood, compare them with various ranges of hypotheses with a low likelihood, and see if there are reasons why prior information, or considerations of acceptability of some sort, should weigh against the evidence of the data. In fact he constructs his weighting function in the light of the likelihood he obtains. And this is a more economical procedure. For the likelihood function has focused attention on the ranges of hypotheses which need detailed consideration from the point of view of prior evidence or acceptability. For example, some hypotheses may have low likelihood, and the researcher may decide they have low acceptability on other grounds. He need not then try to quantify the acceptability more than that.

IV. CHARACTERISTICS OF THE LIKELIHOOD FUNCTION

Traditionally, the likelihood function has not been published. Rather, some particular characteristics have been given. For example, the maximum has been stated, in the form of the maximum likelihood estimator. But even this has been presented as a good estimator judged from the point of view of sampling theory (except in work influenced by Barnard). Such sampling theory has, in turn, when it has been justified explicitly, usually been based on a cost or utility function, and has therefore become more alien to decision theory than to a theory of the presentation of the results of research. However, there is often a case for summarizing the likelihood function; before this case is discussed, it is important to pursue the contrary point of view further, that any presentation of data should give as good a view of the likelihood function as possible.

Take as an example the sampling of a binomial distribution with parameter (probability of defective) θ. A sample of n is taken, and none is found defective. The likelihood function, $L(\theta)$ is, in this case,

$$L(\theta) \propto (1 - \theta)^n.$$

The maximum of the likelihood function is $\theta = 0$. Now on this evidence nobody would believe that it had been established that θ

was in fact zero. If there were some decision to be taken then it is just conceivable that a good decision rule would involve behaving 'as if' $\theta = 0$, and that this in the long run would be a useful one. In fact one would tend to believe that θ was zero or above, but the larger n, the less would one expect θ to be much above zero.

Should one summarize the likelihood function by some single non-zero value? In Barnard *et al.* (1962) we took the view that this should not be done and that the whole likelihood function should be given. This would be far more comprehensible to the reader than any single value in which he did not believe. In that paper, the possibility was raised that the likelihood could be approximated by, say, a four-valued step function. But even such an approximation dividing the plausible range of θ at the points 0, 0·1, 0·2, 0·3, and 0·4 has its dangers. Consider the case where the paper was read by two readers with different information. One has collected a lot of information that $\theta < 0·05$. The new likelihood function published helps him to refine his knowledge. But a later reader knows that there is a mixture of θs, some very small and some quite large, $\theta > 0·4$, say. The experiment, he knows, is done on one of these rare cases. Then the likelihood function may be very valuable in giving knowledge about θ in these rare cases. The point to be emphasized is that in publishing or communicating the result of an experiment, different people may need different parts of the function.

This point about the dangers of summarizing the likelihood function has different weight for different complexities of experiment. For the case given above, a simple statement of the result of the experiment would enable any interested and informed reader to calculate the likelihood function; we shall give an equally familiar but slightly more complicated case below, where presentation of the *data* in a suitable form is one of the best things to be done. As a next stage the formula for the likelihood function could be given. But, better, a graph of the likelihood function could be drawn, for this does provide assimilable information. The emphasis on single numbers arises to quite a considerable extent from our institution of printing. A graph contains much more information than a few figures, and need take up little more space. But figures are kept by the typesetter, where graphs have to have a special block made. The answer seems to be that, where possible, formulae together with some tabulation are best for simple cases.

Having emphasized the importance of *not* summarizing the likelihood function wherever one can avoid it, it must now be admitted that often one has no alternative. Whenever there are more than one or two parameters to be studied (i.e. wherever θ has three or more dimensions), the problem is formidable indeed, for three-dimensional tabulations take up more space than can usually be given. Many regression models are of this sort, and 'complete' systems have many more parameters still.

With such complicated systems, some sort of a scan of the likelihood surface is still desirable. It is quite difficult to find the maximum, it is true, but one stage less than specifying the whole surface might be a specification of the point of maximum likelihood, and the value there, together with the values of the likelihood at some suitable distance on rays leading in various directions away from the maximum point.

This case emphasizes that the likelihood approach returns an emphasis to problems of *descriptive* statistics, to problems of how to describe the likelihood function.

It was suggested above that in work on economics one has not such a confidence in the exact form of relationships as one might have in other disciplines. This point is especially relevant to the likelihood approach, and shows the way to another treatment of descriptive data. A discussion of a 'simple' regression problem will illustrate a way of approach.

Suppose that we have a fairly small sample of treatments and responses.

Suppose we are considering the response of an economic unit (a household, say) to a particular environmental, or treatment, variable. The variables might be income (x_t) and the consumption of some particular good (y_t). Then a natural thing to do would be to fit a regression line, probably a linear one of the form

$$y_t = \alpha + \beta x_t.$$

Assuming the residuals are normally distributed, the log-likelihood function is

$$l = \log L = -1/2 \sum (y_t - \alpha - \beta x_t)^2$$

and there is no particular difficulty in plotting these as a function of α and β. (It is usually convenient to take x_t as measured as deviations from the mean, $\bar{x_t}$.)

Now if we plot a scatter diagram of the x_t and y_t, it is quite easy, with practice, to judge the relative values of four different lines by eye. An example is given in Fig. 1.

All this is standard elementary practice. But, as was remarked before, it is rare that anyone would have very much faith in a linear regression. The range of acceptable hypotheses is very much wider. Another standard procedure would be to fit a quadratic,

$$y = \alpha + \beta x_t + \gamma x_t^2.$$

It would be harder to assess the likelihood function by eye in this case, if only because the various quadratics provide a rather constrained set of forms, difficult to visualize precisely. But again, there is rarely much *a priori* reason for assuming a quadratic. Usually the

Fig. 1

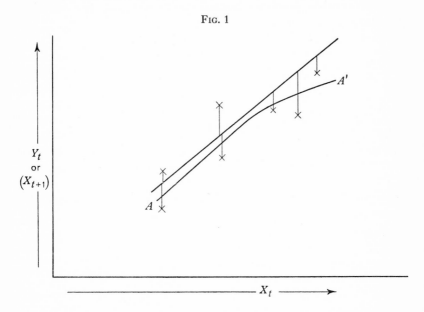

only thing we expect of this sort of data *a priori* is that if the regression is of the form $y = f(x_t)$, then the derivative of $f(x_t)$ does not change too suddenly. Thus a whole variety of shapes are possible for $f(x_t)$, including lines such as AA', not easily put in parametric form.

In this situation, a plot of the likelihood function for the range of acceptable possibilities is not possible. What can be done is to present the original scatter diagram, with some of the range of possible likelihoods, and hope that the trained eye can effectively make estimates of the fit of possible variations of different forms of regression to the data.

Even less often does one find linear regressions in the case of two

or more treatments. Response surfaces are apt to be very complicated, if only because many economic and social forces require a
combination of circumstances to allow them to come into play. For
example, a rapid change in economic efficiency may only come about
when there is both a high income and a high rate of growth of population, so that new equipment is both needed and can be afforded (we
found this sort of effect in a study of retail distribution, for example,
in Barnard *et al.*, 1962). Thus to see the range of plausible regressions, it is necessary to construct the three-dimensional analogues of
scatter diagrams. This author has constructed very many of them,
and has scarcely ever come across one where a multiple linear
regression had a low likelihood comparison with explicable curvi-
linearities of some sort or other.

V. 'EXTENSIBILITY' OF THE LIKELIHOOD FUNCTION

The above argument on regression emphasizes once again the
'extensibility' of the likelihood function. It is always possible to go
back to the *original data*, with a previously unconsidered hypothesis
in mind, calculate the likelihood of the data on the new hypothesis,
and then compare it with the previously obtained likelihood function.
But one does need to preserve the original data, as well as the likelihood function, if this is to be done. The regression case provided
one example; another is the following.

Suppose we collected some data on the number of purchases of an
article in a week. We have at first the hypothesis that the data come
from a Poisson distribution $e^{-\lambda} \dfrac{\lambda^x}{x!}$ For a given x we could publish
the likelihood function

$$L(\lambda) = \lambda^x e^{-\lambda}.$$

The term $1/x!$ is omitted because it is independent of λ.

Now another person reads this. He has the hypothesis that the
reading x came from a geometric distribution

$$(1 - \mu)\mu^x.$$

The extended likelihood for the two hypotheses is

$$(1 - \mu)\mu^x \qquad\qquad 0 < \mu < \infty$$
$$e^{-\lambda}\lambda^x/x! \qquad\qquad 0 < \lambda < \infty.$$

We must now include the $1/x!$ term, for it does not divide through the extended function.

We now briefly consider problems of forecasting from the auto-regressive series. The first point to be noted is that for auto-regressive series, for example

$$x_{t+1} = \alpha x_t + \beta + \epsilon_t,$$

the likelihood function for α and β is exactly the same as for an ordinary regression of the form $y_t = \alpha x_t + \beta + \epsilon_t$.

This fact means that all the considerations about plotting scatter diagrams, etc., that apply to 'ordinary' regression problems apply to this type of problem too. We can look for variations of the linear hypothesis too — an important point when we are predicting x_{t+1} from an unusual x_t.

The distinction between stationary series and explosive series is formally irrelevant. In either case we simply plot the scatter diagram of x_{t+1} against x_t. But if we are dealing with an explosive case (and in situations of economic growth we often are), then it is likely that the most recent x_t will be at the extreme of a range. It will thus be at a place where there is most indeterminacy about the shape of the regression line.

Strictly speaking, in problems of forecasting we are not plotting the likelihood function. Consider the case of a simple linear regression with the ϵ_t independently and normally distributed with unit variance. Then there is a likelihood surface for α and β

$$\log L(\alpha, \beta) = -1/2 \sum (x_{t+1} - \alpha x_t - \beta)^2.$$

The prediction will be taken for some particular value of x_t, $x_t = k$ say, and in principle we should be interested in the likelihood of various values of the parameter $\theta = \alpha k + \beta$. For each value of θ there are many likelihoods, however, corresponding to the various possible α, β.

The simplest solution to this dilemma seems to be to find $\max_{\alpha k + \beta = \theta} L(\alpha k + \beta) = L'(\theta)$, say, and use this as a sort of likelihood function. Since $x_{t+1} = \theta + \epsilon_t$, we can now use $L'(\theta)$ as if it were a probability function and convolute it with the probability density of ϵ_t. The result will be the analogue of a likelihood function of forecast. It will not be a single forecast, nor will it depend on a prior distribution of α. It will give some measure of belief in different forecasts, by a function which, like the likelihood functions, is determined except for a multiplicative constant.

VI. CONCLUDING

The paper has given emphasis to the special importance of passing objective information, whether in publishing research results or in forecasts. In both cases, the information is best passed as an entire function : in the first case as a likelihood function, and in the second case a likelihood function multiplied by a probability function. These problems involve the presentation of a whole function because there is a metric of the sort assumed in problems of decision, and because different recipients of the information are liable to have different prior distributions or other weighting functions.

The problem of conveying the likelihood function focuses attention on how best to describe and summarize it — the problem of 'extending' the likelihood on problems of how to describe the original data. Both, in fact, show the importance of *descriptive statistics*.

There are many subdivisions of the subject of statistics ; this note suggests the following

(1) The conveying of data resulting from an investigation and the problems of description — the typical task of a research report.
(2) The assessment of data involving problems of acceptability or prior probability of the different hypotheses which could give rise to the data ; often most economically examined after the investigation.
(3) Problems of decision, which involve a cost or utility function.

A fourth division, problems of forecasting, contains some of the features of (1) and (2).

REFERENCES

Barnard, G. A. (1949), 'Statistical Inference', *J. Roy. Stat. Soc.* (B), pp. 115–39.
— Jenkins, G. M., and Winsten, C. B. (1962), 'Likelihood Inference and Time Series', *J. Roy. Stat. Soc.* (A), pp. 321–32
Fisher, R. A. (1956), *Statistical Methods and Scientific Inference*, Edinburgh : Oliver & Boyd.
Jeffreys, H. (1948), *Theory of Probability*, 2nd ed., Oxford Univ. Press.
Savage, L. J. (1954), *The Foundation of Statistics*, New York : John Wiley & Son.

Record of Discussion

DISCUSSION OF THE PAPER BY DR. WINSTEN

Dr. Koerts : The message Dr. Winsten wants to bring us is very clear. If we want to communicate information we should publish the likelihood function. In order to reach this conclusion Dr. Winsten has to make the rather drastic assumption that for each value of θ_i, $P(x/\theta_i)$ is known. This implies that his message can only be applied to a rather small part of econometric analysis because we can divide econometric work in which interesting data is used into the following three categories :

(1) The analysis in which data is used but the research worker does not bring the uncertainty explicitly into his analysis. As an example we can think of the work of Professor J. Tinbergen. In this case it goes without saying that the likelihood function cannot be calculated.

(2) The analysis in which the uncertainty is explicitly introduced but no assumption is made with respect to the specific form of the distribution function. One only assumes that certain moments exist. Also in this case the likelihood function cannot be determined.

(3) Finally, we have the work in which the calculation of the likelihood function is possible.

But also in case (3), I have my doubts whether the publication of the likelihood function is really the best thing to do. If we consider more complicated situations than Dr. Winsten is discussing, for example simultaneous equation systems or more complicated regressions equations, the likelihood function also becomes very complicated and we immediately run into the problem of how to describe the likelihood function.[1] Besides this there is the problem of specification errors. Usually we do not know precisely the mathematical form of economic relations. We know beforehand that many specification errors are made. This implies, however, that the likelihood function also contains specification errors. How are we to deal with this problem ?

I think that in many cases the best thing to do is to go back to the original data. That means, publish the original data *together* with the assumptions one has made about the process which generates the data. In many cases this is a simpler procedure and no information is lost.

Finally, I want to make two comments :

(1) Dr. Winsten says that if a research worker is to publish his research he has to pass on to other people the objective parts of his findings. I do not understand this entirely, because if an expert in a certain area is doing research I am also very interested in his prior distribution based on his opinions, before he analyses the data, just because of the fact that this man is an expert.

(2) Dr. Winsten said that likelihood functions are not published. I

[1] In these cases it is no longer possible to draw a graph or to make simple scatter diagrams.

think that this statement is much too strong. In econometric work there are examples in which likelihood functions are indeed published.

Professor Menges : In Dr. Winsten's paper there is one sentence which makes clear the link between his discussion of the likelihood function, on the one hand, and the subject of this Conference on Risk and Uncertainty on the other. And this sentence is the very first of his paper : 'where there is some random variation and therefore some uncertainty'.

Because of the importance of this statement I shall devote the first part of my contribution to just this sentence.

In principle, I agree with Dr. Winsten, but his statement is only one half of the whole matter. Uncertainty has *two* possible sources, not only random variation but also lack of knowledge concerning the possible states of nature or the distribution over the state space respectively. For a Bayesian, I suppose, this distinction is quite irrelevant. But Dr. Winsten is no Bayesian, in so far as he recommends the use of the likelihood function. In order to apply the likelihood function in decision theory, the second source of uncertainty is highly relevant, as I will try to show later.

For the moment let me try to put the whole story of *uncertainty and information* into a tolerably consistent form.

(1) If a well-specified distribution λ over the state space $\Omega = \{\theta\}$ exists, assumed to be independent of the actions, and is *a priori* objectively known, we have the ideal case in the framework of risk and uncertainty. Bayes's criterion is applicable and all is fine.

(2) If objective *a priori* knowledge about λ is not available, one may try to establish λ subjectively. There may be some doubts as to the scientific justification and the empirical validity of personal probabilities. In any case, it will hardly ever be possible to produce *precise* knowledge of the true λ *a priori* subjectively.

(3) If the second source of uncertainty, i.e. lack of knowledge, is total, the application of the pure minimax criterion (whose application is independent of any knowledge about λ) is the only way open. But in most practical cases there is *some* knowledge, i.e. the lack of knowledge is only partial. Empirical data may be obtainable, permitting a meaningful statistical inference and, by this, providing the possibility of 'passing objective information'. This is exactly the situation Dr. Winsten is interested in, and it is the case every reasonable statistician should be interested in.

(4) If the knowledge consists of the information that there exists a certain distribution over the state space, and if, furthermore, it is known that λ lies in a certain subset $\Psi^* \subset \Psi$ of the whole space of distributions, the extended Bayes criterion is applicable.

(5) If an observation X has been made and if it is known (or it seems justified to assume) that the state space is a real one-dimensional parameter space of a certain continuous distribution $f(X \; ; \; \theta)$, where θ itself is distributed according to a continuous distribution $g(\theta \; ; \; \lambda)$, the functional form

of g being known, the observation can be utilized to *reduce the lack of knowledge*.

There are two statistical tools for carrying out this task, both of them belonging to the Fisherian school. One is the likelihood function, the other the fiducial distribution. In our context these two instruments are — to some extent — competing ones, and the question arises as to which should be preferred. In principle, I prefer the fiducial argument, since it provides — from given observations — probability statements either about the unknown θ or about the unknown λ, similar to Bayes *a posteriori* probability but without making use of any *a priori* distribution.

This can be done in several ways, according to the type of uncertainty.

If the uncertainty arises from lack of knowledge concerning θ only, we have to use a fiducial density

$$\frac{\partial F(T;\ \theta)}{\partial \theta}d\theta,$$

where T is a sufficient statistic for θ depending on X, and F the cumulative distribution of T. By weighting the losses with the fiducial densities we obtain a certain risk function. It differs from the ordinary Bayes risk function in that the former is conditional upon the observation T. Bayes's criterion, in a general sense, is applicable.

If the uncertainty arises from randomness of θ and, simultaneously, from lack of knowledge concerning λ, the fiducial distribution $H(T;\ \lambda)$ can be used for the construction of an α_f-fiducial region Ψ^* in which the unknown λ lies with a given fiducial probability α_f close to 1.

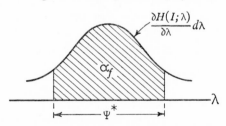

This case, again, leads to the extended Bayes criterion provided the decision-maker considers $1 - \alpha_f$ small enough to ignore the possibility of λ being outside the fiducial region.

(6) If an observation X has been made, but at the same time it does not seem justified to make the assumptions mentioned before, and which are required for the application of the fiducial argument, then my line of reasoning meets with that of Dr. Winsten. We employ the likelihood function. Although it is a weaker measure of uncertainty than fiducial probability, it is less restricted in its applicability. D. A. Spratt has shown to me that the likelihood concept, in the present context, can be used in an *a priori* as well as in an *a posteriori* sense.

If samples have been observed, the distribution of the states of nature $g(\theta ; \lambda)$ can be combined with the likelihood of λ in a way similar to that of R. A. Fisher in an article of 1956. The result is a 'prior relative likelihood' that can be used as the *a priori* distribution in the Bayes sense. After having observed *new* samples the 'prior relative likelihood' can, by means of Bayes's theorem, be transformed into 'likelihood *a posteriori*'.

To conclude, I agree in principle with Dr. Winsten in that

(*a*) the likelihood function is very versatile and of great extensibility ;

(*b*) the likelihood function is important for the objective communication of research results (when uncertainty is involved) ;

(*c*) any presentation of data should give the best possible view of the likelihood function, recognizing the right of everybody to draw their own conclusions and to make their own (highly personal) mistakes.

If the subjective element enters the problem at this stage, it is not so bad by far as the use of subjective probabilities beforehand, because at this stage there has been established a platform for communication based on objective observations.

Mr. Leonardz : I shall confine myself to bringing up for discussion only a few points which I have not understood.

In the middle of the paper there is an example of sampling from a binomial distribution, interpreted as a quality-inspection procedure with unknown probability, θ, of finding a defective item. A sample of n items is taken and none is found defective. The likelihood function attains its maximum for $\theta = 0$ and the argument is that it is not enough to publish this single value as nobody would believe that the true value of θ really is zero. It is claimed that the whole likelihood function should be given on the grounds that different readers have different prior information and need different parts of the likelihood function.

Now, if only $\theta = 0$ is published, it should be perfectly clear to any reader that this is not to be taken literally. Given a description of the experimental set-up he will see that this is just a point estimate. What he might like to have is some kind of confidence interval.

If he is still not happy about things, publication of the likelihood function is not likely to improve the situation, as the reason for his unhappiness will be that he does not believe in the applicability of the probability model used. What he will do is to construct a model of his own and use the original data to calculate his own likelihood function or to perform any other calculations that he finds useful. The extreme example of the reader who knows somehow that θ takes one of two widely separate values is open to the same criticism.

Later on, there is an example which leads to a so-called 'extended' likelihood function. To me this looks like two separate likelihood functions and I do not understand the argument for including the completing multiplicative factor in the second one. I should be very grateful to Dr. Winsten for clarifying this.

Record of Discussion

Professor Bühlmann : The author treats the problem of how to communicate data and proposes that in the case when the parametric family of distributions for the observations is known, the likelihood function would be the best vehicle of information. In cases where a sufficient statistic exists I think that this means that you should communicate the sufficient statistic, an observation which is certainly valuable but not new. However, in the case where no sufficient statistics exist, I should think that it is much more convenient to communicate all the observations rather than the likelihood function.

Professor Hester : I think that Dr. Winsten considers an important topic when he studies the transmission of results of empirical research. But the problem he considers is not the most important. Econometric analyses of time-series data in the United States and other Western countries have become very common. The unfortunate fact is that the same data (perhaps 40 observations) have been analysed hundreds of times by different researchers. I should like to ask him if there is any information in these data to be communicated. Alternatively, does Dr. Winsten have any suggestions for interpreting time-series regression results ?

Owing to shortage of time, it was impossible for Dr. Winsten to reply to the discussion during the session of the Conference and he has waived his right to reply in writing.

Chapter 6

ON SOME OPEN QUESTIONS IN STATISTICAL DECISION THEORY

BY

G. MENGES

I. THE GENERAL STATISTICAL DECISION MODEL

THE concept of decision ranges from predetermined actions, e.g. reflexes or instinctive actions, to chaotic decisions in entirely open situations. Both extremes are excluded from our considerations. We shall deal only with those decisions which terminate a conflict. The person involved in the conflict is the *decision-maker*, an idealized figure assumed to be equipped with unlimited logical faculties and computational capacity.

A certain number of actions are at his disposal, and he faces a certain number of possible states of nature F.

(*a*) If he knows which F is the true one, then he has to make a *decision under certainty*.

(*b*) If he does not know which F is the true one, then he is confronted with a *decision under uncertainty*. The uncertainty can appear in three different forms:

   (1) Nature is his opponent and wants to defeat him. This is the *game-theoretical* case.

   (2) Nature can appear as an opponent which itself is not rational but at the same time not measurable. This is the case of *'complete' uncertainty*.

   (3) Nature can appear as an opponent that is not rational but measurable, i.e. the decision-maker knows the true probability distribution λ over the states of nature exactly (this is the 'case of *pure or genuine risk*'), or he knows λ only approximately, but can, by experimentation, learn more about it (this is the 'case of *approximate or empirical risk*').

In *statistical* decision theory we are concerned only with two of the aforementioned types of decision problems, namely:

(i) decisions under 'complete' uncertainty (case (*b*) 2);

(ii) decisions under 'genuine' or 'empirical' risk (case (*b*) 3).

This means that we omit from our considerations the cases (*a*) and (*b*) 1.

We can now isolate the specializations that are customarily made in the statistical versions of decision theory.

(1) Nature is not taken into account as a rationally acting opponent (while the decision-maker himself is assumed to act rationally).

(2) The decision-maker is given the opportunity to gather information before making his decision. Thus we grant the decision-maker the opportunity to approach his (initial) situation of 'complete' uncertainty to the case of risk as he reduces the uncertainty.

(3) We transform the actions, the states of nature and the outcomes or 'losses' into stochastical terms. We replace the original actions by strategies, the original states of nature by distributions (or distribution parameters), and the 'losses' by risks (expected losses) or even expected risks.

The classical model of statistical decision theory was developed by A. Wald (1950), and is presented, for instance, in the books by Luce and Raiffa (1957) or Chernoff and Moses (1963).

There is given to the decision-maker:

(1) the set of *actions* $A = \{a\}$;

(2) the set of *states of nature* $\Omega = \{F\}$; the elements $F \in \Omega$ are supposed to be probability measures of a certain random variable X which can take values x in a sample space Ξ;

(3) a Borel field σ_1 on A; (A, σ_1) is a measurable space on which probability measures p can be introduced; the set of all probability measures p on (A, σ_1) is denoted by P; the set of all mappings d: $\Xi \to P$ is called D; its elements d, the so-called (randomized) *decision functions*, attach uniquely a probability measure $d(x) \in P$ to every realized value $x \in \Xi$;

(4) the *loss function L*. The states of nature *per se* do not interest the decision-maker; they only concern him as transition stages in the determination of the consequences of the decision — the outcomes, or losses, as they are in most cases defined. An outcome or loss $L(F, a)$ unambiguously corresponds to each possible combination of an action a and a state of nature F. The outcomes can be defined as ordinal or cardinal utility indexes or as losses or profits evaluated in terms of money or other cardinal values. We consider the loss function as a real-valued bounded function L on $\Omega \times A$, the

values $L(F, a)$ of which are called losses. With their help so-called risks $r(F, d)$ on $\Omega \times D$ are defined by

$$r(F, d) = \iint_{\Xi A} L(F, a)\, d\, d(x)\, dF.$$

The risks, also bounded, indicate the expected losses $L(F, a)$ when d is used and F is true.

(5) Finally, the decision-maker adopts a *criterion K* which, on the basis of the risk function, selects one $d_0 \in D$ as the solution of the decision problem, i.e. as the termination of the conflict he was confronted with. Let σ_2 be a Borel field over Ω. On the measurable space (Ω, σ_2) probability measures can be introduced. Let the set of all probability measures λ on (Ω, σ_2) be denoted by Ψ. Ψ is called the set of distribution laws.

(i) If a well-specified distribution law $\lambda \in \Psi$ exists, assumed not to depend on d, and if this well-specified *a priori* distribution is known to the decision-maker, he then faces a decision problem under risk and a Bayes solution is applicable.

A decision function $d_0 \in D$ is called a Bayes solution with respect to $\lambda \in \Psi$, if

$$r^*(\lambda, d_0) = \inf r^* (\lambda, d),$$

where by definition

$$r^*(\lambda, d) = \int_{\Omega} r(F, d)d\, \lambda.$$

Bayes's criterion, which recommends the adoption of just that solution, is practically self-evident and probably the one in favour of which a general consent could be most easily brought about. It has an immediate appeal of rationality. But it may still be questionable as to precisely in what sense the criterion is rational, and for what reasons.

(ii) If nothing is known about the distribution law λ, if it is even doubtful whether such a λ exists at all, the classical theory proposes the minimax criterion as a guide for the decision-maker's behaviour. The minimax solution is defined as follows :

A decision function $d_0 \in D$ is called a minimax solution, if

$$\sup_{F} r(F, d_0) = \inf_{d} \sup_{F} r(F, d).$$

Because this solution does not require any specific knowledge about the elements of Ψ, it is applicable to all decision problems under uncertainty, even (and typically) to the case of complete uncertainty.

I want to limit my considerations to these two basic types of decision criteria, Bayes and minimax, neglecting their variants.

Let us make a stop here and ask the main question of this paper. It is the question of the *applicability of the decision model to empirical situations of risk and uncertainty.* First of all, the answer to this question depends on the assumptions inherent in the general statistical decision model. Each of these assumptions raises at least one specific open question concerning the applicability of the classical decision model.

II. ASSUMPTIONS INHERENT IN THE MODEL

A first assumption in the model is the possibility of enumerating all 'essential' actions and states of nature.

What does 'essential' mean? Which actions and states are 'essential'? Obviously the theory presupposes a rather precise knowledge of the surroundings, the milieu of a specific decision problem, and also a knowledge about the real aims of the decision-maker as well as the initial position of the decision situation. The decision-maker must be able to decide, before solving the actual decision problem, which actions and which states of nature he admits to the problem. Among the actions he will, of course, first eliminate those which are dominated by others. He will also exclude those actions which would make him a (notorious) law-breaker if he chose them. Perhaps he will exclude certain actions just because they are unconventional, or radical — or not radical enough — or because they are, for some reason, inopportune. And perhaps the very best possible action is among those being excluded.

Considerably more serious than these questions, I believe, are those connected with another complex of assumptions, viz., those concerning the possibility of establishing a loss function. In decision theory it is assumed that the decision-maker is familiar with the consequences of a coincidence of an action with a state. If such a familiarity is not at hand but can be supplied, then he may be confronted with another 'decision', namely whether he wants to invest money, time, and effort to provide himself with this knowledge or not.

Furthermore, it is assumed that the decision-maker possesses an unlimited sensitivity for utility differences, because otherwise indifference would be a result of the limited ability to perceive utility differences, and would no longer have the required property of transitivity. Hence it would empirically be led *ad absurdum.* This may actually be so, but the theory would lead to insurmountable troubles if it were to make concessions in this respect. As far as practical application is concerned, it is to be hoped that the empirical utility differences are strong and noticeable enough to be perceived unambiguously. I even believe that numerous decision problems are actually nothing else but problems of establishing a hierarchy of outcomes. The tragic conflict in classical drama often consists in a lack of — at least a weak — ordering of the outcomes of actions. Since the hero cannot order the consequences, he escapes the conflict, for instance by committing suicide. Even in situations of complete certainty a natural conflict can arise if the decision-maker cannot — at least weakly — order the possible consequences. From this point of view there is an analogy, or sometimes perhaps even a competition, between the uncertainty of the states of nature and the uncertainty of the evaluation of the outcomes.

In this context another logical condition should be mentioned : the possibility of expressing the preference relation in real numbers through a utility function. Its basic advantage is computability : instead of a comparison of qualitative descriptions of outcomes, in which one may easily get lost, we get a numerical matrix which can be handled by computational methods. On the other hand it is the most sophisticated feature of a utility function, if it is of the von Neumann–Morgenstern type, that it gives an axiomatic justification of Bayes's criterion. We shall come back to this point in Section IV.

Numerous other assumptions are inherent in the general decision model, of which I want to mention only some of the more problematical and aggravating ones. That the outcome of a decision is completely determined by the action chosen and by the state of nature realized, presupposes at least that these states had been completely separated or 'disaggregated'; in other words, that all relevant features of reality had been taken into account. Another assumption is that the decision-maker is either an individual or, if a group, that it is equipped with a uniform preference system. Besides, it is assumed that the decision-maker wants to act in a rational way, which excludes, for example, his forming his decision by observing ethical precepts or following an aesthetical inspiration; in other words, that he makes his decisions and does not live them. Then the model does not allow for the decision-maker to influence nature, so that it could be considerably changed after a sequence of actions (see Section V).

Thus nature cannot be (gradually) domesticated, nor can the model adapt itself or 'learn' to deal more expertly with the part of nature which is to be faced in the decision situation (see the accommodation principle in Section III). Finally, it is insinuated that the decision is an isolated act, and therefore the interdependence of different decisions (of the same person or of different people) is ignored.

All of these problems can, in principle, be tackled by various ingenious methods; but often only at the price of an inflation of the decision problem — and never completely. The decision model will, therefore, always be an idealized and more or less unrealistic instrument.

III. THE PREDECISION PROBLEM

By predecisions I mean such decisions as constitute the decision problem proper. In the last section we noticed that most of the assumptions, especially the more problematic ones, require certain decisions before the application of traditional decision theory, i.e. *predecisions* which shape the concrete problem.

We may distinguish (at least) five components of the decision structure which have to be laid down by predecisions:

  (i) the action space A;
  (ii) the class P of probability measures p on A;
  (iii) the state space Ω;
  (iv) the sample space Ξ;
  (v) the loss function L.

These components constitute the five-dimensional vector $s = (A, P, \Omega, \Xi, L)$. Let $V_1 = \{A\}$ be the set of all action spaces, $V_2 = \{P\}$ the set of all classes of probability measures p on A, $V_3 = \{\Omega\}$ the set of all state spaces, $V_4 = \{\Xi\}$ the set of all sample spaces, $V_5 = \{L\}$ the set of all loss functions, and let $M = (V_1, \ldots, V_5)$ be the space of the vector s, $M = \{s\}$. The predecision problem is then to select one s out of the whole space M.

By what criteria should this selection be orientated or guided? The reasonable, though somewhat vague, answer is, by the intention to fit the decision model as closely as possible to the empirical decision situation.

The principle behind this intention we call the 'accommodation principle'. The discrepancy between the model and the concrete situation should be as small as possible (see Menges, 1965*a*).

By *M* we may understand the theoretical decision model which is thereby identified with the set of its possible specifications *s* :

$$M = \{s\}.$$

The selection of the *s** ϵ *M* which corresponds best to the empirical decision situation *S* is the predecision problem. Its solution is governed by the accommodation principle.

If the discrepancy between *s* and *S* can be measured by means of a certain metric ρ, we can express the accommodation principle as follows. Choose *s** ϵ *M* such that the distance $\rho(s^*, S)$ between *s** and *S* is an infimum :

$$\rho(s^*, S) = \inf_{s \epsilon M} \rho(s, S).$$

The theoretical model *M*, though it is very general, contains several *a priori* constraints, e.g. that the decision situation must be such that the decision-maker can at least weakly order the outcomes. If the model was so general as not to contain any *a priori* constraints, it would be vacuous.

This implies basically the risk that the model specification fitting the empirical situation perfectly is not contained in *M*; i.e. we run the risk that our model is mis-specified with regard to the empirical situation. Strictly speaking, the decision model is mis-specified with respect to every empirical situation, since we have seen in Section II that it is highly idealized. Reasonably, however, the decision model will not be called mis-specified unless none of its possible specifications comes *near* the empirical situation. And in any case the model contains one specification corresponding 'best' to the empirical situation — however bad this correspondence may be.

In order to solve the predecision problem exactly, one may think of following the algorithm inf $\rho(s, S)$ in a strict sense. Where this way is feasible one may follow it. In numerous practical cases, however, the discrepancy between model and reality, which is to be minimized, is not measurable at all.

Thus the constituting predecision problem is often outside the possibility of direct and exact solvability. Of course one could think of employing another model *M* (of higher order) which determines an optimal rule other than the exacting algorithm inf. $\rho(s, S)$. The specification of that rule could be thought to be again the object of a predecision problem (or rather a 'pre-predecision problem'), guided again by the accommodation principle, and so on *ad infinitum*. But there can be little or no hope of overcoming the original difficulty of constituting the actual (main) decision problem.

On the other hand, however, we may in some special fields be able to devise something like a 'catalogue of frequently encountered situations', indicating (by experience) the best-proved decision models for every instance. Such a thing may be called a *predecision rule* and, wherever it can be elaborated, it will relieve the decision-maker of some of his difficulties.

Furthermore, it may sometimes be possible to incorporate part of the predecision problem into the (main) decision problem itself (Menges, 1965*a*, pp. 8 f.).

Now even if the decision problem proper has been satisfactorily constituted as far as A, P, Ω, Ξ, L are concerned, a decisive point has to be settled. We have to find out the decision-maker's attitude towards information about the distribution law.

IV. KNOWLEDGE ABOUT THE DISTRIBUTION LAW

This knowledge, and even more the decision-maker's fundamental attitude towards information about the distribution law, deeply prejudices his choice of a decision criterion. Which criterion he should choose is the central open question of decision theory.

The application of the Bayes solution can be considered as an immediate expression of objective rationality, if the states of nature obey a probability law λ that is known to the decision-maker (see (i) in Section I, p. 142).

If he succeeded in adjusting his preference behaviour in such an orderly way as to qualify as 'rational' by the von Neumann–Morgenstern characterization, then to follow Bayes's criterion is a must for him, and not much more than a tautology.

What, then, should prevent him from applying it? The answer is, lack of knowledge regarding the distribution law λ.

The decision-maker comes to know λ by three different classical ways: *a priori*, *a posteriori* (both objectively), and subjectively *a priori*. A fourth modern way to overcome the ignorance over λ is to solve the decision problem independently of any knowledge of the distribution law.

Let us start with the classical ways. Whenever *a priori* knowledge about λ exists, it should of course be used, for the sake of the applicability of Bayes's solution. But I could not tell you a single example from the field of economics and the social sciences where such *a priori* knowledge would objectively exist, in contrast to physics, biology and other natural sciences.

Because in our field we do not possess *a priori* knowledge about λ objectively, we take refuge in procuring relevant information, or we follow the proposals of some decision theorists (Koopman, 1940; Kyburg and Smokler, 1964; Savage, 1951, 1954) and use subjective *a priori* knowledge.

The justification for using subjective or personal probabilities may be an open question for some of you, but not for others, and not with me. I have tried to show (Menges, 1965*b*) that the probability subjectivism is a fallacy. The only way open in economics and the social sciences, therefore, is the *a posteriori* one.

Of course it will never be possible, by empirical observation, to find the distribution law λ precisely. We can, however, hope to find a certain subset Ψ^* out of the whole class $\Psi = \{\lambda\}$ of distribution laws.

If we have gained knowledge of $\Psi^* \subset \Psi = \{\lambda\}$, we can apply a certain combination of the Bayes and minimax solutions, which I called the 'extended Bayes solution' (Menges, 1966; see also Schneeweiss, 1964). Choose $d_0 \in D$ with

$$\sup_{\lambda \in \Psi^*} r^*(\lambda, d_o) = \inf_{d \in D} \sup_{\lambda \in \Psi^*} r^*(\lambda, d).$$

The Bayes character of this solution is the more pronounced the smaller Ψ^* is, and vice versa.

In the limiting case, where Ψ^* contains one distribution only, the criterion reduces to the pure Bayes solution. This limiting case may even be attained when Ψ^* still contains more than one element. This happens if and only if Ψ^* lies inside a 'region of invariance' with respect to the Bayes solution. The practical problem consists, then, in finding such regions for the problem on hand.

A certain generalization of the extended Bayes concept consists in decomposing Ω into a few (disjoint) subsets (Menges, 1966, p. 7) $\Omega_1, \Omega_2, \ldots$ with $U_i \Omega_i = \Omega$. If the decision-maker knows that Ω_i occurs with probability $p_i (\sum p_i = 1)$ and Ψ^* is the class of distribution laws attaching the probability p_i to $\Omega_i - (i = 1, 2, \ldots)$, while the probability distribution within Ω_i is unknown, he should choose $d_o \in D$ such that [1]

---

[1] This form is equivalent to

$$\Sigma p_i \sup_{F \in \Omega_i} r (F, d_0) = \inf_d \Sigma p_i \sup_{F \in \Omega_i} r (F, d),$$

which turns to the pure minimax criterion in the case $i = 1$ (Menges, 1966, p. 7).

$$\sup_{\lambda \in \Psi^*} \sum_i \int_{\Omega_i} r(F, d_0) \, d\lambda = \inf_{d \in D} \sup_{\lambda \in \Psi^*} \sum_i \int_{\Omega_i} r(F, d) \, d\lambda,$$

where

$$\bigcup_i \Omega_i = \Omega, \int_{\Omega_i} d\lambda = p_i (i = 1, 2, \ldots) \text{ and } \sum_i p_i = 1.$$

This approach allows the decision-maker to exploit any information available on λ.

Another method, which works in certain situations, utilizes the observations $x_1, \ldots, x_n$ of the random variable X to establish a *fiducial probability* distribution λ_f over Ω. Such a λ_f is an objective measure of what we know about the true state of nature, and may be used directly as the distribution law in Bayes's criterion.

There is a second fiducial possibility. With the help of fiducial methods we can find a region in the space Ψ, in which the true distribution λ lies with given probability, and this region can be considered as Ψ^*.

Finally, let me mention one more approach, estimating the distribution law λ over Ω by means of sampling, which has been pointed out to me by Helmut Diehl.

Let $(F_1, \ldots, F_k)$ be the space of states of nature, where the F_i are possible continuous distribution functions of the real random variable X. The distribution law λ over $(F_1, \ldots, F_k)$ is to be estimated, given observations x_i of the random variable X.

Let us assume that we are given $m - (m \gg k)$ samples

$$x_l^{(n)} = (x_{l1}, \ldots, x_{ln})$$
$$\cdot$$
$$\cdot$$
$$\cdot$$
$$x_m^{(n)} = (x_{m1}, \ldots, x_{mn}).$$

Each of these samples is assumed to be the result of n independent drawings from a certain F, which itself is assumed to be the result of a random drawing from (the unknown) λ.

For each sample $x_i^{(n)} - (i = 1, \ldots, m)$ we form the empirical distribution $S_n^{(i)}(x)$ and calculate the values

$$\sup_x | F_j(x) - S_n^{(i)}(x) | \text{ for all } j = 1, \ldots, k.$$

149

That state F_{ν_i} for which

$$\sup_x \mid F_{\nu_i}(x) - S_n^{(i)}(x) \mid \; = \min_j \; \sup_x \mid F_j(x) - S_n^{(i)}(x) \mid$$

is recorded. With probability 1 there is only one smallest sup. In this way we obtain a set of m states F_j:

$$F_{\nu_1}, \ldots, F_{\nu_m}, \nu_\alpha \in \{1, \ldots, k\} \text{ for } \alpha = 1, \ldots, m.$$

Each of these $F_{\nu_a}(\alpha = 1, \ldots, m)$ gets probability $\dfrac{1}{m}$.

Thus we get a probability distribution over the set $\{F_1, \ldots, F_k\}$, which is considered as ('point') estimation of the true distribution law λ over the space Ω of states of nature. It should be noticed that this estimation is consistent, i.e. if n, $m \to \infty$, the estimation tends to fit the true λ with probability 1. This is evident by the well-known theorem of Glivenko, for if $n \to \infty$, each $S_n^{(i)}(x)$ will tend towards a certain F_j and if furthermore $m \to \infty$, the probability distribution over the F_j will tend towards λ.

Let me now return to the fourth of the ways of overcoming ignorance over λ. Wald (1950) and a few other decision theorists propose to solve the decision problem even if Ψ^* equals the whole class Ψ of all distribution functions. They suggest the pure minimax criterion, which (in its pure form) is independent of any knowledge of the distribution law.

But in doing so they side-step the original decision problem. The decision-maker no longer needs or uses distributions, and he therefore gets no stimulus to look for information about the distribution; that means that the empirical basis has disappeared. If you consider, furthermore, that he behaves, according to the minimax criterion, as if struggling with a rational opponent, you will see that he is in an altogether different decision situation or, at least, that he views his decision situation from a different angle.

I want to point out that the statistical decision-maker practically never has to use the pure minimax criterion because in most cases he has or can obtain empirical data permitting a valid meaningful statistical inference. In this way he may approach the Bayes type of solution better and better, without making use of a doubtful criterion or of doubtful probabilities.

V. INSTABILITY OF THE DECISION SITUATION

We could put a stop to the discussion of open questions in statistical decision theory, had we not to deal with the application to social phenomena, where the free will of human individuals rules, rather than natural determinism. The behaviour of these individuals may change irregularly and rapidly in time, while natural phenomena typically follow time-stable laws.

Instability would raise no further question, if the sequence 'formulation of the decision problem; predecisions; procurement of information; computation of the optimal decision function; concrete action; coinciding of the action with a state of nature; appearance of the outcome' took place with such a speed that there would not occur any change within the decision situation during the process.

This is precisely what the theory assumes. Actually this assumption is most problematical, at least in the field of the social sciences.

In reality that sequence will take a certain amount of time, say a time interval of length G. If the decision situation is stable over the interval of length T and if the process interval G is included by the stability interval T, then the empirical situation is obviously equivalent to the situation assumed in theory.

As the process interval becomes longer and the stability interval becomes shorter, the empirical situation departs from the assumption of the model. We shall not inquire further into the length of the process interval; as a rule it is determined by technological factors, among others by the computing time necessary to arrive at a solution of the decision problem. The stability interval, on the other hand, implies a number of specific problems.

Among the factors limiting the stability interval are:

(1) Changes of the decision-maker's targets as these changes are reflected in the set of relevant actions; or
(2) changes of the set of states of nature that are essential; or
(3) changes in the evaluation of the outcomes.

This limitation is likely to occur even when we are dealing with consequences of decisions which can be measured cardinally, and which can be expressed in terms of money units, if the prices of the goods that make up the consequences change irregularly in time. Changes of a preference field over the set of outcomes can easily occur, if the decision-maker is not completely certain and consistent in evaluating the possible outcomes. Such stability in his evaluations will probably be the harder for him the smaller the utility differences between the various outcomes are. In particular, the empirical transitivity of indifference relations will hardly be preserved for a longer period of time.

Yet the main factor of instability is the possible variation of the distribution law.

In the previous section we considered it desirable to find a region Ψ^* as small as possible. But there exists a deep antagonism between this effort to minimize Ψ^* on the one hand, and the danger of instability on the other. When at a time point t_o a class Ψ_o^* has been fixed, the application of the extended Bayes solution leads to the strategy d_o such that

$$\sup_{\lambda \epsilon \Psi_o^*} r^*(\lambda, d_o) = \inf_{d \epsilon D_o^*} \sup_{\lambda \epsilon \Psi^*} r^*(\lambda, d).$$

Assume that at a time point t_1 the true distribution law is λ_1 and lies outside Ψ_o^*. It may happen in this case that

$$r^*(\lambda_1, d_o) > \sup_{\lambda \epsilon \Psi_o^*} r^*(\lambda, d_o),$$

and another strategy than d_o would have been chosen, had it been known that λ_1 is a possible distribution law, i.e. Ψ_o^* was chosen too small so as to cover the situation at the time point t_1. In order to serve as a basis for decisions realized during the interval T, the class Ψ_o^* must be 'exhaustive' over T, i.e. it must contain all distributions that can possibly occur during T, but simultaneously it must be as small as possible for the sake of the dominance of the Bayes character of the solution. In other words, Ψ_o^* must be a minimal exhaustive set.

Finally, it should be mentioned that not only is the distribution law the main factor of instability, it is also the component of the decision situation hardest to control.

VI. SUMMARY

(1) The concept of decision is introduced and several types of decision problems are distinguished. The principal features of the modern statistical decision model are developed.

(2) Some main assumptions inherent in the model are discussed, showing the high degree of idealization of the model: possibility of

enumerating all 'essential' actions and states of nature, possibility of establishing a loss function, unlimited sensitivity for utility differences, possibility of expressing the preference relation in real numbers, etc.

(3) The concept of predecision is introduced, meaning principally such decisions as define the decision problem. At least five components are subjects of predecisions : the action space A, the class P of probability measures p on A, the state space Ω, the sample space Ξ, and the loss function L. These components constitute the five-dimensional vector s. The decision model M is identified with the set of its possible specifications s: $M = \{s\}$. The selection of that $s^* \epsilon M$ which corresponds best to the empirical situation is the pre-decision problem. Its solution is governed by the accommodation principle. Consequences of this concept are discussed, particularly the problems of mis-specification and mathematical solvability.

(4) The application of the Bayes solution is considered as an immediate expression of rationality, if the states of nature obey a *known* probability law λ. Reasonable possibilities of reaching knowledge about λ are discussed : the extended Bayes solution, finding regions of invariance (with respect to the Bayes solution), a certain generalization of the extended Bayes solution, also establishing a fiducial probability distribution, finding a region in the distribution space Ψ with the help of fiducial methods, and finally a method of estimating directly the distribution law by means of sampling. On the other hand, the statistical decision-maker practically never has to employ the pure minimax criterion, nor is the use of subjective probabilities proposed to him.

(5) Application of statistical decision theory to social phenomena is limited by the instability of the decision-maker's targets, changes in the evaluation of the outcomes, etc. The main factor of instability is the possible variation of the distribution law. Some consequences of this instability are discussed.

Numerous questions remain partially or totally open, in connection with the assumptions of the model, with the objectivity and measurability of the specification of the model, with the recognition of the distribution law, and principally with the phenomenon of instability.

Let us imagine that a 'real decision-maker', e.g. the director of a firm, wants to consult us, the decision theorists. In order to help him, we have to ask him :

Can you enumerate exactly your possible actions ?

Do you know exactly the possible states of nature ?

Do you possess an unlimited sensitivity for utility differences ?

Do your utilities possess the von Neumann–Morgenstern property?

Do you know objectively — either *a priori* or *a posteriori* — the distribution law over the states of nature, or, if not, are you willing to accept the pure minimax rule as the expression of rational behaviour in your actual decision situation ?

Do you know that the decision situation is stable within a certain, not too short, period ?

If he is able to answer these questions in the affirmative, then we can apply the Bayes or minimax criterion or some combination of them.

Otherwise we can possibly give him some help, on the basis of previous experience, to fill up the gaps in his knowledge.

But what should we do if some intrinsic feature of the decision situation dictates a negative answer to one of the above questions ?

REFERENCES

Behara, M., and Menges, G. (1963), 'On Decision Criteria under Various Degrees of Stability', *J. Ind. Stat. Assoc.* 1, pp. 185–95.

Chernoff, H., and Moses, L. E. (1963), *Elementary Decision Theory*, 3rd ed., New York, London 1963.

Hodges, J. L., Jr., and Lehmann, E. L. (1952), 'The Use of Previous Experience in Reaching Statistical Decisions', *Annals of Mathematical Statistics*, 23, pp. 396–407.

Koopman, B. O. (1940), 'The Axioms and Algebra of Intuitive Probability', *Annals of Mathematics*, ser. 2, 42, pp. 269–92.

Kyburg, H. E., and Smokler, H. E. (eds.) (1964), *Studies in Subjective Probability*, New York, London, Sydney.

Luce, R. D., and Raiffa, H. (1957), *Games and Decisions*, New York.

Menges, G. (1965a), 'Predecisions', *Econometric Research Program. R.M.*, no. 71, Princeton University.

— (1965b), 'Über Wahrscheinlichkeitsinterpretationen', *Statistische Hefte*, 6, Heft 2.

— (1966), 'On the "Bayesification" of the Minimax Principle', *Unternehmensforschung*, 10, Heft 2.

Savage, L. J. (1951), 'The Theory of Statistical Decision', *J. Amer. Statist. Assoc.* 46, pp. 55–67.

— (1954), *The Foundations of Statistics*, New York, London 1954.

Schneeweiss, H. (1964), 'Eine Entscheidungsregel für den Fall partiell bekannter Wahrscheinlichkeiten', *Unternehmensforschung*, 8, pp. 86–95.

Wald, A. (1950), *Statistical Decision Functions*, New York, London.

Record of Discussion

DISCUSSION OF THE PAPER BY
PROFESSOR MENGES

Dr. Pelikán : I would start by saying that Professor Menges has given a very interesting account of some of the many open questions of statistical decision theory. I do not think we shall be able to settle them in this discussion, however. I shall concentrate on the problem of predecisions, where I see the main interest of the paper.

I agree with the author that statistical decision theory is concerned with a simplified model of the real decision situation and that the choice of this model represents another decision situation which must be solved beforehand. Sometimes this predecision problem can be more difficult than the decision proper.

I do not fully agree with the author about the manner in which he explains the problem. I do not believe it is possible to speak about the discrepancy between the model and the concrete situation in such a general way and that it makes sense to say that some model corresponds best to reality in an absolute manner. To correspond better to reality is a very vague notion which, moreover, could be understood as implying that more variables are taken into account and that they are measured with greater precision. This is obviously not the case. The author says that in numerous practical cases the discrepancy between the model and reality, which is to be minimized, is not measurable ; I would rather say that it is never measurable and that we cannot speak about its minimization.

The predecision problem could perhaps be looked at as another decision problem with its own loss function, so that we could speak about its minimization. I should like to stress that such a loss function can only rarely be interpreted as the 'distance' between the model and reality. On the contrary, in some cases this function can be minimized for models quite 'distant' if, for example, its value also depends on the amount of information which must be handled in the decision process proper. This would mean that beyond some limit, a better and more 'realistic' model is not worth the effort.

Dr. Leinfellner : I am going to discuss the excellent paper by Professor Menges, which gives an outline of statistical decision theory. Professor Menges's decision model is complementary to my own because it is not based upon utility theory but presupposes it. Professor Menges builds up his statistical decision theory in three steps. In the first he introduces Wald's model where $F_1, F_2, \ldots, F_n$ are states of nature ; $a_1, a_2, \ldots, a_m$ are actions ; and a_{ij} is the outcome, loss, profit, etc., when action a_i is taken and state of nature F_j obtains.

The second step is the introduction of uncertainty and risk into the model. Ignorance on the part of the player about the states of nature brings uncertainty of the three different kinds into the theory

(i) game-theoretical;
(ii) case of 'complete' uncertainty: if for example nature is the opponent of the player and he cannot measure the probability distribution λ of the states of nature F_j;
(iii) nature can appear as an opponent that is not rational but measurable: the decision-maker knows the probability distribution λ exactly or approximately (case of pure or approximate risk).

After a formal outline of the theory he gives in the last step two solutions of the decision problem: Bayes's solution and the minimax solution (as I see it).

Professor Menges limits his discussion to these two basic types of decision rules, and I shall therefore only mention a further criterion: Laplace's. If the probabilities of the different states are unknown, we can assume that they are all equal and the decision rule is to maximize $\Sigma_j a_{ij}/n$. Further, one should mention Hurwicz's and Savage's criteria. Wald's criterion, the minimax solution, is given as the second solution in Professor Menges's paper, as far as I can see.

In Section II Professor Menges gives us a list of assumptions which are made in his model. I very much agree with the statement that 'numerous decision problems are actually nothing else but problems of establishing a hierarchy of outcomes'. That is the leading concept in my own theory Th2.

With regard to learning theory in decision processes I will mention the work of M. Flood, 'Game-learning Theory and Some Decision Making Experiments', in the Thrall–Coombs–Davis volume, where learning is a Markov process.

In Section III Professor Menges develops the predecision problem. He gives a formal theory as an ordered quintuple $s = (A, P, \Omega, \Xi, L)$ where A is the action space, P the class of probability measures p on A, Ω the state space, Ξ the sample space, and L the loss function. The selection of an s^* which corresponds best to the empirical decision situation S Professor Menges calls the predecision problem. If the discrepancy between s and S can be measured by means of a certain metric ρ, this problem can be solved by choosing s^* such that $\rho(s^*, S)$ is an infimum (the accommodation principle). In other cases it may be possible to find the best-proved decision models by a catalogue of frequently encountered situations. This seems to be equal to my method of finding a super-decision rule.

As pointed out by Professor Menges, the solution of the predecision problem is often merely hypothetical. He therefore tries to find out the decision-maker's attitude towards information about the distribution law, because this attitude can deeply influence his choice of decision criterion or his choice of a super-decision rule. There are three classical ways: *a* *posteriori, a priori* (both objectively), and subjectively *a priori*. As a Bayesian, Professor Menges decides in favour of the *a posteriori* method by the extended Bayes solution. As that solution has been discussed already, I would add only a suggestion. If we assume that at the time point t_1 the true distribution law is λ_1 and lies outside Ψ'^*, there exists an inequality

$$r^*(\lambda_1, d_0) > \sup_{\lambda \in \psi_0^*} r^*(\lambda, d_0).$$

If it should be possible to transform this inequality into a difference, this difference gives us the range of instability and perhaps a useful factor expressing instability. On the value of this range depends the possibility of finding a solution, i.e. a decision rule.

Dr. Winsten: Professor Menges's paper shows much unease about decision theory. I must confess that as somebody who has in fact used decision theory in industrial situations I was quite surprised at these feelings. Perhaps all of us have the same sort of feelings about economic theory or sociological theory, but decision theory has always seemed to me much more clear-cut than other theories. The feeling in Professor Menges's paper is perhaps summed up by his statement that the decision-theory model will always be an idealized and more or less unrealistic instrument. Idealized, yes ; unrealistic, no — not if you use it in the right situations. We have had several good examples today, taken from the insurance business, of problems which seem to be admirably suited to the use of decision theory. In industrial sampling — the field in which I have used decision theory — we often have very clear-cut situations where one can make useful gains by using what are, after all, directly relevant mathematical results. However, decision theory has often been used for much more general situations than these : it has been used partly to explain how people make decisions and partly to describe how people ought to make decisions under all possible circumstances. We must therefore look for more refinement of the theory, for more general theories, and for more special theories.

Consider some of the problems mentioned by Professor Menges. For example, there is one where the utility function is not very well differenti-ated. Here I feel we are dealing with a shadow problem. If you do not have a well-differentiated utility function then it does not matter what decision you make. You could do what you like and no theory will help you to decide. Further, if one is interested in decisions, one should not make too strong a distinction between prior distributions and minimax theory. One of the most useful theorems in decision theory is that, as a rule, a minimax decision is in fact also a Bayes decision with a particular prior distribution. If it is found that a minimax decision implies a prior distribution that is felt as quite implausible, then surely minimax theory should not be used.

Many problems of decision are broad and complicated, and one should develop a philosophy for dealing with complicated, open-ended problems. The first element of this philosophy would surely be that complicated, open-ended problems do not have simple solutions involving only a little analysis. If one looks for a quick solution in problems in which nothing is well defined or well known, then one is going to be disappointed.

How can this situation be dealt with ? One way I will suggest is in strong contrast to what Professor Menges called the accommodation principle. He suggested that what should be done is to look for the nearest realistic case. But here there would be difficulties in finding an appropriate definition of 'nearness'. Instead I suggest that one should try to span the nature of real-world problems by different theories. The theories and problems can be regarded as points in a space on which a metric is not defined. One should try to surround one's actual case with points representing theories, theories whose consequences it is possible to examine. Some, for example, might have particularly simple prior distributions which admit algebraic solution. Others might have the sort of utility function which enables a solution to be found by computer. Having done this, one might notice that the solution is sensitive to some aspects of the assumptions but not to others. But then one has found what is important in the specification of the problem. It is not a question of finding what theory is closest to reality but of doing a comprehensive sensitivity analysis. Of course, one may find oneself in a situation where the results are very sensitive to assumptions. This simply means that decision theory is not yet able to help.

Mr. Bessière : It seems to me that the notion of the 'distance' between a model and reality is fundamentally subjective and thus that its introduction is in contradiction with the aim of *maximum objectivity* which we agreed upon and which to me seems to be the aim of any science. On the other hand I believe that the suggestions of Dr. Pelikán give us an objective means of evaluating, let us say, a 'deviation' (*écart*), the psychological meaning of which would be the same as that of Professor Menges's 'distance'.

My objections to this notion of 'distance' go even further, however, because in order that this distance be defined we must admit that we can know, or at least define, a 'reality' which would be independent of any model. This is not the case, however, because any description we can make of this reality must be given by a verbal representation, or at least a conceptual one, which is already a model. Moreover, everything that we can *know* about reality comes through the nervous inflows received by our brains and these inflows are already symbols. We live in a world of symbols. We perceive reality only as it is coded by our concepts, and even in the best case we are only able to know it as it is coded by our nervous inflows. We shall never know what there is on the other side of the translators which are our eyes, our hands, etc.

This has two consequences. On the one hand, the 'distance' ρ cannot be defined, and the best thing we can do is to evaluate the quality of our models by the success of the decisions that they generate; this is the method of the experimental sciences. On the other hand, there will always remain in our knowledge, and *a fortiori* in the decision, an irreducible subjective component, which, however, should not keep us from always seeking the maximum of objectivity.

I would also like to mention — without going into details — that under the initiative of Professor Pierre Massé, Électricité de France has for several years been using a method for preparing decisions in the face of major uncertainties. This method I have called the 'method of minimax regret' because it uses the same mathematical formalization as that of the minimax regret criterion. The point is that this criterion is not used as a real decision *criterion*, but as a *tool* for facilitating the difficult calculations which the strict use of 'subjective' probabilities would lead to. But we justify this use by taking the classical Bayes theories as our starting-point. On the practical level the method is, of course, satisfactory. I wanted to mention this in defence of, and as an illustration of the minimax regret methods.

Professor Menges: Perhaps there are a few minor misunderstandings which I should clarify first.

(1) If and only if the discrepancy between s and S can be measured by means of a certain metric ρ can we formulate the accommodation principle in an operational way. I admitted already in my paper that $\rho(s, S)$ will in most practical cases not be measurable. On the other hand, it seems to me that there might be practical cases where $\rho(s, S)$ is indeed measurable. But even where $\rho(s, S)$ is not measurable, the accommodation principle is not to be abolished completely. It may well serve as an (admittedly more or less subjectively orientated) guide.

(2) The term 'measurability of uncertainty' in my paper is used in the sense of Knight, meaning simply some knowledge of the probability distribution over the states of nature.

(3) 'Best correspondence to reality' is indeed a highly vague notion. But I did not at all mean it in a sense of taking into account more and more variables. The desire to obtain a 'good correspondence to reality', e.g. in Frisch's sense of the autonomy principle, can even lead to the selection of only a very few 'autonomous' (or 'causal') variables.

(4) The extended Bayes solution has as its two limiting cases the Bayes solution and the minimax solution. A special case of the Bayes solution is the Laplace solution. With the application of Hurwicz's criterion there is connected the strong difficulty of quantifying the optimism degree. Savage's regret criterion is really an interesting one, but I doubt that its inclusion into the discussion of open questions could 'close' one or the other of them.

(5) It is to be conceded that a prediction model, or at least some sort

of prediction, is necessary to find the optimal solution of a decision problem. We must assume, of course, that the outcome of an action depends on some aspect of nature, say on the value of some variable θ. Then we simply have to predict something about θ in order to find a good action.

On the other hand, in a decision model the prediction process may and often will be concealed in the process of finding the optimal (or a good) decision, which is the model's proper aim. Still, concealed or not, prediction is inherent in decision-making, sometimes, however, only in a mutilated form, e.g. when the only important thing is to know if $\theta_1 < \theta < \theta_2$ or not. This depends on the loss function.

The less the decision structure is sensitive to θ, the less important is the role played by a prediction of θ in solving the decision problem.

May I come now to more detailed points made in the discussion ? I am afraid I cannot agree with some of the comments made by the discussants. Here they are :

(1) I cannot consider lack of empirical strongness and noticeability of utility differences as a shadow problem. To me (and others) it seems to be a highly disturbing and uncomfortable difficulty.

(2) Dr. Winsten reminds me of the theorem by Wald that a minimax decision is in general also a Bayes decision relative to a least favourable *a priori* distribution. I can by no means recognize the usefulness of this theorem in order to overcome any difficulty mentioned in my paper.

The said theorem holds under a very restrictive assumption : P and Ψ contain all possible randomized decision functions or *a priori* distributions respectively (then the risk function $r^*(\lambda, d)$ has a saddle point). In practical problems, however, there are often only finite subsets $P^* \subset P$ and $\Psi^* \subset \Psi$ under consideration, and in this case the Bayes solution with respect to the least favourable *a priori* distribution in Ψ^* is in general not identical with the minimax solution.

(3) Mr. Bessière's objection is a fundamental one. I am nearly in complete agreement with his statements, e.g. if he requires maximal objectivization. And I even admit the strong dependence of model and reality in both directions. It is not without models that we recognize reality. But in spite of all this I think it is at least comfortable and useful in scientific work to postulate the existence of an outside world. Although reality can only be represented in one's mind by notions, concepts, terms, models, and other abstractions (and not in itself), following the old Heidelberg school of philosophy (Rickert, Windelband, Max Weber) I consider — at least in the field of social sciences — a strong need for something like accommodation. Reality can be captured in generic notions only ; social and economic models are expressed in 'ideal' notions only (*Idealbegriffe* in the sense of Max Weber). The scientist's task is to try to define both the generic and the ideal notions in such a way as to minimize the discrepancy between them. But this is a vast and controversial field.

Record of Discussion

There came up in the discussion a few suggestions and points of view which seem very interesting and valuable.

(1) I agree with Dr. Pelikán that it may be worth while (and that even some of the predecision difficulties might thereby be overcome) to take reflexes and instinctive as well as subconscious actions into consideration.

I want furthermore to pick up Dr. Pelikán's idea to consider eventually a loss function of the predecision problem as the basis of defining a distance between reality and model. One may define the distance $\rho(s, S)$ between reality S and model s as the loss $L(s, S)$ to be suffered if the true empirical situation is S and the model s has been specified. One may doubt that (Ls, S) can be determined, but this attempt shows at least that there *are* possibilities of quantifying 'nearness', 'discrepancy', or 'distance' between reality and model. A similar idea has been used by A. Wald when he defined the so-called intrinsic metric in order to 'metrize' very general spaces like action spaces.

(2) Dr. Leinfellner is right when stating complementarity between his model and mine. From his theory Th2 there follows a lot of interesting aspects with regard to my model. And there seems to be a close relationship between his super-decision and my predecision problem.

(3) The inclusion of the methods and concepts of learning theory into the decision model in order to overcome some of the difficulties, as suggested by Dr. Leinfellner, should indeed be practised more.

(4) The suggestion of transforming the inequality

$$r^*(\lambda_1, d_0) > \sup_{\lambda \epsilon \psi_0^*} r^* (\lambda, d_0)$$

into a difference so as to reach a measure of instability is very interesting, and I shall try to examine it in more detail.

(5) Dr. Winsten demands more refinement of the theory, for more general and for more special theories. So do I. I also agree when he states that the decision theory in its more classical forms serves well in insurance problems and in industrial sampling. The more stable the general conditions of the decision situation, i.e. the more determined by technological or biological factors they are, the better serves the present theory.

(6) Dr. Winsten suggests that we try to cover actual real-world problems by a set of proper but different theories. If I understand him right he suggests some sort of sensitivity analysis instead of trying to accommodate the actual decision problem and the model specification, whereas I propose to introduce such hypotheses into the model that can be considered close to real conditions.

Dr. Winsten : I only wish to make one clarification. Professor Menges talks of the 'closeness' of a hypothesis to real conditions. The only measure of such closeness would, in fact, be the usefulness of the hypothesis for prediction, and this notion of 'closeness' is circular. By any other definition a hypothesis may be close, yet because the predictions

161

from a hypothesis are very sensitive to the exact specification of the hypothesis, it may be a very bad predictor. That is why I should prefer the notion of a very extended sensitivity analysis to Professor Menges's 'accommodation principle'.

Professor Menges: To me, however, accommodation and sensitivity analysis are not antagonistic. It depends on the aim one follows in the application of the decision model to which degree one will employ one of them or even both. If one desires to base one's decision upon a 'real-valid' judgement about reality and upon an explanation of real-world phenomena (i.e. the statistician's desire), one will probably be inclined to follow the accommodation principle. If, on the other hand, one wants to make sure decisions, regardless of what the real-world conditions are (i.e. the game-theoretical aspect), one will perhaps do better by analysing the model's sensitivity. In any case, I agree with Dr. Winsten that a sensitivity analysis of the assumptions is important in the specification process of any model.

Chapter 7

A THEORY OF BINARY DECISIONS

BY

PETRU L. IVANESCU

I. INTRODUCTORY

IN this paper we shall be concerned with problems involving binary decisions, i.e. problems which can be described using functions with bivalent variables (0, 1) and real values; such functions will be called pseudo-Boolean functions.

A variable takes the value 1 if the corresponding action is to be carried out, and the value 0 in the opposite case. We shall suppose that the constraints of the problem are deterministic, while the utilities are expressed by means of pseudo-Boolean functions, whose coefficients $c_1, c_2, \ldots, c_\rho$ can take on (at random) values in the finite sets $T_1, T_2, \ldots, T_\rho$.

In the first two sections we shall describe methods for obtaining the complete list of all those binary decisions which fulfil the constraints. The use of this result for finding the 'best' action, under complete ignorance about the values c_i are to take in T_i $(i = 1, \ldots, p)$, is described in Section III; however, it is not the aim of this paper to enter into discussions concerning the criteria to be used in the definition of 'best' actions.

In Section IV, assuming that the probability distribution of all c_i is known, methods are described for finding the minimum expected value of a pseudo-Boolean function the variables of which can be subject to certain constraints.

The methods are based on the results obtained previously by the author and Sergiu Rudeanu, which are described in Ivanescu and Rudeanu (1967). Different applications of pseudo-Boolean programming are described in Ivanescu (1965).

The methods were programmed for a MECIPT–1 computer with satisfactory results.

Notation. The two-element Boolean algebra $\{0, 1\}$ will be denoted by B_2; disjunction will be denoted by $\cup$, conjunction by . (or simply juxtaposition), negation by ‾. If $f(x_1, \ldots, x_n)$ is a mapping of the Cartesian product $\underbrace{B_2 \times B_2 \times \ldots \times B_2}_{n \text{ times}}$ into the field R of reals, it will be termed a 'pseudo-Boolean function'. If $f(x_1, \ldots, x_n)$ is a pseudo-Boolean function, then

$$f(x_1, \ldots, x_n) = 0$$

is termed a pseudo-Boolean equation, while

$$f(x_1, \ldots, x_n) < 0$$
$$f(x_1, \ldots, x_n) \geqslant 0$$

are termed pseudo-Boolean inequalities.

II. LINEAR PSEUDO-BOOLEAN CONDITIONS

The aim of this section is to describe an algorithm for solving systems of linear equations and inequalities of the form

$$\sum_{h=1}^{m} (a'_{ih}x_h + a''_{ih}\bar{x}_h) \overset{<}{\underset{>}{=}} b_i \qquad (i = 1, \ldots, m) \tag{1}$$

where the unknowns $x_h - (h = 1, \ldots, m)$ can take only the values 0 or 1, where

$$\bar{x}_h = 1 - x_h, \tag{2}$$

and where a'_{ih}, a''_{ih} and b_i are given real numbers.

Let us consider the case of a single inequality of the form

$$\sum_{h=1}^{m} (a'_h x_h + a''_h \bar{x}_h) \geqslant b \, ; \tag{3}$$

it is easy to see that it can be brought to the form

$$\sum_{i=1}^{n} c_i X_i \geqslant d \tag{4}$$

where X_i is equal either to x_i or to $\bar{x}_i$, and c_i and d are given real numbers; we shall further assume that

$$c_1 \geqslant c_2 \geqslant \ldots \geqslant c_n \geqslant 0.$$

A solution $S^* = (X_1^*, \ldots, X_n^*)$ of (4) will be called a 'basic solution', if for each index i for which $X_i^* = 1$, the vector $(X_1^*, \ldots, X_{i-1}^*, 0, X_{i+1}^*, \ldots, X_n^*)$ does not satisfy condition (4). Let I be the set of those indices i, for which $X_i^* = 1$, and let $\mathcal{J}$ be a set of indices so that $I \subset \mathcal{J}$. We shall denote by $F(S^*, \mathcal{J})$ the set of vectors $S = (X_1, \ldots, X_n)$ for which $X_j = 1$ for each $j \epsilon \mathcal{J}$. It is obvious that every vector $S \epsilon F(S^*, \mathcal{J})$ fulfils condition (4); the set $F(S^*, J)$ will be called a 'family of solutions' of (4).

In order to determine all the basic solutions of (4), we have to apply repeatedly the following rules:

(i) If $d \leqslant 0$, then the unique basic solution is $X_1 = \ldots = X_n = 0$.

(ii) If $d > 0$ and $c_1 \geqslant \ldots c_p \geqslant d > c_{p+1} \geqslant \ldots \geqslant c_n$, then ($\alpha$) for each $k = 1, 2, \ldots, p$, the vector $X_k = 1$, $X_j = 0$ $(j \neq k)$ is a basic solution; (β) the other basic solutions are to be sought among the vectors for which $X_1 = \ldots = X_p = 0$ and which fulfil $\sum\limits_{i=p+1}^{n} c_i X_i \geqslant d$.

(iii) If $d > 0$, $c_i < d$ $(i = 1, \ldots, n)$ and $\sum\limits_{i=1}^{n} c_i < d$, then (4) has no basic solutions.

(iv) If $d > 0$, $c_i < d$ $(i = 1, \ldots, n)$ and $\sum\limits_{i=1}^{n} c_i = d$, then the unique basic solution is $X_1 = \ldots = X_n = 1$.

(v) If $d > 0$, $c_i < d$ $(i = 1, \ldots, n)$, $\sum\limits_{i=1}^{n} c_i > d$ and $\sum\limits_{i=2}^{n} c_i < d$, then the basic solutions are to be sought among the vectors for which $X_1 = 1$ and which fulfil $\sum\limits_{i=2}^{n} c_i X_i \geqslant d - c_i$.

(vi) If $d > 0$, $c_i < d$ $(i = 1, \ldots, n)$, $\sum\limits_{i=1}^{n} c_i > d$ and $\sum\limits_{i=2}^{n} c_i \geqslant d$, then we have to examine separately the two cases $(\gamma_1) X_1 = 1$ and $\sum\limits_{i=2}^{n} c_i X_i \geqslant d - c_1$, and $(\gamma_2) X_1 = 0$ and $\sum\limits_{i=2}^{n} c_i X_i \geqslant d$.

Let $S^* = (X_{k1}^*, \ldots, X_{kn}^*)$ $(k = 1, \ldots, K)$ be all the basic solutions of (4). For each k let $u(k)$ be defined by $X_{k,\,u(k)}^* = 1$, $X_{kj}^* = 0$ $(j > u(k))$, and let $\mathcal{J}_k = \{1, 2, \ldots, u(k)\}$. Then we have:

THEOREM 1. The families of solutions $F(S_k^*, \mathcal{J}_k)$ $(k = 1, \ldots, K)$ contain all the solutions of (4), and are pairwise disjoint.

Example 1. For solving

$$-x_1 + 7x_2 + 7\bar{x}_3 - 2x_4 - 9\bar{x}_5 + 3x_6 \geqslant 9, \qquad (5)$$

we put $X_1 = x_5$, $X_2 = x_2$, $X_3 = \bar{x}_3$, $X_4 = x_6$, $X_5 = \bar{x}_4$, $X_6 = \bar{x}_1$, and we obtain

$$9X_1 + 7X_2 + 7X_3 + 3X_4 + 2X_5 + X_6 \geqslant 21. \tag{6}$$

As we are in case (v), we put $X_1 = 1$, obtaining thus $7X_2 + 7X_3 + 3X_4 + 2X_5 + X_6 \geqslant 12$, which is in case (vi); we have thus to split the discussion according to the two values of X_2.

For $X_2 = 1$ we obtain the inequality $7X_3 + 3X_4 + 2X_5 + X_6 \geqslant 5$. According to case (ii) we find the basic solution (i) $X_3 = 1$, $X_4 = X_5 = X_6 = 0$, and it remains the case $X_3 = 0$, $3X_4 + 2X_5 + X_6 \geqslant 5$; the last inequality has the unique basic solution (ii) $x_4 = X_5 = 1$, $X_6 = 0$ (obtained by applying rule (v) twice).

For $X_2 = 0$, we have the inequality $7X_3 + 3X_4 + 2X_5 + X_6 \geqslant 12$, the unique basic solution of which (repeated application of (v)) is (iii) $X_3 = X_4 = X_5 = 1$, $X_6 = 0$.

The basic solution of (6) corresponds to the three 'partial solutions' (i), (ii), (iii); $S_1^* = (1, 1, 1, 0, 0, 0)$, $S_2^* = (1, 1, 0, 1, 1, 0)$, $S_3^* = (1, 0, 1, 1, 1, 0)$. Consequently, $\mathcal{J}_1 = \{1, 2, 3\}$, $\mathcal{J}_2 = \mathcal{J}_3 = \{1, 2, 3, 4, 5\}$. Returning to the original inequality (5), we obtain the following table of the three families of solutions (here '—' means arbitrary: 0 or 1):

TABLE 1

No.	x_1	x_2	x_3	x_4	x_5	x_6
1	—	1	0	—	1	—
2	—	1	1	0	1	1
3	—	0	0	0	1	1

Similar rules can be established for the solution of linear pseudo-Boolean equations, as well as for that of systems of linear pseudo-Boolean equations and inequalities.

Example 2. Let us consider the system

$$3\bar{x}_1 + 6x_2 + 2x_3 + 4x_4 \geqslant 7 \tag{7.1}$$

$$x_1 + 2\bar{x}_2 + 3\bar{x}_3 + 8x_4 \geqslant 5. \tag{7.2}$$

Let us first put $x_4 = 1$. The system (7.1), (7.2) reduces to the inequality $3\bar{x}_1 + 6x_2 + 2x_3 \geqslant 3$, which has the families of solutions (i) $x_2 = 1$, $\bar{x}_1$ and x_3 arbitrary; (ii) $x_2 = 0$, $\bar{x}_1 = 0$, x_3 arbitrary.

For $x_4 = 0$ the system becomes

$$3\bar{x}_1 + 6x_2 + 2x_3 \geqslant 7 \tag{8.1}$$

$$x_1 + 2\bar{x}_2 + 3\bar{x}_3 \geqslant 5. \tag{8.2}$$

Case (v) shows that (8.1) implies $x_2 = 1$, whereas (8.2) implies $\bar{x}_2 = \bar{x}_3 = 1$. The contradiction shows that for $x_4 = 0$ there are no solutions.

Thus the families of solutions of (7.1), (7.2) are:

TABLE 2

No.	x_1	x_2	x_3	x_4
1	—	1	—	1
2	0	0	—	1

III. SYSTEMS OF NONLINEAR PSEUDO-BOOLEAN CONDITIONS

The aim of this section is to give a method for the determination of all the solutions of a system $\sum = \sum (x_1, \ldots, x_n)$ of non-linear pseudo-Boolean equations and inequalities.

The Boolean function

$$\Phi(x_1, \ldots, x_n) = \begin{cases} 1, \text{ if } (x_1, \ldots, x_n) \text{ fulfils } \sum \\ 0, \text{ in the opposite case} \end{cases} \qquad (9)$$

will be termed the 'characteristic function' of $\sum$; the Boolean equation $\Phi(x_1, \ldots, x_n) = 1$ will be termed the 'characteristic equation' of $\sum$.

If $(\xi_{11}, \ldots, \xi_{1n}), \ldots, (\xi_{m1}, \ldots, \xi_{mn})$ are the solutions of a linear equation (determined, for instance, as in Section I), then the characteristic function is:

$$\Phi(x_1, \ldots, x_n) = x_1^{\xi_{11}} \ldots x_n^{\xi_{1n}} \cup \ldots \cup x_1^{\xi_{m1}} \ldots x_n^{\xi_{mn}}, \qquad (10)$$

where

$$x^\xi = \begin{cases} x, \text{ if } \xi = 1 \\ \bar{x}, \text{ if } \xi = 0. \end{cases} \qquad (11)$$

In the case of a linear inequality or of linear systems, the procedure described in Section I gives the solutions grouped into families, and this simplifies formula (10).

Example 3. In Example 2 of Section I we have shown that the families of solutions of the system

$$3\bar{x}_1 + 6x_2 + 2x_3 + 4x_4 \geqslant 7 \qquad (7.1)$$
$$x_1 + 2\bar{x}_2 + 3\bar{x}_3 + 8x_4 \geqslant 5 \qquad (7.2)$$

are given by the Table 2.

The characteristic function is hence

$$\Phi = x_2 x_4 \cup \bar{x}_1 \bar{x}_2 x_4. \tag{12}$$

Let us now consider a non-linear equation or inequality. If we denote each conjunction

$$\alpha_{i_1} \cdot \cdot \cdot \cdot \alpha_{i_{k(t)}}$$
$$x_{i_1} \cdot \cdot \cdot \cdot x_{i_{k(t)}}$$

appearing in it by a new variable y_i, then we obtain a linear equation or inequality, the characteristic function of which can be obtained as above. Returning to the original variables, we obtain the characteristic function of the original equation or inequality.

Example 4. Let us consider the inequality

$$x_1 x_4 + 2x_1 \bar{x}_2 \bar{x}_3 - 4x_2 x_4 + 3x_3 \bar{x}_4 > -1 ; \tag{13}$$

putting $x_1 x_4 = y_1$, $x_1 \bar{x}_2 \bar{x}_3 = y_2$, $x_2 x_4 = y_3$, $x_3 \bar{x}_4 = y_4$ we get the linear inequality

$$y_1 + 2y_2 - 4y_3 + 3y_4 > -1, \tag{14}$$

the characteristic function of which is

$$\Psi = \bar{y}_3 \cup y_3 y_4 \cup y_3 \bar{y}_4 y_2 y_1 ; \tag{15}$$

hence the characteristic function of (13) is

$$\Phi_2 = \bar{x}_2 \cup x_2 \bar{x}_4. \tag{16}$$

Finally, if $\phi_1, \ldots, \phi_p$ are the characteristic functions of the different equations and inequalities of a system $\sum$, then the characteristic function of $\sum$ is

$$\Phi = \phi_1 \ldots \phi_p. \tag{17}$$

(If the system contains a linear part $\sum_1$, it is recommended to compute first the characteristic function of $\sum_1$, as it is done in Example 5.)

Example 5. Let us consider the system

$$7x_1 x_2 x_3 - 2\bar{x}_1 x_4 x_8 + 5x_2 x_4 x_6 x_7 x_8 - 4x_3 x_8 - x_4 \bar{x}_5 x_6 \leqslant 3, \tag{18.1}$$
$$3x_1 - 2x_2 \bar{x}_6 + 14x_5 \bar{x}_6 \bar{x}_8 + 2x_1 x_2 x_3 - 7x_8 > -8, \tag{18.2}$$
$$8x_4 x_5 \bar{x}_8 - 4\bar{x}_3 \bar{x}_7 x_8 + 3x_1 x_2 + \bar{x}_3 + \bar{x}_4 + \bar{x}_5 \leqslant 2 \tag{18.3}$$
$$2x_3 + 3x_5 - \bar{x}_5 x_6 + 4x_6 \bar{x}_7 x_8 - 2x_5 x_6 x_7 x_8 > 1, \tag{18.4}$$
$$4x_1 \bar{x}_2 + 3x_2 > 2 \tag{18.5}$$
$$3\bar{x}_1 - 5x_2 + 6x_3 - 7x_7 - 8\bar{x}_8 > 1 \tag{18.6}$$
$$-2x_1 + 4x_3 + 7\bar{x}_4 + x_6 - 3x_8 > 6. \tag{18.7}$$

The characteristic functions of the inequalities (18.1), ..., (18.5) are:

$$\phi_1 = \bar{x}_1 \cup \bar{x}_2 \cup \bar{x}_3 \bar{x}_8 \cup (\bar{x}_3 \cup x_8)(\bar{x}_4 \cup \bar{x}_6 \cup \bar{x}_7), \qquad (19.1)$$

$$\phi_2 = x_1 \cup \bar{x}_2 \cup x_6 \cup \bar{x}_8, \qquad (19.2)$$

$$\phi_3 = \bar{x}_3 \bar{x}_7 x_8 \cup (\bar{x}_1 \cup \bar{x}_2)(x_3 \cup x_4 \cup x_5)(\bar{x}_4 \cup \bar{x}_5 \cup x_8), \qquad (19.3)$$

$$\phi_4 = x_3 \cup x_5 \cup x_6 \bar{x}_7 x_8, \qquad (19.4)$$

$$\phi_5 = x_1 \cup x_2, \qquad (19.5)$$

while the characteristic function of the linear sub-system (18.6), (18.7) is

$$\phi_{6,\,7} = x_3 \bar{x}_4 \bar{x}_7 x_8 \cup \bar{x}_1 \bar{x}_2 x_3 \bar{x}_4 x_7 x_8 \cup \bar{x}_1 \bar{x}_2 x_3 \bar{x}_4 \bar{x}_7 \bar{x}_8. \qquad (19.6)$$

Applying formula (17), we obtain the characteristic function of the system (18):

$$\Phi = \phi_1 \cdot \phi_2 \cdot \phi_3 \cdot \phi_4 \cdot \phi_5 \cdot \phi_{6,\,7} =$$
$$x_1 \bar{x}_2 x_3 \bar{x}_4 \bar{x}_7 x_8 \cup \bar{x}_1 x_2 x_3 \bar{x}_4 x_6 \bar{x}_7 x_8. \qquad (20)$$

THEOREM 2. The solution of a system $\sum$ of pseudo-Boolean equations and inequalities can be reduced to that of solving its characteristic equation

$$\Phi(x_1, \ldots, x_n) = 1. \qquad (21)$$

The disjunctive form of (21) permits the direct listing of the families of solutions of $\sum$ (which correspond to the conjunctions of (21)).

Note. It is easy to obtain Φ in a form yielding pairwise disjoint families of solutions.

Example 6. The families of solutions of (18) can be obtained directly from the disjunctive form of the characteristic equation (20):

TABLE 3

No.	x_1	x_2	x_3	x_4	x_5	x_6	x_7	x_8
1	1	0	1	0	—	—	0	1
2	0	1	1	0	—	1	0	1

Note. The characteristic function of systems containing also logical conditions can be obtained easily. Let $E_1, \ldots, E_p$ be p pseudo-Boolean equations (inequalities), the characteristic functions of which are $\phi_1, \ldots, \phi_p$. If we are interested, for instance, in finding those values of the variables which fulfil at least one of the conditions $E_1, \ldots, E_p$, it is sufficient to write the characteristic equation $\phi_1 \cup \ldots \cup \phi_p = 1$. Other logical conditions can be treated in a similar way.

General Decision Theory

IV. BINARY DECISIONS UNDER COMPLETE UNCERTAINTY

Let us consider a problem of binary decisions, whose constraints are deterministic:

$$f_i(x_1, \ldots, x_n) \begin{smallmatrix} \leqslant \\ = \\ \geqslant \end{smallmatrix} a_i \tag{22}$$

$$x_j = 0 \text{ or } 1, \tag{23}$$

while the objective function

$$f_0(x_1, \ldots, x_n) \tag{24}$$

has uncertain coefficients

$$c_1, c_2, \ldots, c_q. \tag{25}$$

More precisely, each c_h $(h = 1, \ldots, q)$ can take on one of the values

$$c_{h1}, c_{h2}, \ldots, c_{hr_h}. \tag{26}$$

Thus the vector $C = (c_1, c_2, \ldots, c_q)$ can take on the values $(c_{11}, c_{21}, \ldots, c_{q1})$, $(c_{12}, c_{22}, \ldots, c_{q2}), \ldots$, which we shall denote by $C_1, \ldots, C_r$.

The methods described in Sections I and II allow us to obtain a full listing of the possible actions $A_1, A_2, \ldots, A_t$ $(A_u = (x_1^u, \ldots, x_n^u)$, $u = 1, \ldots, t)$ satisfying the constraints (22) and (23).

Let us denote by U_{vw} the value of (24) for action A_v (i.e. $(x_1^{(v_1)}, \ldots, x_n^{(v_n)})$) when the coefficients are in the state C_w.

We obtain in this way a complete listing of the possible decisions along with their corresponding utilities:

TABLE 4

	C_1	. . . .	C_w	. . . .	C_r
A_1			.		
.			.		
.			.		
.			.		
A_v	. . . . .		$.U_{vw}.$	. . . .	.
.			.		
.			.		
.			.		
A_t			.		

If there is an index v_0 so that

$$U_{v_0w} > U_{vw} \qquad (w = 1, \ldots, r), \tag{27}$$

then A_{v_0} is called a 'dominating activity', and it obviously constitutes an optimal decision.

If there are two indices v_1 and v_2 so that

$$U_{v_1w} > U_{v_2w} \qquad (w = 1, \ldots, r), \tag{28}$$

then A_{v_1} 'dominates' A_{v_2}, and it is obvious that A_{v_2} is not an optimal decision.

In the general case, after defining what an optimal decision is (using for instance the maximin criterion, or the minimax risk criterion, or the pessimism-optimism index of Hurwicz, or the criterion based on the principle of insufficient reason, or any other criterion),[1] the optimal decisions can immediately be obtained from Table 4.

Example 7. Let us consider the problem of maximizing the linear pseudo-Boolean function

$$c_1x_1 + c_2x_2 + c_3x_3 + c_4x_4 \tag{29}$$

under constraints (7.1), (7.2), and so that

$$c_1 \in \{-3, 0, 1\}$$
$$c_2 \in \{-1/2, +1/4\}$$
$$c_3 \in \{2, 5/2\}$$
$$c_4 = 4.$$

As was shown in Example 2, the possible decisions are

$$A_1: x_1 = 1, x_2 = 1, x_3 = 1, x_4 = 1$$
$$A_2: x_1 = 0, x_2 = 1, x_3 = 1, x_4 = 1$$
$$A_3: x_1 = 1, x_2 = 1, x_3 = 0, x_4 = 1$$
$$A_4: x_1 = 0, x_2 = 1, x_3 = 0, x_4 = 1$$
$$A_5: x_1 = 0, x_2 = 0, x_3 = 1, x_4 = 1$$
$$A_6: x_1 = 0, x_2 = 0, x_3 = 0, x_4 = 1.$$

The vectors C_w are

$$C_1 : c_1 = -3, c_2 = -1/2, c_3 = 2, c_4 = 4$$
$$C_2 : c_1 = -3, c_2 = -1/2, c_3 = 5/2, c_4 = 4$$

[1] For a complete discussion of these see Luce and Raiffa (1957).

$$C_3 : c_1 = -3, c_2 = \quad 1/4, c_3 = 2 \ , c_4 = 4$$
$$C_4 : c_1 = -3, c_2 = \quad 1/4, c_3 = 5/2, c_4 = 4$$
$$C_5 : c_1 = \quad 0, c_2 = -1/2, c_3 = 2 \ , c_4 = 4$$
$$C_6 : c_1 = \quad 0, c_2 = -1/2, c_3 = 5/2, c_4 = 4$$
$$C_7 : c_1 = \quad 0, c_2 = \quad 1/4, c_3 = 2 \ , c_4 = 4$$
$$C_8 : c_1 = \quad 0, c_2 = \quad 1/4, c_3 = 5/2, c_4 = 4$$
$$C_9 : c_1 = \quad 1, c_2 = -1/2, c_3 = 2 \ , c_4 = 4$$
$$C_{10}: c_1 = \quad 1, c_2 = -1/2, c_3 = 5/2, c_4 = 4$$
$$C_{11}: c_1 = \quad 1, c_2 = \quad 1/4, c_3 = 2 \ , c_4 = 4$$
$$C_{12}: c_1 = \quad 1, c_2 = \quad 1/4, c_3 = 5/2, c_4 = 4.$$

Hence the utilities are :

TABLE 5

	C_1	C_2	C_3	C_4	C_5	C_6	C_7	C_8	C_9	C_{10}	C_{11}	C_{12}
A_1	5/2	3	13/4	15/4	11/2	6	25/4	27/4	13/2	7	29/4	31/4
A_2	11/2	6	25/4	27/4	11/2	6	25/4	27/4	11/2	6	25/4	27/4
A_3	1/2	1/2	5/4	5/4	7/2	7/2	17/4	17/4	9/2	9/2	21/4	21/4
A_4	7/2	7/2	17/4	17/4	7/2	7/2	17/4	17/4	7/2	7/2	17/4	17/4
A_5	6	13/2	6	13/2	6	13/2	6	13/2	6	13/2	6	13/2
A_6	4	4	4	4	4	4	4	4	4	4	4	4

As A_5 dominates both A_4 and A_6, while A_1 dominates A_3, we can restrict the discussion to Table 6 :

TABLE 6

	C_1	C_2	C_3	C_4	C_5	C_6	C_7	C_8	C_9	C_{10}	C_{11}	C_{12}
A_1	5/2	3	13/4	15/4	11/2	6	25/4	27/4	13/2	7	29/4	31/4
A_2	11/2	6	25/4	27/4	11/2	6	25/4	27/4	11/2	6	25/4	27/4
A_5	6	13/2	6	13/2	6	13/2	6	13/2	6	13/2	6	13/2

Hence Table 7 gives the optimal actions for the different cs.

TABLE 7

No.	Coefficients of (29)	Optimal decisions
1	$C_1, C_2, C_3, C_4, C_5, C_6$	A_5
2	C_7, C_8	A_1 or A_2
3	$C_9, C_{10}, C_{11}, C_{12}$	A_1

Now it is clear that Table 7 reduces to Table 7′ because A_1 is obviously preferable to A_2.

TABLE 7′

No.	Coefficients of (29)	Optimal decisions
1′	$C_1 - C_6$	A_5
2′	$C_7 - C_{12}$	A_1

Hence in any case a necessary condition for a decision to be optimal is

$$x_1 = x_2; \quad x_3 = x_4 = 1. \tag{30}$$

Example 8. Let us consider the problem of maximizing the pseudo-Boolean function

$$c_1 x_1 x_3 \bar{x}_4 + c_2 \bar{x}_5 \bar{x}_7 + c_3 \bar{x}_2 x_6 \bar{x}_8, \tag{31}$$

under constraints (18), and so that

$$c_1 \epsilon \{ -2, 0, 1 \}$$
$$c_2 \epsilon \{ -1, +1 \}$$
$$c_3 \epsilon \{ 0, 1, 2 \}.$$

As was shown in Example 6, the possible decisions are those included in Table 8.

TABLE 8

No.	x_1	x_2	x_3	x_4	x_5	x_6	x_7	x_8
A_1	1	0	1	0	1	1	0	1
A_2	1	0	1	0	0	1	0	1
A_3	1	0	1	0	1	0	0	1
A_4	1	0	1	0	0	0	0	1
A_5	0	1	1	0	1	1	0	1
A_6	0	1	1	0	0	1	0	1

The vectors C_w are given in Table 9:

TABLE 9

No.	c_1	c_2	c_3
C_1	-2	-1	0
C_2	0	-1	0
C_3	1	-1	0
C_4	-2	-1	1
C_5	0	-1	1
C_6	1	-1	1
C_7	-2	-1	2
C_8	0	-1	2
C_9	1	-1	2
C_{10}	-2	1	0
C_{11}	0	1	0
C_{12}	1	1	0
C_{13}	-2	1	1
C_{14}	0	1	1
C_{15}	1	1	1
C_{16}	-2	1	2
C_{17}	0	1	2
C_{18}	1	1	2

The utilities are then given in Table 10:

TABLE 10

No.	C_1	C_2	C_3	C_4	C_5	C_6	C_7	C_8	C_9	C_{10}	C_{11}	C_{12}	C_{13}	C_{14}	C_{15}	C_{16}	C_{17}	C_{18}
A_1	-2	0	1	-2	0	1	-2	0	1	-2	0	1	-2	0	1	-2	0	1
A_2	-3	-1	0	-3	-1	0	-3	-1	0	-1	1	2	-1	1	2	-1	1	2
A_3	-2	0	1	-2	0	1	-2	0	1	-2	0	1	-2	0	1	-2	0	1
A_4	-3	-1	0	-3	-1	0	-3	-1	0	-1	1	2	-1	1	2	-1	1	2
A_5	0	0	0	0	0	0	0	0	0	0	0	0	0	0	0	0	0	0
A_6	-1	-1	-1	-1	-1	-1	-1	-1	-1	1	1	1	1	1	1	1	1	1

If we now apply, for instance, the maximin criterion, we see that the corresponding 'best' decision is A_5.

If we apply, on the other hand, the minimax risk criterion of Savage, we see from the table of 'risks' (Table 11) that the corresponding 'best' decisions are A_5 and A_6.

TABLE 11

No.	C_1	C_2	C_3	C_4	C_5	C_6	C_7	C_8	C_9	C_{10}	C_{11}	C_{12}	C_{13}	C_{14}	C_{15}	C_{16}	C_{17}	C_{18}
A_1	2	0	0	2	0	0	2	0	0	3	1	1	3	1	1	3	1	1
A_2	3	1	1	3	1	1	3	1	1	2	0	0	2	0	0	2	0	0
A_3	2	0	0	2	0	0	2	0	0	3	1	1	3	1	1	3	1	1
A_4	3	1	1	3	1	1	3	1	1	2	0	0	2	0	0	2	0	0
A_5	0	0	1	0	0	1	0	0	1	1	1	2	1	1	2	1	1	2
A_6	1	1	2	1	1	2	1	1	2	0	0	1	0	0	1	0	0	1

If we apply, for instance, the criterion based on the 'principle of insufficient reason', i.e. compute the expected utility: $U_r = \dfrac{1}{r} \sum_{w=1}^{r} U_{vw}$,

TABLE 12

A_r:	A_1	A_2	A_3	A_4	A_5	A_6
U_r:	$-\dfrac{6}{18}$	$-\dfrac{6}{18}$	$-\dfrac{6}{18}$	$-\dfrac{6}{18}$	0	0

we find that the best decisions are A_5 and A_6 (Table 12).

It is beyond the scope of this paper to enter into discussions concerning the criterion to be used.

V. MINIMIZING EXPECTED VALUES OF PSEUDO-BOOLEAN FUNCTIONS

It is well known (see, for instance, Dantzig, 1963, 25–1, Theorem 1) that if the coefficients of the objective function of a problem of mathematical programming are randomly distributed independently of the x_j, then the minimum expected total cost solution is obtained by finding the x_j satisfying the restrictions and minimizing the objective function in which the coefficients $c_1, \ldots, c_r$ are replaced by their expected values $e_1, \ldots, e_r$.

(1) Linear Objective Function

If the objective function is linear, we first obtain the families of solutions to the constraints as in Sections II and III, and replace the dashes in their table by 1 if the corresponding coefficient is negative, and by 0 if the corresponding coefficient is positive, and have the dash for those having the coefficient equal to 0. Thus we obtain the best solution of each family, and then we have to choose that (those) one(s) of them yielding the lowest value of the objective function.

Example 9. Let us minimize the linear pseudo-Boolean function (in which the coefficients were replaced by their expected values)

$$-5x_1+6x_2+2x_3+3x_4 \tag{32}$$

under the linear constraints (7.1), (7.2).

It was shown in Example 2 that the families of solutions to those constraints are given in Table 2. Replacing the dashes we obtain the best solutions of each family as in Table 13.

TABLE 13

No.	x_1	x_2	x_3	x_4	Value of (32)
1	1	1	0	1	4
2	0	0	0	1	3

As $3 = \min (3 ; 4)$, the sought point minimizing the expected value is:

$$x_1 = x_2 = x_3 = 0, \ x = 1.$$

Example 10. Let us minimize the linear pseudo-Boolean function (in which the coefficients were replaced by their expected values):

$$3x_1 - 2x_2 - x_3 + 4x_4 - 6x_5 + 4x_6 + 2x_7 + 3x_8 \tag{33}$$

under the non-linear constraints (18.1)–(18.7).

It was shown in Example 6 that the families of solutions to the constraints are those in Table 3. Replacing the dashes, we obtain:

TABLE 14

No.	x_1	x_2	x_3	x_4	x_5	x_6	x_7	x_8	Value of (33)
1	1	0	1	0	1	0	0	1	-1
2	0	1	1	0	1	1	0	1	-2

As $-2 = \min (-1 ; -2)$, the sought point minimizing the expected value of (33) is

$$x_1 = x_4 = x_7 = 0, \ x_2 = x_3 = x_5 = x_6 = x_8 = 1.$$

(2) *Non-linear Objective Function — No Constraints*

Let us consider the problem of minimizing the expected value of a non-linear pseudo-Boolean function

$$\mathscr{F}(x_1, \ldots, x_n). \tag{34}$$

After replacing the coefficients by their expected value, the problem reduces to that of minimizing the pseudo-Boolean function

$$f_1(x_1, \ldots, x_n) = \mathscr{E}[\mathscr{F}(x_1, \ldots, x_n)]. \tag{35.1}$$

It is easy to show that f_1 can be put into the form

$$f_1(x_1, \ldots, x_n) = x_1 g_1(x_2, \ldots, x_n) + h_1(x_2, \ldots, x_n). \tag{36.1}$$

Let $\phi_1'(x_2, \ldots, x_n)$ and $\phi_1''(x_2, \ldots, x_n)$ be the characteristic functions of the inequality $g_1(x_1, \ldots, x_n) < 0$ and of the equation $g_1(x_1, \ldots, x_n) = 0$ respectively, and let

$$\phi_1(p_1, x_2, \ldots, x_n) = \phi_1'(x_2, \ldots, x_n) \cup p_1 \, \phi_1''(x_2, \ldots, x_n), \tag{37}$$

where p_1 is an arbitrary parameter taking the values 0 or 1.

Let us put

$$f_2(x_2, \ldots, x_n) = f_1[\phi_1'(x_2, \ldots, x_n), x_2, \ldots, x_n] \tag{35.2}$$

and write f_2 in the form

$$f_2(x_2, \ldots, x_n) = x_2 g_2(x_0, \ldots, x_n) + h_2(x_2, \ldots, x_n); \tag{36.2}$$

the functions $\phi_2'(x_3, \ldots, x_n)$, $\phi_2''(x_3, \ldots, x_n)$, $\phi_2(x_3, \ldots, x_n)$ are now determined as above, etc.

At stage n we obtain the function

$$f_n(x_n) = f_{n+1}[\phi_{n-1}'(x_n), x_n], \tag{35.n}$$

which will be written in the form

$$f_n(x_n) = x_n g_n + h_n, \tag{36.n}$$

where g_n and h_n are constants; we now define ϕ_n' and ϕ_n'' as above, and put $\phi_n = \phi_n' \cup p_n \phi_n''$.

THEOREM 3. The constant

$$f_{n+1} = f_n(\phi_n') \tag{35.n+1}$$

is the minimum expected value of $\mathscr{F}(x_1, \ldots, x_n)$. The minimizing points are characterized by the relations

General Decision Theory

$$x_n = \phi_n(p_n) \tag{37.n}$$

$$x_{n-1} = \phi_{n-1}(p_{n-1}, x_n) \tag{37.n-1}$$

$$\cdot \quad \cdot \quad \cdot \quad \cdot \quad \cdot$$

$$x_1 = \phi_1(p_1, x_2, \ldots, x_n), \tag{37.1}$$

where $p_1, p_2, \ldots, p_n$ are arbitrary parameters taking the values 0 or 1.

Practice has shown that the number of parameters effectively appearing in (37) is very small.

Example 11. Let us minimize the function

$$f_1 = -2x_1 x_3 + 5x_1 x_2 x_4 - 8x_3 \bar{x}_5 + 4x_2 \bar{x}_5 - 4\bar{x}_1 x_3 x_5 + 6x_2 x_3 x_5 + 5x_6 - 5x_7 + 2x_8, \tag{38.1}$$

the coefficients here standing for the expected values of the original coefficients.

Stage 1: $g_1 = -2x_3 + 5x_2 x_4 + 4x_3 x_{,5}$ so that $\phi_1{}' = x_3 \bar{x}_5 (\bar{x}_2 \cup \bar{x}_4)$, $\phi_1{}'' = \bar{x}_3 (\bar{x}_2 \cup \bar{x}_4)$, hence

$$\phi_1 = (x_3 \bar{x}_5 \cup p_1 \bar{x}_3)(\bar{x}_2 \cup \bar{x}_4) \tag{39.1}$$

and

$$f_2 = x_3 \bar{x}_5 (\bar{x}_2 + x_2 \bar{x}_4)(-2x_3 + 5x_2 x_4 + 4x_3 x_5) + (-8x_3 \bar{x}_5 + 4x_2 \bar{x}_5 - 4x_3 x_5 + 6x_2 x_3 x_4 + 5x_6 - 5x_7 + 2x_8) = -2\bar{x}_2 x_3 \bar{x}_5 - 2x_2 x_3 \bar{x}_4 \bar{x}_5 - 8x_3 \bar{x}_5 + 4x_2 \bar{x}_5 - 4x_3 x_5 + 6x_2 x_3 x_4 + 5x_6 - 5x_7 + 2x_8. \tag{38.2}$$

Stage 2: $g_2 = 2x_3 \bar{x}_5 - 2x_3 \bar{x}_4 \bar{x}_5 + 4\bar{x}_5 + 6x_3 x_4 = 2x_3 x_4 \bar{x}_5 + 4\bar{x}_5 + 6x_3 x_4$, hence $\phi_2{}' = 0$, $\phi_2{}'' = x_5(\bar{x}_3 \cup \bar{x}_4)$, and

$$\phi_2 = p_2 x_5(\bar{x}_3 \cup \bar{x}_4), \tag{39.2}$$

and

$$f_3 = -10x_3 \bar{x}_5 - 4x_3 x_5 + 5x_6 - 5x_7 + 2x_8. \tag{38.3}$$

Stage 3: $g_3 = -10\bar{x}_5 - 4x_5$, hence $\phi_3{}' = 1$, $\phi_3{}'' = 0$,

$$\phi_3 = 1 \tag{39.3}$$

and

$$f_4 = -10\bar{x}_5 - 4x_5 + 5x_6 - 5x_7 + 2x_8. \tag{38.4}$$

Stage 4: $g_4 = 0$, hence $\phi_4{}' = 0$, $\phi_4{}'' = 1$,

$$\phi_4 = p_4 \tag{39.4}$$

and

$$f_5 = -10 + 6x_5 + 5x_6 - 5x_7 + 2x_8. \tag{38.5}$$

Stage 5: $g_5 = 6$, hence $\phi_5' = 0$, $\phi_5'' = 0$

$$\phi_5 = 0 \tag{39.5}$$

and

$$f_6 = -10 + 5x_6 - 5x_7 + 2x_8. \tag{38.6}$$

Stage 6: $g_6 = 5$, hence $\phi_6' = 0$, $\phi_6'' = 0$,

$$\phi_6 = 0 \tag{39.6}$$

and

$$f_7 = -10 - 5x_7 + 2x_8. \tag{38.7}$$

Stage 7: $g_7 = -5$, hence $\phi_7' = 1$, $\phi_7'' = 0$,

$$\phi_7 = 1 \tag{39.7}$$

and

$$f_8 = -15 + 2x_8. \tag{38.8}$$

Stage 8: $g_8 = 2$, hence $\phi_8' = 0$, $\phi_8'' = 0$,

$$\phi_8 = 0 \tag{39.8}$$

and hence the expected minimum value is

$$f_9 = -15. \tag{38.9}$$

Formulae (39.8), . . ., (39.1) give us the minimizing points:

$$x_8 = 0,\ x_7 = 1,\ x_6 = 0,\ x_5 = 0,\ x_4 = p_4,\ x_3 = 1,\ x_2 = 0,\ x_1 = 1 \tag{40}$$

$$(f_1)^{\min} = f_1(1,\ 0,\ 1,\ p_4,\ 0,\ 0,\ 1,\ 0) = -15. \tag{41}$$

(3) Non-linear Objective Function with Constraints

The above algorithm together with the results of Sections II and III offer a procedure of minimizing any pseudo-Boolean function the variables of which are subject to certain constraints. Let $f(x_1, \ldots, x_n)$ be the objective function, whose coefficients were replaced by their expected values. Let $F_1, \ldots, F_q$ be the families of solutions to the constraints (determined as in Sections II and III). A family F_k is described by fixed values of $s(k)$ of the variables, and arbitrary values of the remaining variables. Introducing those $s(k)$ fixed values in f, we obtain a function $f^{(k)}$ of $n - s(k)$ variables. This can be minimized using the method described in 2. We obtain in this way $f_{\min}^{(1)}, \ldots, f_{\min}^{(q)}$. Obviously

$$f_{\min} = \min_{1 \leqslant k \leqslant q} f_{\min}^{(k)}. \tag{42}$$

We obtain the minimizing points of f, applying the second part of the algorithm given in 2 for those functions $f^{(h)}$ which realize $f_{\min}^{(h)} = f_{\min}$.

179

Example 12. Let us minimize the function (having the coefficients replaced by their expected values):

$$f = 3x_1x_2 + 9x_2x_3x_4 - 7\bar{x}_1x_5x_6 + 2x_3x_4\bar{x}_6 +$$
$$4x_1\bar{x}_2x_3\bar{x}_4\bar{x}_5x_6 - 5x_7 + 5x_8 + 2x_7\bar{x}_8 \tag{43}$$

under the constraints (18.1)–(18.7). The families of solutions of (18) were found in Example 6 and are given in Table 15:

TABLE 15

No.	x_1	x_2	x_3	x_4	x_5	x_6	x_7	x_8	$f^{(k)}$	$f_{min}^{(k)}$
1	1	0	1	0	—	—	0	1	$f^{(1)} = 4\bar{x}_5x_6 + 5$	$+5$
2	0	1	1	0	—	1	0	1	$f^{(2)} = -7x_7 + 5$	-2

Hence,

$$f_{min} = f_{min}^{(2)} = f(0,\,1,\,1,\,0,\,1,\,1,\,0,\,1) = -2. \tag{44}$$

Similar procedures hold when minimizing the variance of a pseudo-Boolean function.

VI. THE MAXIMIN OF A PSEUDO-BOOLEAN FUNCTION

Let us consider the problem of finding those bivalent variables for which the minimum of

$$\mathscr{F}(x_1, \ldots, x_n) \tag{45}$$

when the coefficients $c_1, \ldots, c_p$ of $\mathscr{F}$ take on all their possible values

$$c_i \epsilon \{c_{i1}, \ldots, c_{ik_j}\} \qquad (i = 1, \ldots, p) \tag{46}$$

is maximum.

Putting

$$c_i = \sum_{j=1}^{k_i} y_{ij} c_{ij} \qquad (i = 1, \ldots, p) \tag{47}$$

and

$$\sum_{j=1}^{k_i} y_{ij} = 1 \qquad (i = 1, \ldots, p), \tag{48}$$

where y_{ij} are new bivalent variables, we see that the problem is now that of finding

Ivanescu — A Theory of Binary Decisions

$$\text{MAX MIN} \quad \mathscr{F}(x_1, \ldots, x_n; \, y_{11}, \ldots, y_{pk_p}) \qquad (49)$$
$$x_i \quad y_{ij}$$

under conditions (48).

A method for solving this problem, similar to that in Section V (2), is given in Ivanescu and Rudeanu (1967), chap. vii.

That method also allows us to solve such problems when the variables are subject to constraints.

REFERENCES

Dantzig, G. B. (1963), *Linear Programming and Extensions*, Princeton : Princeton Univ. Press.

Ivanescu, P. L. (1965), 'Pseudo-Boolean Programming and Applications', *Lecture Notes in Mathematics*, No. 9, Berlin–Heidelberg–New York : Springer-Verlag.

— and Rudeanu, S. (1967), *Boolean Methods in Operations Research and Related Areas*, Berlin–Heidelberg–New York : Springer-Verlag.

Luce, R. D., and Raiffa, H. (1957), *Games and Decisions : Introduction and Critical Survey*, New York : John Wiley & Sons.

DISCUSSION OF THE PAPER BY DR. IVANESCU

Dr. Leinfellner : I have only one question. Would it be possible to use your method in game theory — and even for automatic computations in game theory ?

Dr. Pelikán : I should like to mention that there is a logical problem — and a technical device — which can be used in connection with the pseudo-Boolean function as introduced by Dr. Ivanescu. This device is known under such names as threshold mechanism, neutron model, or Perceptron. Such a device has n Boolean inputs x_i which become weighted with real numbers w_i. There is one output, y, which is also Boolean, attaining the value 1 if and only if $\Sigma w_i x_i \geqslant T$, where T is a real number representing the threshold value. It then appears possible to use the theory of threshold devices which is well developed, or to *simulate*, by means of such devices on a computer, methods to solve systems of inequalities such as those of Dr. Ivanescu.

Mr. Bessière : I just wish to remind you of the existence of a method, somewhat similar to Dr. Ivanescu's, which has been developed by a group of French mathematicians. It is the so-called 'SEP-method', SEP meaning 'séparation et évaluation progressive'.

Dr. Ivanescu: Dr. Leinfellner asks me whether an application of pseudo-Boolean programming to the theory of games could be imagined. I suppose that it could. First of all I have in mind a possibility of describing coalitions by means of pseudo-Boolean functions. But a discussion I have had with Dr. Selten seemed to indicate also a certain connection between kernels of a game and pseudo-Boolean functions.

Pseudo-Boolean programming was applied until now to various problems arising in 'finite mathematics'. So, for instance, problems arising in the theory of games (determination of the number of equilibrium points, conditions for internal and external stability, the kernels of a graph, the chromatical number of a graph), in the theory of flows in networks (determining the value of a maximal flow, the minimal cuts, as well as certain feasibility conditions), in integer linear and non-linear programming, in the theory of finite partially-ordered sets, etc., may all be translated into a pseudo-Boolean language and solved by means of pseudo-Boolean programming. A fairly complete description of the various applications of pseudo-Boolean programming which were developed in the last years is given in reference (2) in my paper.

I think that Dr. Pelikán's idea of using thresholds in pseudo-Boolean programming could prove to be very useful.

As was pointed out by Mr. Bessière, there is a strong connection between our method of pseudo-Boolean programming and the SEP procedures developed in France. In fact there is also a strong connection with the 'branch and bound' techniques developed in the U.S.A. The main difference between our procedure and the other ones consists in the fact that we are making an intensive use of Boolean techniques, and these allow us to solve problems of non-linear programming. As a matter of fact the linearity plays in pseudo-Boolean programming a much less important role than in other techniques.

Chapter 8

PROGRAMMES FOR HUMAN DECISION-MAKING

BY

PAVEL PELIKÁN

I. INTRODUCTION

OUR subject belongs to what we could call the economic theory of organization and information or what is sometimes called the application of cybernetics in the economy. Roughly speaking, such studies deal with information structures and their function in economic systems, such systems being firms or even the economies of whole nations. In the study of these problems we are interested in the manner in which messages are received, treated, and transmitted in such systems, especially with regard to their efficiency. In doing so we can either study real systems with real people and ask questions why systems are as they are and why people behave as they do (descriptive approach), or we can try to design some projects as to what systems should be like and how they should work (normative approach). In the words of Jacob Marschak, we act either like students in comparative zoology or like engineers. No doubt the final aim of these studies is to act like engineers, which seems to be more useful and attractive. To design projects, however, necessitates a knowledge of reality, that is a knowledge of what we are going to make them from; this will probably force us to have some dealings with comparative zoology as well.

If we want to make use of human decision-making elements, and I really do not see any other possibility, we must learn to know them so that our plans will not be upset by some of their apparently irregular but nevertheless real features. The concept of the classical *Homo œconomicus* will surely not do because he really does not know any of the difficulties in the understanding and treating of messages. We have to seek help from the other sciences, especially psychology and sociology. Unfortunately their results are often formulated in such a way as to make them of little use for our purposes. In this

183

paper I should like to propose a way of introducing more consideration of the human element into our studies so that we could take more
account of some psychological and sociological findings, without
nevertheless abandoning clarity and without being ambiguous.

All statements I am going to make about the behaviour of human
beings, and especially of their nervous systems, have the form of
basic suppositions. I should like to be simple and clear enough not
to discourage mathematical economists whilst at the same time I want
to respect and not hurt too much the feelings of psychologists and
sociologists. In doing so I naturally risk falling into disgrace with
all of them.

II. THE PROBLEM

When we study a social system wherein individuals control different action variables and base their decisions on different information, the questions of communication structure and of the decision
functions of individuals arise. The decision functions indicate to
each individual what to do, i.e. what actions he is to perform or what
messages he is to send and to whom in response to some received set
of messages. We could write it, for instance, in this way:

$$a_i = f_i^a(m_{Ei}),$$

$$m_{iE} = f_i^m(m_{Ei}),$$

where a_i means the state of action variables that the individual i
controls, m_{Ei} the set of messages that he receives from his environment, and m_{iE} the set of messages that he sends to his environment.
The functions f_i^a and f_i^m are his decision functions.

If the communication structure and the payoff function of the
whole system are given, we could, as engineers, interest ourselves in
finding the optimal decision functions f_i^a and f_i^m for all individuals.[1]
Here we are not going to do so but rather we want to study in what
form we could expect to find general solutions of this problem, and
what could be our expectation of individuals understanding them,
accepting them, and following them. It is true that in some simple
special cases this need not be a problem, but generally it would not
be at all simple. Let us imagine, without too much fantasy, what
'sending messages' or 'treating messages according to the decision
function f' could sometimes mean in practice in the bureaucracy of

[1] See, for instance, J. Marschak, 'Elements for a Theory of Teams', *Management Science*, vol. 1, no. 2, Jan. 1955, or R. Radner, 'Team Decision Problems',
Annals of Mathematical Statistics, vol. 33, no. 3, Sept. 1962.

a real social system. It is not even necessary to have read Kafka or Parkinson to have one's own ideas upon this subject.

The problem I should like to discuss here is that of the uncertainty due to people's limited consciousness of the ways of their own decision-making and to the limited possibilities of language as a means of communication for describing decision functions. I suppose that this problem is of some importance for normative methods in the theory of human decision-making and, in particular, for their practical use when organizing social systems.

III. OPERATIONS ON MESSAGES

We shall only deal with messages because it is obvious that even a choice of an action means a choice of message which is sent to some effector (e.g. in the human body it could be a message sent from the nervous system to a group of muscles). As far as this paper is concerned, operations on messages have the same meaning as treatment of messages and both of these terms will be used.

When studying an operation on messages we are going to divide participating messages into two groups which we call (*a*) data, and (*b*) programmes.

The data are the messages upon which the operation is performed and the programme is the message which governs the operation. Instead of programmes we could speak about algorithms. I have chosen the word 'programme' because it is used in computer programming where I have often found some inspiration for my ideas.

For expressing programmes we need the notion of elementary operations. When speaking about programmes we must always suppose that a set of elementary operations is given (e.g. basic logical and arithmetical operations). The programme is the message giving the order of execution in these elementary operations so that a given, complex operation can be executed as a final effect of such a procedure. (In a special case, one elementary operation could be considered as well as a complex one, and the programme would then, of course, be trivial.)

IV. OPERATIONS ON MESSAGES IN THE HUMAN CENTRAL NERVOUS SYSTEM

Let us now consider the central nervous system (CNS) as the system where all messages in which we are interested are treated. If we want to use the concept of programme as we have introduced it, we must first ask what the set of elementary operations could mean in the case of the human CNS. There is no simple answer to this question and many possibilities are open. For instance, if the neuron hypothesis is right, we could consider that set as being one of elementary logical operations performed by single neurons. Although I tend to believe in this hypothesis myself, I do not believe in the utility of such a view.

Let us look for some inspiration from the treating of messages by computers, where programmes of complex problems are also not described in terms of elementary operations of logical circuits, although we know that during the computation they are really disintegrated into such operations. This is because a certain hierarchy of programmes is introduced, every level of which has its own set of elementary operations (e.g. the elementary operations of an automatic coding system, of the computer, of its arithmetic unit, and of its simple circuits). Elementary operations at a certain level can be described by programmes in terms of elementary operations of the level next below it.

For our purposes it will be sufficient to introduce a two-level hierarchy of programmes in the human CNS:

        (*a*) conscious programmes;
        (*b*) unconscious programmes.

We define conscious programmes as those which people can describe and communicate to others. The unconscious programmes are all the other programmes which people can use for their operations on messages but cannot describe and communicate.

Let me stress that we are speaking about programmes and not about data. Conscious programmes can govern operations on conscious data only. Unconscious programmes can, however, govern operations on both conscious and unconscious data.

Unconscious programmes use elementary operations which we can suppose to be operations as simple even as those on the neuron level. We may suppose that many complex operations in the human CNS are governed by unconscious programmes.

Only when operations are of a certain minimum complexity can the human CNS take consciousness of some of their input and output data so that it can express them and use them in communication with others. It does not mean, of course, that at the same time the human CNS must be conscious of their programmes. On the contrary, the case of treating conscious data according to unconscious programmes seems to be very usual. This is so, for instance, in what we call 'intuition' and 'intelligence'.

People's unawareness as to some programmes of their mental operations does not, of course, mean that these programmes do not exist. If we accept that the brain is the tool of thought, these programmes really must exist and be imprinted in its structure because otherwise people could not use them. There is an important difference between using a programme and knowing how to describe it.

Some of the operations governed by unconscious programmes, if they are complex enough, can have the following properties :

(*a*) All their input and output data are conscious.
(*b*) Different people can perform them identically, and this can be checked because of (*a*).
(*c*) They are designed by conventional symbols in a language.
(*d*) They can be performed with reasonable reliability by the CNS whenever designed by their symbols.

Only such operations can serve as elementary operations for conscious programmes. We shall call them conscious elementary operations. The sets of conscious elementary operations available to different individuals can be different. We may consider their size to be connected with the level of people's education and especially with their capacity to think abstractly.

V. INDIVIDUAL FORMATION OF NEW PROGRAMMES

The human CNS is a very complicated system which can not only treat input data and change them into output data, but also form new programmes for its own consequent use. If these new programmes are unconscious, they are strictly individual (e.g. conditioned reflexes), but if they are conscious they can become socially shared (e.g. discovered natural laws, rules of social behaviour).

The formation of new programmes is a special sort of operation on messages. New programmes are found as a result of some operations, the programmes of which have already existed in the CNS. We shall call learning operations the operations for forming new programmes.

Example: When given a confusion matrix (i.e. ordered input and output data of an operation governed by some unknown programme) and a set of elementary operations, new programmes can be formed as the result of trial and error procedures. Different combinations made of the given elementary operations are proposed and checked as to whether they give results conforming with the given confusion matrix. If not, the proposed combination is rejected and some new one tried. The programme of the learning operation in this case can be divided into two parts: (*a*) the generating of proposals; (*b*) the checking of them. The proposals seem to be very often generated according to some unconscious programme because people usually do not know how they get 'good ideas'. There are hardly any normative theories prescribing how to get from one's own CNS an abundant source of good ideas when this does not arise spontaneously. Sometimes we can look at generated proposals as at random messages issued from some internal Monte Carlo element. Sometimes when studying the human CNS it is necessary to speak about random messages in other cases too. In general, random messages can act either like a noise distorting other messages in the CNS, or they can be used as substitutes for missing information. Thanks to them we can imagine, for example, that decisions can be made even if all the necessary data are not available or some parts of their programmes have not been determined. Naturally the probability of success is consequently affected. Of course, if there is a possibility of repeating some activity and in this way approaching the right solution, e.g. the trial and error method already mentioned, random messages play the very important role of those messages which determine the first phases of this activity (as data and/or as programmes) and without which the activity could not start. Naturally, the definition of random messages is relative and depends on the aim of our studies. Messages that we consider as random from one point of view can be considered from the other as unconscious messages coming from some very determined unconscious source (e.g. the point of view of an economist versus that of a psychoanalyst).

When operating on messages, the CNS can make some mistakes. The mistakes must not, of course, be so substantial as to affect the survival of the CNS. Mistakes in a newly formed programme mean that the results obtained according to it do not coincide with the given confusion matrix. Such mistakes can be due, for instance, (*a*) to the confusion matrix which is not given at once for all possible values of input data; (*b*) to the impossibility (or to the lack of will) of checking up on the proposed programmes over the given confusion matrix; (*c*) to the objective impossibility (or to the subjective incapacity) of ordering the elementary operations from the given set into a programme which could give a satisfactory coincidence with the given confusion matrix.

VI. THE ORIGIN OF PROGRAMMES IN THE HUMAN CNS

If we first study some learning operation and afterwards the operation for which the learning operation has established the programme, we must admit that the same message which we consider as treated data when studying one operation can be considered as programme when studying another operation. This is well in accordance with our previous statement about the relative difference between data and programmes. Nevertheless, sometimes we may find it useful to speak about programmes in the CNS as the group of all messages that can be at least once considered as programmes in the studies of different operations.

We may distinguish three different groups of programmes, according to their origin, in the human CNS:

(*a*) inborn programmes;
(*b*) individually-formed programmes;
(*c*) programmes communicated from the social environment.

Usually we may consider most of the inborn programmes in the human CNS as programmes for learning operations, although we could even find between them programmes for data-processing (e.g. unconditioned reflexes). The individually-formed programmes and the communicated ones may often be considered as programmes for data-processing, but we could also find between them programmes for learning operations (man can learn how to learn).

VII. HUMAN ACTIONS AND SOCIAL COMMUNICATION

The above division of programmes is related to their division into conscious and unconscious ones; we may consider the inborn programmes as unconscious, the individually-formed programmes as either unconscious or conscious, the communicated programme as conscious.

People can act, of course, according to both their conscious and unconscious programmes, while they can communicate only their conscious ones. It means that people can perform more different operations on messages than they are capable of describing by conscious programmes. Naturally, the situation can change to a certain extent: people can form conscious programmes even for some operations that they have been able previously to perform only unconsciously. It can be done, for instance, by the observation of others or, even better, by the observation of oneself (introspection). The formation of conscious programmes for unconsciously performable operations must be done, of course, by some sort of learning operation, as is the case for any other formation of new programmes. Even mistakes can be committed for similar reasons to those already mentioned. Possible mistakes in forming such conscious programmes have a particular consequence for human social behaviour: people can decide about their actions by using other operations on messages than those about which they are speaking when communicating conscious programmes.

Example: A man can commit mistakes when introspecting on his own unconsciously performed operations for some of the following reasons:

(*a*) He does not check up on the proposed conscious programme for all possible input data. This can happen, for instance, because he cannot know for certain how he would behave in some situations or because he does not want to do so, even if it were possible. This unwillingness can be motivated by a fear of admitting to society the real programme of his decision-making (e.g. hypocrisy or even bluffing, especially if declaration of using some programmes and not using other programmes can be advantageous), or even to himself (e.g. repressed motivation which we can consider as a part of some unconscious programmes). The case of bluffing is, of course, slightly different because the real programme can be found; it is just that it is not socially communicated. From the point of view of social communication, the result is the same: a difference between the programme which is used and that which is communicated.

(*b*) He cannot find the corresponding conscious programme because he cannot find any satisfactory combination of the conscious elementary operations which are available to him (e.g. a chess champion who is capable of excellent decisions when playing but incapable of communicating the programme for finding them).

When people are not capable or willing to find exact conscious programmes of their decision-making, they may tend to communicate by means of symbols which do not mean any exactly defined elementary operation on messages (e.g. words like 'think it over', 'take into account', 'decide with the most possible regard to . . .', etc.). In this case, of course, the conveyed information can decrease nearly to zero. The receiver of such a message (I propose to call it 'pseudo-programme') cannot use it as a programme for his own decision-making. He must use some parts of his own programme which he considers most conform to the received message or at least, conform to it to the extent that nobody could prove, by using communication in language, that he had not respected it. Naturally, the possible individual interpretations of such vague messages (pseudo-programmes) can differ substantially.

VIII. CONCLUSIONS

In the possible differences between how people really make decisions and how they describe the programmes for their decision-making, we can see one of the sources of uncertainty in the functioning of social organizations. Here we can see the explanation why, if two men are doing the same thing according to some language description, it may not be the same thing according to the programmes actually used in their decision-making and thus to the actual results.

We can see that the social communication of programmes for decision-making can be restricted not only because of different interests of different people in the case of non-co-operative games (e.g. a man can be reluctant to follow the prescribed programme for his decision-making because he finds it against his interests), as has been stressed often, but also in the case of co-operative games because of reasons which I would call limits in human rationality. I mean by this the limits of decision-making for which people are really using the same conscious programmes that they are communicating. In the limits of human rationality we must see at the same time the limits of normative methods when organizing social systems.

The over-estimation of human rationality and the consequent exaggerated use of normative methods leads to the formation of pathologic bureaucratic systems where circuits of messages can be very complicated but at the same time very independent of some important actions.

I do not want to preach against normative methods, which have undoubtedly been responsible for considerable progress in the managerial sciences, in operational research, in decision theory, etc. Thanks to them, the set of well-defined conscious programmes for human decision-making has increased and the uncertainty in social organizations, ensuing from the use of individual unconscious programmes of non-guaranteed quality, has diminished.

Nevertheless, it is also necessary to admit that people sometimes must decide without being too well aware as to how they should do so. Social organizers may, of course, feel uneasy when facing the uncertainty ensuing from other people's individual and non-communicated programmes which may influence substantially and unpredictably the real behaviour of the organized social system. The way out of this situation, however, seems not to consist in developing the normative methods to the extent that all human decision-making would be prescribed by centrally determined conscious programmes. Even if we ignored the ethical reasons which would not allow us to accept a world in which all human individuality and personality would be excluded from decision-making (except, perhaps, in some restricted group of social organizers), there are the reasons which we have just studied — the limits of human rationality.

We must study very critically the possibility of using normative methods which are based on language communication. Since the possibility of using them reasonably does not usually cover all the activities in social organizations, it is necessary to complete them by other arrangements. It is possible, for instance, to influence indirectly the individual formation of programmes for decision-making and to assure their participation in social activity according to their quality, without communicating them as social messages. In the economic system, such arrangements seem to be connected with decentralization where the central unit allows individual parts of the whole system a more or less independent interaction with some objective environment (e.g. the market, the natural environment). Then it is possible to assure the choice of successful individual programmes without necessarily communicating them and to make the whole system more resistant to possible degeneration. Naturally, this does not exclude some risk and uncertainty as to the quality of the actual results. Such uncertainty, however, seems to be better than the certainty of disorganization due to the over-estimation of human rationality. Some risk and uncertainty are probably inherent in the life of individuals as well as in that of societies ; people can diminish them but never get rid of them completely. When people are speaking of having diminished them, that is the time when we must look carefully to see whether they have not, in fact, increased them.

DISCUSSION OF THE PAPER BY DR. PELIKÁN

Professor Marschak : I think this is a courageous and innovatory paper, and I think that in some sense an introduction was given to it by some of the discussion of my own paper this morning. It may really be that in their obsession with descriptions of optimal situations and their equal obsession with economic man, who is a creature of more or less unlimited capabilities, economists have reached the point where there is not much more for them to say. There have been several ways proposed out of this dilemma. One, which has also been mentioned here, is associated with the name of Herbert Simon. He has developed a concept of 'limited rationality' in which economic agents have much more modest goals and much more modest abilities than the globally rational classical economic man. I am not really a member of the group that works in this direction, but it is my impression that this model has not, so far, been very well articulated, i.e. we are not yet in a position to discuss an economy made up of Simon-type individuals. The concept of individual limited rationality has just not been that well formulated.

In a sense we can regard the proposals of Dr. Pelikán as an alternative to this approach. I am not at all familiar in this territory, but I believe his proposal also draws on some topics in psychology and other behavioural sciences, and in addition, it seems, from the computer-design literature. It is far too early to make any choice between these two approaches, but to me Dr. Pelikán's definitely has a quite different flavour. The difference is, I think, that there is a stress in Dr. Pelikán's model on the two parts of an individual's behaviour : the conscious part and the unconscious part. It seems to me that this is an important aspect of human behaviour, and a theory which recognizes it may very well have considerable appeal. If I understand him correctly, what Dr. Pelikán deplores about some of the 'normative' models developed by economists (and I suppose I am one of the guilty parties) is that we are talking about black boxes or robots and not about human beings, and that if we are trying to design organizations composed of such robots, then we are depriving ourselves of some important tools. In Dr. Pelikán's model the unconscious part of man is not something that should be bothersome to the designer of organizations but something that should be attractive to him. It has important potentialities for operating organizations which the more traditional sort of model leaves out.

I think we might get a better feeling for what Dr. Pelikán is doing if he would try to answer some more direct questions. One main question that I have is the following. If economists are asked to clutter up their nice, neat models with some new complications, they would like to be told, however vaguely and imprecisely, what this will get them in terms of interesting and unexpected properties of economic organizations. Is it possible to sketch in a very vague form what a theorem might look like in this new terminology ? What kind of assumptions on the various elements of the model might one be able to use in order to demonstrate some unexpected (or perhaps expected) consequences ?

Professor Siroyezhin : From my point of view Dr. Pelikán has missed one important point in considering a two-stage system of decision processes. I think that in constructing models like those developed by Dr. Pelikán we have to distinguish two subdivisions of the unconscious part of behaviour : one which acts equally in all human beings independently of social conditions, and one which depends upon individual social experience. I feel that with such a structure the model would be much more valuable for further development and would give more useful implications for organization theory. I should like to add that I read the paper with interest and that I consider the work done as an original contribution.

Professor Menges : I refer to the basic attitude of Dr. Pelikán's paper. 'No doubt', we read, 'the final aim of these studies is to act like engineers.' I don't know if I would like to live in an economy managed by persons who act like engineers. In any case I think we shall have to go a long way before social processes can be mastered and controlled. Before we get there, concepts will have to be defined in measurable terms, causal relations will have to allow formal mapping, and, finally, a broad arsenal of explanatory answers to questions of the types 'What is ?' and 'Why is something ?' will have to be available. So far research in the social sciences has been mostly normative and explanatory ; the social sciences are only at the very beginning of their explanatory phase, and I cannot believe that by some information-theoretical tricks the social sciences can skip the explanatory phase and go directly into the operational or engineering phase, answering directly the question, 'How are we to operate ?' Our knowledge about social phenomena and their conditions is much too deficient.

Mr. Bessière : I wish to bring your attention to the notion of conscious and unconscious programmes and to the possibility of interpreting them when studying animals or computing machines. For animals we should of course delete the conscious programmes and for computers the unconscious ones. This proves, in particular, that the existence of conscious programmes (in the meaning Dr. Pelikán gives this word) does not imply *consciousness of the self*. But perhaps consciousness of the self can be interpreted by the fact that, as far as I can see, man is the only being which has at the same time conscious and unconscious programmes.

But I see another difference between man and computers which cannot be interpreted in terms of consciousness, but which comes from the supposed existence of a *stochastic generator*. Dr. Pelikán assumes this existence, and I think it is a very important feature. I shall give you an argument to sustain this assumption. You have probably heard about Buridan's ass — this poor creature that was placed at exactly equal distances from two equally desirable piles of hay and that became mad before starving to death. I think such a thing could also happen to a computing machine looking for an optimal solution and which finds the optimum is not unique without having any programme to solve this internal contradiction. But I believe this could not happen to a real man, nor to a real donkey, and that the explanation for this is that both the man and the donkey have got some Monte Carlo generator somewhere in their common basic unconscious part.

Dr. Pelikán : I thank Professor Marschak for his discussion and for his appreciation of my paper. I agree with him that my approach means some complications in comparison with the classical one. I apologize for not being able to say, for the time being, anything interesting about the theorems in this new terminology. I want to look for such theorems in my future work, to which the paper presented is only an introduction. I simply believe that the unconscious part of man does exist and that it influences rather sensibly his behaviour even in economic organizations.

Professor Siroyezhin's valuable remark about the introduction of three-level hierarchy would complicate the theory. It is possible, of course, to increase the number of levels ; I even mentioned this possibility in my paper. Trying to keep, however, the theory relatively simple and considering the criterion of social communication as decisive in this study, I rather believe that the two-level hierarchy (conscious and unconscious levels) is quite sufficient here.

As to Professor Menges's discussion, I think we have not understood each other in the meaning of the word 'engineering' in human organizations. I simply meant by this the application of normative methods when organizing and managing social and economic systems. I think that anybody who prepares realizable projects is, with a little fantasy, comparable to an engineer.

I thank Mr. Bessière for his valuable and stimulating remarks. As to the problem of the consciousness of the self, I agree with him that it could be connected with the notion of conscious and unconscious programmes. It should perhaps be more stressed that the existence of conscious programmes is due to the use of socially conventional symbols.

Chapter 9

GENERALIZATION OF
CLASSICAL DECISION THEORY

BY

WERNER LEINFELLNER

I. THE FUNDAMENTAL PERSONALISTIC VIEW OF THE DECISION THEORY

THE decision theory of today is a mixture of several independent theories, such as utility theory, statistical decision theory, and game theory. This paper tries to give an outline of a more general decision theory founded upon some aspects of basic research. It is mainly the personalistic view of decision-making under uncertainty and risk based upon human valuation, clearly expressed by Savage, who said that valuation (utility) is the first and probability the second. The following reasoning takes further into account that there are two fundamental attitudes towards the surrounding world. Firstly, man can be conscious of a part of the world by *recognition*. Especially scientific recognition means mapping a part of the world (D) into his mental consciousness, i.e. into symbols of language to find out the empirical structure of this part (D) of the world. Secondly, man can be conscious of a part (D) of the world by *evaluation*. Evaluation means mapping of objects, actual states of the world, of actions into his mental consciousness, i.e. into symbols of language, to find out the order created by ordering relations of preference (Pref). There is a fundamental difference between the basic ordering of an empirical set M_0 of things $a'_1, a'_2, \ldots, a'_n$ by empirical relations, as 'a'_i is greater than a'_j, and a'_i is equal to a'_k', and the ordering by relations of preference, as 'a'_i is preferred to a'_j' ($P(a'_i, a'_j)$ in symbols), or 'a'_i is indifferent to a'_j' ($I(a'_i, a'_j)$). The former are objective inter-subjective empirical relations (observable), basic information about the empirical structure of nature; the latter are subjective ones, which impress man's order of interests and preferences upon his surroundings. To recognize this impressed order gives the individual a fundamental orientation about all possible states of the world in

196

relation to himself. With such an orientation in mind he is able to find the best decisions to make. A simple decision rule — the normative aspect of valuation — is for example selecting the highest or the lowest value from his order of values. This is the protomodel of social and economic behaviour and rational decision-making, if it is applicable to dual and plural (multipersonal) decision-making. What is a little difficult to understand is the fact that valuation and decisions can be objects of scientific recognition, of scientific theories. But there is a parallel in logic, for since Aristotle there is a recognition of rational inference and today we have complicated theories about this, including probable inference. Aristotle found the formal rules of inference, Bernoulli the first formal rule of valuation.

Within the frame of a theory it is possible to express all information in a descriptive language (L_0) and to represent the empirical descriptions in a purely theoretical language (L_t), of the same theory. L_t expresses the orderings of values — usually *in mente* — in mathematical or logical symbols. To guarantee the right theoretical reconstruction of valuation and decisions within the framework of a theory, the theories must be consistent and their results empirically confirmable.

II. THE FORMAL ASPECT OF INDIVIDUAL DECISION-MAKING UNDER UNCERTAINTY

Human valuation presupposes individual valuation. From this protomodel we have a theoretical aspect, the theory Th1. Th1 consists of two parts, the descriptive (L_0) and the pure theoretical part (L_t). There are rules of correspondence, based upon non-numerical and numerical value-functions.

(1) *Sketch of the Framework of Th1*

L_t = pure theoretical frame of representation of values and decisions within Th1. It deals with a representation space, normally a finite Euclidean space, or an ordered vector space, with theoretical statements as Bernoulli's rule, which predict optimal decisions of the form $\text{Pref}(a'_1, a'_2)_{\text{Th1}}$. The subscript 'Th1' means that we are only regarding decisions belonging to the special theory Th1. Consistency and empirical confirmation are the characteristics of Th1. The theoretical sentences, especially the theoretical laws, are valid only over D of Th1. The structure of the pure theoretical part L_t can be defined by axioms.

Formalism

First a law:

If $\sum \alpha_i a_i \geqslant \sum \beta_i a_i$, then $\alpha_i \geqslant \beta_i$.

Value space consists of numerical sets: M_z, vectors, numerical relations, functions, operations, as $=, >, +$.

Mixture space consists of: real numbers representing probabilities: $(\alpha_1, \alpha_2, \ldots, \alpha_n)$; $(\beta_1, \beta_2, \ldots, \beta_n)$, where $(p(e_1) = \alpha_1, p(e_2) = \alpha_2, \ldots, p(e_n) = \alpha_n)$ $\epsilon[0, 1]$.

$$M_t^p = (\alpha_1 a_1, \alpha_2 a_2, \ldots, \alpha_n a_n)$$
$$M_t = (a_1, a_2, \ldots, a_n)$$

ordered by $\succ\!\!-\!\!-$, $\sim$.

For example a_i, b_i are values, $\alpha_i a_i$, $\beta_j b_j$ etc. are probable values.

Rules of correspondence based upon non-numerical and numerical valuation functions defined on M_0.

Rules of correspondence based upon numerical representation of accidental events by probability measure function defined on E.

L_0 = description of empirical decisions within the range D $(M_0 \subset D)$, dealing with:

empirical sets M_0
$(a'_1, a'_2, \ldots, a'_n) \epsilon M_0$
$(b'_1, b'_2, \ldots, b'_n) \epsilon M_0$
empirical relations P, I indicating empirical decisions (behaviouristic basis).

events $(e_1, e_2, \ldots, e_n) \epsilon E$.

Note: All theoretical sentences, notions, etc., are valid only within the frame of a theory they belong to. For example, decision rules within Th1 make sense only for a single person (Sagoroff, 1964).

(2) *Formal Definition of the Structure of Th1*

If the symbols and signs given in Section II (1) are used, so that the conditions $A1$–$A9$ below are satisfied, $A1$–$A9$ define the formal structure of Th1 (definition of the basic (individual) valuation scheme). If these conditions are consistent and empirically testable, they are a representation of $(M_0; P, I)$ and $e_1, e_2, \ldots, e_n$ unto $(M_t^p; \succ\!\!-\!\!-, \sim, 0)$. For $(M_t^p; \succ\!\!-\!\!-, \sim, 0)$ is an objective expression $(M_z^p; >, =, +)$. Each role of theoretical and mathematical reasoning about valuation and probability should enable this person to detect and remove inconsistencies in his own real decisions or in his possible decisions (= values or envisaged behaviour). This is the process of development towards rational valuation and deciding. There is no absolute behaviour which is called rational. There exists only a rational type of decision-making, which is approaching rational valuation and deciding = rational behaviour.

The following properties, which can be regarded as behavioural laws of Th1, are of importance:

L1. If $P(a'_i, a'_j)$ or $I(a'_i, a'_j)$, then $a_i \succ\!\!- a_j$ or $a_i \sim a_j$ and $u(a_i) \geqslant u(a_j)$ (law of representation).

L2. $u(\alpha_1 a_1, \alpha_2 a_2, \ldots, \alpha_n a_n) = u(a_1)p(e_1) + u(a_2)p(e_2) + \ldots, u(a_n)p(e_n) =$
$$\sum_{i=1}^{n} u(a_i)p(e_i)$$

(Bernoulli's rule, when the decision rule of Th1 is maximized). In case of $\alpha_1 = \alpha$, $\alpha_2 = 1 - \alpha$, *L2* is diminishing to $u(\alpha a_1, (1 - \alpha)a_2)$ $= u(a_1)p(e_1) + u(a_2)p(e_2)$. $p(e_i)$ can be a probability distribution $f(x)$ for tickets in lotteries.

As we have a theory (Th1), it is necessary to prove the consistency of *L1* and *L2* by deriving from *A1–A9* (Section II (3)).

A1. The empirical relation system $(M_0; P, I)$ is a quasi-ordering. if for a'_i, a'_j, a'_k
I is reflexive: $I(a'_i, a'_i)$,
I is symmetrical: if $I(a'_i, a'_j)$, then $I(a'_j, a'_i)$,
I is transitive: if $I(a'_i, a'_j)$ and $I(a'_j, a'_k)$, then $I(a'_i, a'_k)$,
P is transitive: if $P(a_i', a'_j)$ and $P(a'_j, a'_k)$, then $P(a_i', a'_k)$,
P is connected: for all $a'_i, a'_j \epsilon M_0$ either $P(a'_i, a'_j)$ or $P(a'_j, a'_i)$ or $I(a'_i, a'_j)$.

Within Th1, *A1* is merely a hypothesis fulfilled only by individuals of the type *r* (rational).

A2. From *E* and a probability measure *p* over *E* we get $\alpha_i \epsilon[0, 1]$,

$$\sum_{i=1}^{n} \alpha_i = 1, i = 1, 2, \ldots, n.$$

From a set of pure alternatives $(a'_1, a'_2, \ldots, a'_n)$ ordered by *A1* we get M_i^p by the event-matching assumption: If $(a'_1, a'_2, \ldots, a'_n) \epsilon M_0$ and $(e_1, e_2, \ldots, e_n) \epsilon E$, then $(\alpha_1 a_1, \alpha_2 a_2, \ldots, \alpha_n a_n) \epsilon M_i^p$. E.g. if pure alternative a'_1 is given and if e_1 occurs ($\alpha_1 = 1$), and if pure alternative a'_2 is given and if e_2 does not occur ($\alpha_2 = 0$), then ($\alpha_1 a_1$, $\alpha_2 a_2$). Note that if $a_1 = a_2$ and if $a \sim \alpha a$, $(1 - \alpha)a$ where $\alpha = 1$ or $\alpha = 0$, then a is a sure value (sure value-assumption or reduction of probable values to sure values). We have only this simultaneous definition of sure values by probable values and vice versa. Therefore absolute sure values are merely fictitious. There is no probability without valuation and no valuation without a closed unit interval $[0, 1]$, which satisfies the usual probability axioms.

*A*3. There are binary ordering relations $\rangle$— and $\sim$ over the elements of M_t^p. (Note that $\rangle$— and $\sim$ are relations between values of non-numerical character.)

*A*4. For all x, $x \epsilon M_t$, there are max and min elements a_i and a_j:

$$a_i \rangle — x \rangle — a_j.$$

*A*5. If $(a_i \rangle — a_j \rangle — a_k)$, then there exists an α which can be found by an experiment, so that

$$a_j \sim (\alpha a_i, (1 - \alpha)a_k).$$

(Of course there exists an empirical *I*.) This Archimedian hypothesis may even be dropped (Aumann, 1964).

*A*6. If $a_i \overset{\rangle}{\sim} a_j$ and there is an $\alpha \epsilon [0, 1]$, then:

$$(\alpha a_i, (1 - \alpha)a_j) \overset{\rangle}{\sim} ((1 - \alpha)a_j, \alpha a_i)$$

(commutativity assumption).

*A*7. If $a_i \overset{\rangle}{\sim} a_j$, then $(\alpha a_i, (1 - \alpha)a_j) \overset{\rangle}{\sim} (\beta a_i, (1 - \beta)a_j$ if and only if $\alpha \geqslant \beta$ (monotonicity assumption).

*A*8. For all $\alpha, \beta, \gamma, \delta \epsilon [0, 1]$ if $\delta = \alpha \gamma + \beta(1 - \gamma)$ then CM_t^p exists.

$$CM_t^p = (\gamma_1 M_{t1}^p, \gamma_2 M_{t2}^p, \ldots, \gamma_n M_{tn}^p).$$

Those compound value sets (CM_t^p) can be reduced to simple value sets (M_t^p) by *A*5. For example:

$$(\gamma_1 M_{t1}^p, \gamma_2 M_{t2}^p) \sim M_t^p, \text{ or}$$

$$(\gamma(\alpha a_i, (1 - \alpha)a_j), (1 - \gamma)(\beta a_i, (1 - \beta)a_j)) \sim (\delta a_i, (1 - \delta)a_j).$$

If *A*8 is fulfilled, it is possible to compute compound probabilities (Luce, 1964).

*A*9. If $m(\alpha_1 a_1, \alpha_2 a_2)$ is the amount of money indifferent to the gamble $(\alpha_1 a_1, \alpha_2 a_2)$, then, if

$$m(\alpha_1(a_1+c),\ \alpha_2(a_2+c)) = m(\alpha_1 a_1,\ \alpha_2 a_2) + c$$

and if the numerical value function u is continuous and satisfies the expected utility hypotheses, then

$$u(x) = px + q \qquad (p>0),\ \text{or}$$
$$u(x) = p\lambda^x + q \qquad (p>0,\ \lambda>1,\ \text{or}\ p<0,\ \lambda<1).$$

(3) *Proof of L1 and L2*

If we define that $u(a_1) = 1$, $u(a_n) = 0$, then by *A4* $a_1 \overset{\displaystyle\succ}{\sim} x \overset{\displaystyle\succ}{\sim} a_n$. By *A5* we get: If there exists an α_1, then

$$x \sim (\alpha_1 a_1,\ \alpha_n a_n).$$

If we define that $u(x) = \alpha_1$, u must fulfil *L1*, *L2*. For *L1* we get: There is of course in the same way a y and if there exists a β_1, then

$$y \sim (\beta_1 a_1,\ \beta_n a_n).$$

By *A6, 7*

$$(x \overset{\displaystyle\succ}{\sim} y) \longrightarrow ((\alpha_1 a_1,\ \alpha_n a_n) \overset{\displaystyle\succ}{\sim} (\beta_1 a_1,\ \beta_n a_n)),$$

if and only if $\alpha_1 \geqslant \beta_1$.

By definition of u this is equivalent to $u(x) \geqslant u(y)$.

For *L2*:

$$(\gamma x,\ (1-\gamma)y) \sim (\gamma(\alpha_1 a_1,\ \alpha_n a_n),\ (1-\gamma)(\beta_1 a_1,\ \beta_n a_n)) \sim (\delta_1 a_1,\ \delta_n a_n).$$

By *A6, 8* hence

$$u(\gamma x,\ (1-\gamma)y) = u(\delta_1 a_1,\ \delta_n a_n) = \delta_1.$$

By definition

$$\alpha\gamma + (1-\gamma)\beta = u(x)\gamma + u(y)(1-\gamma).$$

There are ways of testing this theory by experiments (Davidson *et al.*, 1957). Individuals could either accept or reject each of a series of gambles in the form $(\alpha_1 x_1,\ \alpha_2 6\phi)$ for example. There arises the problem of subjective versus objective probability. In Th1, values are regarded as subjective, but probability not. There are two variants of this theory — the probabilistic value theory and the subjective value theory. The first considers the probability that alternatives are chosen, the second is based upon the expected subjective probability. There are two ways of avoiding these difficulties, shown in the work of Savage and of Davidson, Suppes, and Siegel

(Leinfellner, 1964). Savage assumes that there is no 'objective probability' at all, but only the subjective variety. According to Savage probability is the second concept, valuation is the first. Without a value-measure we cannot talk about probability. Only if there exists a personal mapping of the states (events) of the world into the closed unit interval $[0, 1]$, is there a way to satisfy the usual probability axioms and there is a mapping of the consequences $(\alpha_1 a_1, \alpha_2 a_2, \ldots, \alpha_n a_n)$ unto the real numbers, which behave like a value function. One action is preferred, if its expected utility (= value) is greater. Given that, there exists a rational decision rule. But each probability-measure must be obtained by a single individual and is therefore 'subjective'. Objective probabilities arise only through an interpersonal consensus, as well as 'norms' are created by this consensus. Therefore this theory can be regarded as a cornerstone of individual decision-making based upon individual valuation and uncertainty.

III. DUAL DECISION THEORIES FROM TYPE Th2

Dual decision processes are performed by two participants ($n = 2$). Th2 is the type of a strictly competitive theory and presupposes Th1. Th2 is based upon human valuation : (1) each decision-maker must have in mind not only his own order of valuation, but also the order of his partner ; (2) orderings of values range over sequences of possible subdecisions = strategies (s_i) ; (3) a common constant valuation function (payoff function) is given by the empirical conditions and rules of the special decision process (game) ; (4) by means of this constant valuation function the underlying structure of evaluation of the strategies of both decision-makers is given in a state diagram of all possible outcomes of the decision process (game) = matrix $A =$ (a_{ij}). Uncertainty is brought in by Th1, by probability measure over the constant valuation function and over the strategies. Multipersonal decision-making ($n > 2$, in dual decision processes $n = 2$) is characterized by the fact that people have the same valuation function, but uncertainties (probabilities) are not the same if an act is chosen (= made a decision) from a finite set S_i ($i = 1, 2, \ldots, n$) of available acts.

Considerable simplifications can be achieved if we assume that values (utilities) are interpersonally transferable, i.e. that the different admissible scales given by Th1 belong to different individuals, participants of the same decision process. This is always regarded as a miracle — and it is without consideration of the frame given by Th2. There is only one way of justification of the assumption of 'transferable value' — to regard the whole theory Th2 as a proof for it. With the exception of interpersonal agreement and some automatic mechanism of instincts we have no other justification for the phenomenon of orientation of values in common orders during a dual decision process.

Before giving the formal outline we shall discuss some basic symbols of L_0 and L_t of Th2, whose scientific use will be defined later on by axioms $A1$–$A11$.

The extension of valuation of Th1 in Th2 over possible sequences of subdecisions gives man an orientation about the possible complex actions of his neighbour if he is a partner in a well-known decision process. Sequences of subdecisions can be regarded as single possible decisions like the M_ts, the M_t^ps, and the CM_t^ps. Strategies are something like motives, complete enumerations of actions leading to an aim, which is evaluated according to the underlying valuation structure of each decision process given by the constant valuation function. Everything that has happened and that will happen is taken into account in this set of subdecisions. There must be good, bad, optimal, pure or mixed strategies, and we must therefore use the same valuation scheme of Th1 with slight modifications. From this valuation scheme it is possible to derive decision rules, i.e. predict optimal strategies for each participant. Strategies are treated here as vectors of the rows and columns of the value matrix $A = (a_{ij})$. But what is a matrix in a dual decision process? It is a methodical description of the empirical frame, the empirical conditions and rules of each decision process, and belongs partly to L_0, partly to L_t. It is a state diagram, which tells how a participant has to evaluate the strategies in accordance with the rules and conditions of each decision process. This is obtained by a special linear value function, the interpersonal valid payoff function of the matrix games, defined over the strategies and telling how much player 1 may expect to win from player 2 if player 1 decides for a particular strategy from his set. All empirical basic information, all rules, i.e. the empirical frame of decisions, is given by the state diagram, the matrix (a_{ij}). The payoff function is always evaluated in terms of the appropriate value (utility) function and units of Th1. Each matrix game is therefore a decision process and defined by a triplet (S^1, S^2, K), where $s_1^1, s_2^1,$ ..., $s_n^1 \epsilon S^1$ and $s_1^2, s_2^2, ..., s_m^2 \epsilon S^2$. S^1 and S^2 are represented in a representation space, usually a Euclidean space, as convex, closed and bounded sets and the payoff function is theoretically a convex, linear function, including the uncertainty of the choice of strategies after the event-matching assumption:

$$K((\mu_1 s_1^1 + \mu_2 s_2^1), s_j^2) = \mu_1 K(s_1^1, s_j^2) + \mu_2 K(s_2^1, s_j^2),$$
$$K(s_i^1, (\mu_1 s_1^2 + \mu_2 s_2^2)) = \mu_1 k(s_i^1, s_1^2) + \mu_2 K(s_i^1, s_2^2),$$

where μ_1, $\mu_2 \in [0, 1]$ and $i = 1, 2, \ldots, m$, $j = 1, 2, \ldots, n$. The representation of strategies as points in a Euclidean space simplifies the formulation of theoretical laws in Th2. Matrix decision processes are obtained, when S^1, S^2, $\ldots$, S^n are taken as simplices in finite dimensional Euclidean space and it is taken into consideration that there is a second moment of uncertainty given by a distribution over the finite strategies, i.e. the rows and columns of the matrix (a_{ij}). Symbolizing the distribution by the vector

$$x = (x_1, x_2, \ldots, x_m),$$

where $x_i > 0$ and by

$$y = (y_1, y_2, \ldots, y_n),$$

where $y_j > 0$ and

$$\sum_{i=1}^{i=m} x_i = 1, \qquad \sum_{j=1}^{j=n} y_j = 1,$$

the payoff kernel has the form

$$K(x, y) = \sum_{i=1}^{i=m} \sum_{j=1}^{j=n} x_i a_{ij} y_j = (\chi, A\gamma),$$

where A is the matrix (a_{ij}). With this symbolic representation of a dual decision process Th2 can be structurally defined.

Formal Definition of the Structure of Th2

If the symbols and signs given in Section III (1) are used, so that the following conditions $A1$–$A11$ are satisfied, $A1$–$A11$ define the formal structure of Th2.

$A1$. There are binary ordering relations $\succ\!-$ and $\sim$ over α_i, $i = 1$ $2, \ldots, m$ (column vectors) and β_j, $j = 1, 2, \ldots, m$ (row vectors), where α_i, $\beta_j \epsilon V$.

$A2$. The relational system $(V; \succ\!-, \sim)$ is a quasi-order, if the following conditions are fulfilled:

$$\alpha_i \sim \alpha_i; \quad \alpha_i \sim \alpha_j \rightarrow \alpha_j \sim \alpha_i;$$
$$\alpha_i \sim \alpha_j; \quad \alpha_j \sim \alpha_k \rightarrow \alpha_i \sim a_k;$$

For all α_i, α_j, $\alpha_k \epsilon V$ either $\alpha_i \rangle\!\!-\!\alpha_j$, or

$$\alpha_j \rangle\!\!-\!\alpha_i, \text{ or } \alpha_i \sim \alpha_j \ (1 \leqslant i, j, \ k \leqslant m).$$

The same is valid for all β_i, β_j, β_k $(1 \leqslant i, j, \ k \leqslant n)$.

The ordering is independent of the numbering of the vectors.

A3. If each $a_{ij} > a_{kj}$, then $\alpha_i \rangle\!\!-\!\alpha_k$; $i, k = 1, 2, \ldots, m, j = 1, 2, \ldots, n$;
If each $a_{ij} > a_{ik}$, then $\beta_j \rangle\!\!-\!\beta_k$; $j, k = 1, 2, \ldots, n, i = 1, 2, \ldots, m$.

A4. There is a probability distribution (after the event-matching assumption) over the rows and columns (vectors) of (a_{ij}).

A5. In α_i and β_j there are minimal components a_{ij}^1 for decision-maker 1 ($= 1$) and a_{ij}^2 for decision-maker 2 ($= 2$) as well as maximal components $\bar{a}_{ij}^1$ for 1 and $\bar{a}_{ij}^2$ for 2 ($i = 1, 2, \ldots, m$, $j = 1, 2, \ldots, n$), or

A6. If $\alpha_i \overset{\rangle\!\!-}{\sim} \alpha_j$ $(1 \leqslant i, j \leqslant m)$ and there is an $x_i \epsilon [0, 1]$, then

$$(x_1 \alpha_1, x_2 \alpha_2, \ldots, x_m \alpha_m) \sim C^1 \qquad \text{and}$$
$$(y_1 \beta_1, y_2 \beta_2, \ldots, y_n \beta_n) \sim C^1$$

(C^1, $C^2 =$ decision for a mixed strategy by 1 or 2).

A7. If $\alpha_i \overset{\rangle\!\!-}{\sim} \alpha_j$ $(1 \leqslant i, j \leqslant m)$ and there is an $x_i \epsilon [0, 1]$, then

$$(x_i \alpha_i, (1 - x_i)\alpha_j) \overset{\rangle\!\!-}{\sim} ((1 - x_i)\alpha_j, x_i \alpha_i).$$

The same is valid for all β_i, β_j and y_i $(1 \leqslant i, j \leqslant n)$.

A8. If $\alpha_i \overset{\rangle\!\!-}{\sim} \alpha_j$, then

$$(x_i \alpha_i, (1 - x_i)\alpha_j) \overset{\rangle\!\!-}{\sim} (x_k \alpha_i, (1 - x_k)\alpha_j),$$

if and only if $x_i \geqslant x_k$ $(1 \leqslant i, j \leqslant m; \ x_i, x_k \epsilon [0, 1])$. The same is valid for all β_i, β_j and y_i, y_k $(1 \leqslant i j \leqslant n; \ y_i, y_k \epsilon [0, 1])$.

A9. If the a_{ij}^k converge to a_{ij} and if, e.g., $\alpha_i^k \overset{\rangle\!\!-}{\sim} \alpha_j^k$ for each k ($k = 1$, $2, \ldots, m$), then the limit vectors satisfy $\alpha_i \overset{\rangle\!\!-}{\sim} \alpha_j$. The same is valid for all β_i, β_j.

A10. If for all α_i, α_j $(1 \leqslant i, j \leqslant m; \ x_i \epsilon [0, 1])$
$w(x_i(\alpha_i + c), (1 - x_i)(\alpha_j + c))$, then
$(x_i \alpha_i, (1 - x_i)\alpha_j) + c$.
The same is valid for all β_i, β_j $(1 \leqslant i, j \leqslant n)$ and $y_i \epsilon [0, 1]$.

*A*11. If each decision-maker in Th2 is maximizing his level of
security according to the axioms of Th1, this is equal to a
stable value configuration based upon a (mixed strategy)
equilibrium between the order of values of 1 (VO^2) and the
order of values of 2 (VO^2). In the case of the strict competitive
dual decision process VO^1 is the inversion of VO^2 and vice
versa.

If these axioms hold for two participants (decision-maker, adversary),
there are the following laws in Th2:

*L*1. If $\alpha_i \rangle\!\!-\alpha_j$ and $\beta_i \rangle\!\!-\beta_j$, or $\alpha_i \sim \alpha_j$ and $\beta_i \sim \beta_j$, then

$$w(\alpha_i) > w(\alpha_j) \text{ and } w(\beta_i) > w(\beta_j)$$

(law of representation). By definition

$$w(\alpha_i) = |\,a_{ij}\,| \text{ etc.}$$

*L*2. The ordering relation is not changed, if the matrix (a_{ij}) is replaced by (a_{ij}^*), where

$$a_{ij}^* = pa_{ij} + q,\ p > 0.$$

$$w(C^1) = v(\chi_1 A \gamma) = \sum_{i=1}^{m} \sum_{j=1}^{n} x_i a_{ij} y_j,$$

where

$$\sum_{i=1}^{m} x_i = 1,\quad x_i \epsilon [0,\ 1] \qquad (i = 1, 2, \ldots, m),$$

$$\sum_{j=1}^{n} y_j = 1,\quad y_j \epsilon [0,\ 1] \qquad (j = 1, 2, \ldots, n).$$

If there are in a dual decision process (two-person zero game)
with matrix A mixed strategy χ and γ:

$$w(\chi_0,\ \gamma) > w(\chi_0,\ \gamma_0) > w(\chi,\ \gamma_0),$$

then χ_0 and γ_0 are optimal strategies and $w(\chi_0,\ \gamma_0)$ is the value of
the dual decision process (game) formalized in Th2, based upon
the concept of a possible equilibrium between the ordering of
values of the two participants. For 1 a decision rule is formulated:

*L*3. Choose a probability mixture $\chi_0 (= C_0^1)$, so that the quantity

$$\min_j (x_1 a_{1j} + x_2 a_{2j} + \ldots + x_m a_{mj}), \qquad (j = 1, 2, \ldots, n)$$

is maximized to get a stable equilibrium.

Other criteria such as domination, linearity, row adjunction, column linearity, column duplication, can be obtained from $A1-A11$.

Discussion of Th2

There are other possibilities of axiomatizing even multipersonal decision theories based upon personal valuation. Already in the von Neumann–Morgenstern (1944) theory of utility there are strong intuitive grounds for accepting the close connection of valuation and decisions. In the sense of this paper, values are only possible decisions (in mind) and decisions are realized values. The axiomatic treatment of individual decision-making (Th1) and dual decision-making (Th2) expresses the theoretical connection between valuation, probability and decisions by axioms, which may be interpreted as maxims of individual and dual rational behaviour. Utility theory, game theory, and decision theories are melting together and are only hypotheses within a general decision theory. Therefore the mere conclusion that every valuation is leading to Bernoullian utility, is only a theoretical reasoning within the theory and must not be confirmed (it is not possible to demand this in all cases). There is a terminological confusion, because in decision theories only the empirical confirmation of optimal decisions given by a decision rule must be confirmable. It is a classical aspect of the decision; theory that there should exist in all cases a classical utility satisfying Bernoulli's basic hypothesis:

$$u(\alpha_1 a_1 + \alpha_2 a_2) = \alpha_1 u(a_1) + \alpha_2 u(a_2).$$

This is only an intermediary but necessary hypothesis, leading to the concept that valuation is an increasing linear function of every other, even of functions belonging to different individuals. But not even that. Only the resulting decision rules must be empirically confirmable to test the whole theory. The reconstruction of the reasoning and the valuation in the mind of each decision-maker in theoretical concepts should result in computing optimal decisions; that is the real aim of theoretical reasoning.

There are variants which enlarge our theory Th1, e.g. decision rules can belong to a single individual decision-maker or to a group acting like a single person. Or there are optimal decisions selected from an infinite set of strategies. Further, there are variants which restrict our theory Th2. Especially decision processes with 'complete' ignorance about possible decisions (= values) of the second decision-maker. Milnor's (1954) games against nature consider

nature as a fictitious adversary having no known objective probability and no known strategy. In this case of no-information decision
processes we must add some hypotheses *ad hoc* to our theory Th2
which express our assumption concerning the possible states of the
adversary (of course only for some concrete decision problems).
The problem of decision-making against an adversary (nature) is
therefore either to get some partial information about the adversary
or to use some hypotheses *ad hoc* about possible (*a priori*) states of
nature. The four hypotheses described below are different, as are
their decision rules. The decision-maker, who uses such a theory
with a certain hypothesis *ad hoc* about the theoretically possible state
of strategies of his adversary, chooses an act by a decision rule which
is the best against the theoretical distribution of strategies of his
adversary. If we use the Laplace hypothesis we assume that the
different states are all equally probable. We find that the decision-
making is given by the average

$$(a_{i1}+a_{i2}+\ldots+a_{in})/n,$$

if the decision-maker 1 chooses the ith row. Following a decision
rule he should choose a row for which this average is maximized.
This theory does not fulfil $A6$, $A8$, $A12$, $L2$ of Th2 and is therefore a
restriction of Th2. Similar restrictions we obtain by using Wald's
hypothesis expressing the pessimistic assumption of expecting the
worst (minimax decision rule). Hurwicz's hypothesis suggests
selecting a constant as an index $(0 \leqslant q \leqslant 1)$ which measures the
decision-maker's optimism. For each row or mixture of rows there
is a smallest component and a largest $\bar{a}_{ij}$. The decision rule is to
choose a row or a mixture for which

$$\beta \bar{a}_{ij}+(1-\beta)\bar{a}_{ij}$$

is maximized. If $\beta = 0$ we obtain Wald's decision rule. Savage uses
the hypothesis of minimaxing the regret. If we define the negative
regret matrix (r_{ij}),

$$(a_{ij} - \max a_{kj}),$$

(r_{ij}) measures as an index the difference between the payoff which is
actually obtained and the payoff which could have been obtained if
the true state of the strategies which the adversary uses had been
known. Application of Wald's decision rule to the matrix (r_{ij})
means to choose a row or a mixture for which

$$\min_{j} r_{ij}$$

is maximized. Here we see that the decision-maker may be free to choose in a certain empirical situation (f) any of the available theories and use their decision rules. Although these theories have a common structure (a valuation-scheme expressing Bernoulli's principle and the von Neumann–Morgenstern ordering of values, Borch, 1968), they do not give a common single decision rule. But what decision rule should the decision-maker objectively use ? Is there any criterion, a super-decision rule, which could select the best optimal decision rule DR_i^0 from the set of all decision rules, DR ? Of course there is a possibility, if the decision-maker uses the valuation scheme again. He could estimate and even compute the value $u(DR_i, f)$ which a certain decision rule DR_i has with regard to a certain empirical basis $f(f \epsilon D)$. The use of the valuation scheme after Th1 — or even a shortened scheme — gives values if we compare two rules :

$$u(DR_i, f) \gtrless u(DR_j, f).$$

A decision rule DR_i belonging to an optimal set of decision rules DR^0 is admissible, if it is not strongly (or weakly) dominated by any other rule DR_j belonging to DR. If we have assertained the existence of a minimal admissible set of super-decision rules, we can try to select one single super-decision rule which is the best one. That is an outline of a statistical decision theory of the future, which uses the valuation scheme again and again to find optimal super-decision rules.

This sketch as a conception of the statistical decision theory may be conceptually plausible and can be made feasible mathematically in several cases. But there is a fundamental difficulty in getting the right adequate values :

$$u(DR_i, f) \gtrless u(DR_j, f),$$

if we consider decision rules with regard to social and economic empirical states. Which one of the possible class of decision rules is the optimal ? Which decision rule is the more rational, etc. ? We do not even have a definition or a description of rational valuation and decision-making. Therefore it is nearly impossible to find an optimal super-decision rule, because man is only — instead of having a constant rational behaviour — developing towards rational behaviour (as I hope) in a process of approximation. That means that he himself is creating norms and standards of rational behaviour, rational valuation, rational decision-making, if he recognizes his own valuation and decision-making. The formal and theoretical aspects of decision theories give him the proofs and guarantees of consistent and fruitful valuation and decision-making, fruitful for his development within human society. Just as recognition of logical reasoning and logical inference has at last created fruitful logical and scientific thinking, the recognition of valuation and decision-making means finding a way of getting rid of inconsistencies. Consistent valuation and decision-making will produce step by step the rational behaviour of man within human society.

REFERENCES

Aumann, R. J. (1964), 'Utility Theory without the Completeness Axiom', *Econometrica*, 1964.

Borch, K. (1968), *The Economics of Uncertainty*, Princeton Univ. Press.

Davidson, D., Suppes, P., and Siegel, S. (1957), *Decision-Making*, Stanford Univ. Press, chap. ii, pp. 19–81.

Leinfellner, W. (1964), 'Werttheorien und ihre formale Behandlung', Teil I und II, *Wissenschaft und Weltbild*.

Luce, R. D. (1964), 'Utility Theory', in *Mathematics and Social Sciences*, John Wiley & Sons.

Milnor, J. W. (1954), 'Games against Nature', in *Decision Processes*, John Wiley & Sons.

Neumann, J. von, and Morgenstern, O. (1944), *Theory of Games and Economic Behavior*, Princeton Univ. Press.

Sagoroff, S. (1964), 'Ökonometrie: ein Teil der Ökonomie', *Zeitschrift für Nationalökonomie*, Bd. xxiv.

———

DISCUSSION OF THE PAPER BY DR. LEINFELLNER

Dr. Ivanescu : The paper by Dr. Leinfellner offers an interesting and elegant way of generalizing classical decision theories.

The first part of his paper is devoted to an axiomatic treatment of individual decision-making under uncertainty. The author considers a set M_0 of objects, organized by some 'empirical' relations $R_1, R_2, \ldots, R_n$. From the point of view of valuation, two relations, P (meaning preference), and I (meaning indifference), are introduced. The basic problem here is to find conditions under which a mapping of M_0 into the field Z of reals could be found, so that preference and indifference should be translatable into order-relations in Z.

The following concepts and notations are revised:

Let $(a^{1'}, \ldots, a_n') \epsilon M_0$; the set M_0 is organized by means of the empirical relations P and I.

Let $(e_1, \ldots, e_n)$ be an element of a set E of possible events. The corresponding outcome probabilities are denoted by $(\alpha_1, \ldots, \alpha_n)$.

Let the 'values' of objects a'_i be a. The set $\{(a_1, \ldots, a_n)\}$ is denoted by M_t. Let the 'probabilistic utility' of a'_i be $\alpha_i a_i$. The set $\{(\alpha_1 a_1, \ldots, \alpha_n a_n)\}$ is denoted by M_t^p. The set M_t and M_t^p are organized by the order relations $\rangle$— and $\sim$, transcribing the preference and indifference relations acting in the empirical set M_0 into the utility sets M_t and M_t^p. Finally, the numerical value of the utility of a_i is denoted by $u(a_i)$.

The following axioms are introduced:

$A1'$. I is an equivalence relation (reflexive, symmetrical, and transitive).

$A1''$. P is a complete, transitive ordering.

$A2$. For any $(a'_1, \ldots, a'_n) \epsilon M_0$ and $(e_1, \ldots, e_n) \epsilon E$, if $\alpha_1, \ldots, \alpha_n$ are the corresponding probabilities $(\alpha_i \geq 0, \Sigma \alpha_i = 1)$ then $(\alpha_1 a_1, \ldots, \alpha_n a_n) \epsilon M_t^p$.

$A3$. For each $P_1 = (\alpha_1^1 a_1, \ldots, \alpha_n^1 a_n)$ and $P_2 = (\alpha_1^2 a_1, \ldots, \alpha_n^2 a_n)$ one and only one of the following three situations holds:

$$P_1 \rangle\!\!- P_2$$
$$P_1 \sim P_2$$
$$P_2 \rangle\!\!- P_1.$$

$A4$. For any $x \epsilon M_t$, there are elements a_i and α_j in M_t such that

$$a_i \rangle\!\!- x \rangle\!\!- a_j.$$

$A5$. If $a_i \rangle\!\!- a_j \rangle\!\!- a_k$, then there is an $\alpha (0 \leqslant \alpha \leqslant 1)$ such that

$$a_j = \alpha a_i + (1 - \alpha) a_k.$$

$A6$. If $a_i \overset{\rangle\!\!-}{\sim} a_j$, then there is an $\alpha (0, 1)$ such that

$$[\alpha a_i + (1 - \alpha) a_j] \overset{\rangle\!\!-}{\sim} [(1 - \alpha) a_j + \alpha a_i]$$

(commutativity).

$A7$. If $a_i \overset{\rangle\!\!-}{\sim} a_j$ then

$$[\alpha a_i + (1 - \alpha) a_j] \overset{\rangle\!\!-}{\sim} [\beta a_i + (1 - \beta) a_j]$$

holds if and only if $\alpha \geqslant \beta$ (monotonicity).

$A8$. — axiom permitting computation of compound probabilities.

$A9$. — axiom implying equivalence of utility definitions up to addition of constants.

Under the above nine axioms, it is proved that the corresponding theory satisfies the following two properties:

General Decision Theory

L1. Preservation of Order.

If $P(a'_i, a'_j)$ or $I(a'_i, a'_j)$ then $a_i \succ\!\!- a_j$ or $a_i \sim a_j$ and $u(a_i) \geqslant u(a_j)$.

L2. Additivity of Utility.

$$u(\alpha_1 a_1 + \ldots + \alpha_n a_n) = u(a_i)p(e_1) + \ldots + u(a_n)p(e_n).$$

On the basis of this generalized utility theory, the author develops in the second part of his paper an extension of it to the study of two-person games. This very interesting axiomatization of the theory of two-person games is concluded with discussions of several variants of it.

The paper is elegant and important. Its style is unfortunately rather condensed, however, making the understanding of it rather cumbersome. Some more personal remarks :

(1) It seems to me realistic to suppose that the elimination of the transitivity assumption on P could leave the essentials of the theory unchanged.

(2) I do not understand why the number of events $e_1, \ldots, e_n$ is supposed to be equal to the number of objects $a'_1, \ldots, a'_n$.

(3) I think it would be useful to see whether the used systems of axioms are or are not independent.

Mr. Bessière :

(1) I have found Dr. Leinfellner's paper most interesting, in particular because of its philosophical aspects. As the mathematical axiomatic aspect has just been surveyed by Dr. Ivanescu, I shall concentrate on the philosophical point of view. However, before this, I shall have to ask Dr. Leinfellner to clear up one minor point : I did not see the usefulness of the distinction between the languages L_o and L_t.

(2) Right at the beginning of the introduction, the author makes a distinction between two possible attitudes towards the surrounding world : *attitude* 1, the aim of which is *recognition*, especially *scientific recognition* ; and *attitude* 2, the aim of which is *evaluation*.

Attitude 1, especially when it is scientific, tries to attain *objectivity*. But at the first appearance of this word, the author defines it as *intersubjectivity*. I think this is a very important point. Indeed, if we want to interpret 'objective' as meaning 'directly attached to an object', we implicitly assume that this object can be known in itself. However, we cannot know any object other than by receiving *messages* from it, through the channel of *our* nerves. This truth is rediscovered every day by modern science : microphysics, information theory, cybernetics, etc. But this implies that all knowledge must be 'subjective' in this particular meaning that it requires the existence of a knowing subject. Thus, knowledge is said to be 'objective' when the models used by different persons to represent their personal recognition of the world are isomorphic, that is *independent of the subject*. I think we shall define objectivity by this independence. But there is no absolute objectivity, for the objective knowledge remains dependent on time, and changes as science advances.

I must apologize for insisting on such trivialities. But I think it is quite important always to keep these trivialities in mind, and furthermore, I think it is necessary to agree on definitions before speaking. Many futile debates about the so-called 'subjective probability theory' could have been avoided if everybody agreed on the meaning of words such as 'subjective' and 'objective'.

(3) Now some remarks on attitude 2. Here, the author says, everything is subjective because our valuations reflect our own interests and preferences. We choose our decisions so as to realize the highest possible value. This is the protomodel of all decision theory.

One could object that this is a mere tautology, for we cannot define value other than as a characteristic of our preferences. I would reply that this is a *fruitful* tautology. For it has been a long time since man invented and used the concept of value, and this is nearly enough to prove that our preferences may be represented by a numerical scale. And this shows the possibility and the practical validity of axiomatic theories such as the author's Th1.

Before arriving there, we must be aware, as the author says, that 'valuation and preferences can be objects of scientific recognition', of objective knowledge. This is very important. It means that if several 'knowing subjects' (*Homo sapiens*) observe, or perhaps make experiments on, the same 'acting subject' (*Homo oeconomicus*), showing his preferences through his behaviour, they may agree on the same representation of his preferences. The fact that such a possibility does exist is somewhat puzzling but is implied by the very existence of decision theories.

And now comes a fundamental remark. As for every experimental scientific theory, the assumptions and axioms of a decision theory need *not* be empirically tested. Of course, there is nothing wrong in doing so, but it is not necessary. 'To guarantee the right reconstruction . . ., the theories must be consistent and their results empirically confirmable.' And that is sufficient.

(4) In describing Th1, the author says: '(The) role of theoretical reasoning . . . about valuation and probability (is to enable every) person to detect and remove inconsistencies from his own decisions. . . . *There is no absolute behaviour which is called rational. There exists only a rational type of decision-making.*'

I feel this affirmation to be important. For the aim of decision theory is not to dictate to everybody the same uniform behaviour, but to help each person in determining the best behaviour to achieve his own goals.

After the part of the paper dealing with Th2, we enter the conclusions. Just before this, the author states the different criteria (Laplace, Wald, Hurwicz, Savage) used for games against nature, and Milnor's well-known result about their incompatibility. Then he says: 'The decision-maker may be free to choose . . . any of (these criteria).'

This is a point on which I cannot agree. And I think that the author must have felt somewhat uncomfortable when writing this, for he immediately proposes a method for choosing among these criteria. More precisely, he proposes to use again the valuation scheme which constitutes Th1, but this time at the level of criteria (instead of decisions). He presents this as a way of building so-called 'super-decision rules'. And, in a rather bewildering way, the author seems to establish a connection between this method and an affirmation of the unity of decision theory. A few pages earlier he has written : 'Utility theory, game theory, and decision theories are melting together . . . within a general decision theory.' All right. But now he goes on : '[This method] is an outline of a statistical decision theory of the future, which uses the valuation scheme again and again.'

I shall have to discuss this point. But before doing so, I want to say how much I appreciate the hopeful conclusion of Dr. Leinfellner. Anyone who has not read it will have missed something important.

(5) I have said enough about how much, on the whole, I agree with Dr. Leinfellner's opinion, and now I have to come back to my major point of disagreement, which concerns so-called 'games against nature'.

In reality, could a game against such a mythical opponent as nature be anything but an individual decision problem ? I think not, and I therefore feel that the problem of 'games against nature' has been completely resolved, at least from the theoretical point of view, by Savage's theory. And in my mind, the *only* rational interpretation of Milnor's incompatibility result is that *it is not possible, in front of uncertainty, to reject probabilities.*

We may call this uncertainty 'Nature'; we may want to speak of subjective probabilities ; that is unimportant because it is nothing more than a question of words. But we cannot reject the fact that the ten Milnor axioms are incompatible. And I know nobody to whom an omission of any of these ten conditions for rationality in non-probabilistic decision-making would be acceptable. I think that this proves that *none of the proposed criteria* (Laplace, Wald, Hurwicz, and even the minimax regret criterion — which I think is very useful, however, if carefully handled) *may be taken as rational.*

Now, as the ten Milnor axioms were purposely selected so as to keep probabilities out of the picture, their incompatibility is something of a proof that *we cannot prevent using probabilities.*

That is why I think that the problem of the determination of a super-decision rule is a false problem : for individual decisions under uncertainty, *the only possible decision rule is the maximization of expected utility —* being computed from 'objective' probabilities and/or utilities when such objective things are available, and from subjective ones when not.

(6) Now, in conclusion, I should like to come back to the distinction

between the recognition attitude and the valuation attitude. I think it is a very useful distinction ; a very practical shorthand device which makes it unnecessary to state, before or after each sentence : 'if we adopt the point of view of mere understanding' or 'if you pay attention to actual decision-making'.

But this distinction should not go too far. For *Homo sapiens* and *Homo oeconomicus* are two inseparable parts of that strange animal we call *Homo*. And indeed, I think that knowledge will be not only useless, which is evident, but even of no interest if it were not oriented by some aim, by some need for action. This is true even for so-called 'fundamental research'. I find the proof for this in the fact that this kind of research never developed faster than nowadays, in our 'technical' world. The reason is that secular experience has proved to us that a better understanding of the world is always useful, sometimes a little, and often quite a lot.

Another point which shows that there is no complete separation between recognition and valuation is that any recognition implies a value judgement : 'true' or 'false'. And how can we know that such a theory or such a model is 'true' if not by looking at what it gives when it is empirically tested in actual practice ? Scientific evolution goes exactly as biological evolution, through a 'struggle for truth', and the selection of the best adapted.

Professor Menges : The paper by Dr. Leinfellner seems to me of very great importance, because it leads to a well-axiomatized and unified decision theory. I understand that such a decision theory is primarily a personalistic one. This for several reasons.

(1) Personalistic is the element of self-determination, the element of concern on the part of the decision-maker.

(2) The preference field is rather subjectively oriented as far as its subject is a utility range that is valid for the decision-maker.

(3) The decision criteria, at least the so-called strong criteria, are to be called subjective rather than objective ones.

Such affinity promotes the desire to use the ideas of subjective probability. But probability can be presented only objectively as long as it is expected to make valid judgements on reality. On the other hand, I agree that there is a strong need for 'something like probability' in a personalistic context. I want to make a terminological suggestion, viz., to call this 'something like probability' degree of belief.

The degree of belief can be axiomatized in a fashion similar to subjective probability. And there is a certain reasonableness in the subjective evaluation of degree of belief. If the decision-maker evaluates his degree of belief wrongly, then this is his own fault and he will have to take the consequences. Therefore he will try hard to produce as true an expression of his degree of belief as possible. Even if he does not succeed, he can still act rationally and without contradicting himself.

I agree completely with Dr. Leinfellner that there is no absolute behaviour which can be called rational. I understand rationality as a filter which is to exclude illogical, completely irrational or inconsistent behaviour.

Concerning Mr. Bessière's comments on Milnor's games against nature, I want to point at the philosophy of the 'as if' of Vaihinger.

Professor Siroyezhin: We have to state finally that the relation of dynamic dependency between 'subjective' and 'objective' in our progress which has been briefly outlined is a fruitful basis for the development of a generalization of decision theory. The need for such a generalization is very correctly pointed out in Dr. Leinfellner's paper. Then we could establish the soundest set of postulates and axioms for such a theory.

Dr. Leinfellner: I thank Dr. Ivanescu for his mathematical and logical review as well as for his suggestions. He suggested eliminating transitivity in Axiom 1 of the theory Th1. I think we can only weaken the strong transitivity, for example to a stochastic transitivity:

$$p(a \overset{\succ}{\sim} b) \geqslant \frac{1}{2} \text{ and } p(b \overset{\succ}{\sim} c) \geqslant \frac{1}{2} \text{ then } p(a \overset{\succ}{\sim} c) \geqslant \begin{cases} p(a \overset{\succ}{\sim} b) \\ \\ p(b \overset{\succ}{\sim} c) \end{cases}$$

In this formula p can be regarded as a subjective probability. But if we do that we obtain a weakened valuation scale. Instead of the linear transformation of Th1 (Axiom 9)

$$u(x) = px + q$$

we get only

$$u(x) = x + q,$$

i.e. an interval scale instead of a ratio scale.

Of course, the numbers of the e_is and the a_js need not be the same, as Dr. Ivanescu has pointed out. In this case we have a homomorphic mapping, where $i > j$.

As for the problem of subjective and objective probability, I suggest a simple distinction. The α or β in my paper can be regarded as subjective or objective values of probability. If we have events $e_1, \ldots, e_n$ which we can regard as outcomes in a mechanical, physical, system — an apparatus or a chance-mechanism, such as tossing a coin — I suggest that we speak in terms of objective probability. If I cannot find any events or I cannot substitute possible events by an observable empirical process or mechanism, then the αs are unknown. I am forced to estimate them, etc. In this case I speak of subjective probabilities.

Regarding Mr. Bessière's contribution I am very glad that he pointed out some philosophical questions of philosophy of science which are closely connected with theoretical reasoning. Science in the form of theories is — to speak simply — our best one. We must try to reach this highly developed form in the science of decision-making. If we base decision-making upon utility we have within our theoretical framework two levels of language. The language L_0 (o means observable) consists only of statements ; terms which can be tested empirically. Statements about preference or indifference between two things, objects, etc., are behavioural observations and must be tested empirically. But the whole theory consists of a second language L_t (t means theoretical). In L_0 we state descriptions and measurements ; in L_t we represent the empirical structures we have described or measured in mathematical structures, as I have shown in my paper. Consistent theoretical representation of our world, which can be confirmed to a high degree by empirical observations, measurements — that is what I call scientific recognition. It is clear that the methods and results must be intersubjective. In this sense 'intersubjective' is merely a circumspection of interpersonal use ; of the fact that science is a real international means of communication. I consider only the use of scientific theories as intersubjective.

I think that there is a little misunderstanding with regard to games against nature. In all cases where we have complete or partial ignorance about the second decision-maker in a dual decision process of type Th2 we can consider games against nature as a special subcase of this general one.

Before I finish my answer with a discussion of the problem of rationality I should like to answer Professor Menges. I do not think that axiomatizations have no use in clarifying the problem of subjective probability. Axiomatization of decision-making should have two aims. Firstly, to lay down in axioms the behavioural postulates. If and only if we lay down these postulates can we recognize our assumptions of preference structure. Secondly, we must embed basic theoretical and mathematical concepts into reality ; e.g. Axioms 6–8 of Th1 allow the application of computing compound probabilities etc. Behavioural postulates and theoretical assumptions together allow the deduction of a ratio scale of utilities (values) and allow even the measurement of them. I think that this is the only way to get a theoretical aspect of human decision-making based upon valuation.

Last but not least, there is the problem of rationality. My own position is a pragmatic one. I am convinced that up to now, i.e. up to the beginning of scientific reasoning about decision-making, we have not known much about rational behaviour or rational decisions. Let me illustrate how we got knowledge about rational inference. Before Aristotle's famous work about Syllogism in *Analytica*, nobody had known anything about rational inference. Today we have many formal systems of logic ; we have formal theories of inference. Now we know exactly what rational inference is. If a scientist is reasoning, he uses the rules and axioms of an underlying logic which gives him the standards of correct rational inference. We are obliged to obey these rules — otherwise nobody will trust our speaking and reasoning. If and only if we use a scientific (a theoretical) language, we must fulfil all rules of rational inference, even if we do not know logic in detail.

With regard to decision-making up to now, nobody knows even simple rules. But if we make a real intellectual effort and construct decision theories — that are theoretical and therefore consistent aspects of human decision-making — we are laying down (finding out) norms and rules which will be (so I hope) standards of rational decision-making for now and even for the future. Just as we are using standards of rational inference only in science, so we are using standards of rational decision-making only if we make decisions within human society, as we do as economists *par excellence*. If we are making private decisions nobody will care about standards of decision-making. Our main aim is to get consistent decisions. Consistent decisions are possible only within the framework of a theory ; only here can we prove the consistency. If these consistent theories are, moreover, fruitful for human society, then decision-making after the pre-scription of these theories will lay down fundamentals of rational be-haviour for the future, just as Syllogism and theories of rational inference have done it for rational inference. That is my opinion about rationality. Dealing with decision theories is an approach to a rational standard of decision-making in the future.

PART III

GROUP DECISIONS AND
MARKET MECHANISMS

Chapter 10

PSYCHOLOGICAL VARIABLES AND COALITION-FORMING BEHAVIOUR[1]

BY

REINHARD SELTEN

AND

KLAUS G. SCHUSTER

I. INTRODUCTION

GAME theorists have proposed several theories of coalition-forming behaviour. In this paper we shall consider only those which seem to be applicable to our experimental set-up (von Neumann and Morgenstern, 1944; Shapley, 1953; Luce, 1955; Aumann and Maschler, 1964; Davis and Maschler, 1963). These theories are generally considered normative, but even normative theories should have some proximity to real behaviour. Therefore it is interesting to compare experimental results with theoretical predictions.

Our experiment is based on a game in characteristic function form. If such games are played in a laboratory setting, a social-psychological situation is created, and it must be expected that social and psychological factors are more or less strongly influencing the results of the experiment.

In order to gather some information about relevant psychological variables we have tried to measure several personality factors and interpersonal relations.

Our experiment does not intend to test specific psychological hypotheses formulated in advance. It is not primarily an instrument to decide theoretical questions; rather, it should be considered as an analogue to important real-life conflict situations. The purpose of such laboratory analogues is to provide an empirical basis for the development of new hypotheses which may be helpful in the construction of predictive theories.

The experiment described here is similar to some earlier experimental studies on games in characteristic function form (Kalish *et al.*,

[1] The research reported here was supported by Deutsche Forschungsgemeinschaft. We are indebted to Otwin Becker, Volker Häselbarth, and Reinhard Tietz, who helped to conduct the experiment.

1954; Maschler, 1965). Other experiments are related but not really similar in purpose and content (Hoffmann *et al.*, 1954; Mills, 1954; Vinacke and Arkoff, 1957; Fouraker, 1964).

The characteristic function game underlying our experiment has gained a certain notoriety among game theorists. It is known under the name 'Me and my Aunt' and has been introduced by Davis and Maschler as an example where their kernel concept seems to lead to counter-intuitive results. In their paper 'The Kernel of a Co-operative Game' they cite from letters of many well-known game theorists who expressed their opinions about probable outcomes of this game (Davis and Maschler, 1963).

II. THE EXPERIMENT

A five-person characteristic function game with real money payoff was played twelve times by different sets of players. The subjects were 60 male undergraduates of Frankfurt University, 59 majoring in economics and 1 in psychology; all of them were volunteers. As far as we know, there were no close acquaintances and friendships between members of the same experimental group.

After the subjects had entered the laboratory, they were asked to take a seat on the outside of a horseshoe-shaped arrangement of tables. Each of the five subjects received two identical 'number-cards' which were fixed on the lapels and the backs of the players; thereby the participants were numbered from 1 to 5. The session was opened by a brief discussion about a controversial political issue; this discussion served to give the subjects some impressions about each other and took about fifteen minutes.

After the opening discussion the subjects were told to rate each other on four nine-point rating-scales measuring sympathy, perceived bargaining ability, trust, and perceived fairness. The rating-scales were headed by written instructions. The sympathy-scale was introduced as follows (translation from German): 'Think of the following situation: you have to choose one of your co-participants in this experiment as a companion for a vacation trip. Please indicate how much you would like to have each of your participants as a companion; your ratings should not be influenced by economic con-siderations; thus it should not be important whether your companion has a car or not.'

In the corresponding instructions concerning the trust scale the subjects were asked how much they would like to lend a considerable sum of money to each of their co-participants, if they would have to be sure to get the money back soon. Estimates on bargaining ability and fairness of the other players were obtained by similar questions. There were separate scales for each of the co-participants with respect to each of the four criteria. The end-points were explained as 'I'd like to very much' (*sehr gern*) and 'I'd hate to' (*sehr ungern*). The participants were not able to see the judgements of each other.

After these sociometric measurements, sets *D* and *E* of the Raven Progressive Matrices Test (standard form) were administered.[1] Tasks *B*8 and *B*9 were used to explain how to solve Raven items. The subjects could risk between one and four points for each item. The subjects were told that points for correct answers are counted as positive and points for false answers are counted as negative; they were supposed to maximize the sum of points. The maximum sum of points within each experimental group was rewarded by DM5. The players who were second and third best received DM3, and DM2 respectively. The remaining two got nothing. Scores were not announced and rewards were not paid until the end of the whole session. The subjects were allowed only fifteen minutes to solve the Raven items.[2] This Raven test procedure was intended as a combined measure of problem-solving ability and risk-taking propensity.

After the Raven test the subjects were asked to answer an eighty-five item personality questionnaire measuring three personality factors. The items were keyed in opposite directions to operate against response sets as acquiescence and nay-saying. Two of these three personality factors, which may be called 'dominance' and 'rigidity', do not seem to be relevant to the questions analysed in this paper; therefore we shall not discuss them here.[3]

The third factor is measured by fifteen items, which were originally intended as a control against the tendency to give incorrect answers. Symptomatic answers to these questions contain the assertion that the subject behaves extraordinarily ethically in a sample of situations. The following example may serve to illustrate the nature of these items: 'Sometimes I have been secretly satisfied when other students got lower grades than I did' (the symptomatic answer is 'no').

We have decided to call this factor 'conformism', or more precisely 'ethical conformism'. Accordingly, the scores on that scale

[1] In session number 1 sets *C* and *D* were administered. These sets were too easy.
[2] There was no time restriction in session 1.
[3] We plan further investigations.

will be referred to as 'C-scores'. We could have chosen other names like 'need for social approval' or 'social desirability', but 'ethical conformism' seems to be less misleading.

We cannot exclude the possibility that some subjects with high C-scores do behave ethically or at least intend to do so; but we think that most of them are somewhat hypocritical about their real behaviour tendencies.

After a short break the rules of the game were explained. These rules were as follows.

Rules: One player is called 'big' and the other four are called 'small'. There are five types of winning coalitions:

Type 1: the big player and one small player.
Type 2: the big player and two small players.
Type 3: the big player and three small players.
Type 4: the four small players.
Type 5: all players.

A winning coalition gets DM 40 (about $10). Coalitions which are not winning coalitions receive nothing. In the course of the game intermediary 'registered coalitions' are formed; such coalitions become final only after a ten-minute registration time. Within those ten minutes a member may leave the coalition and thereby terminate its existence. In order to register a coalition the members have to agree about the division of the payoff. (Play number 1 was conducted with only five minutes registration time.) Only the payoff agreements of the final coalition are paid out at the end of the play.

The device of registered coalitions was used in order to get reliable material about intermediary coalitions.

The following economic interpretation was given to the players. The Government is willing to give certain mining rights on the continental shelf to a group of firms; the winning coalitions are determined by some minimum requirements on capital and technological know-how.

As long as the game was played all players had to stay within the 'bargaining space', which was the inside of the horseshoe-shaped arrangement of tables. The subjects were free to take a seat or to remain standing or to move around in the bargaining space. Only open negotiations were allowed. All players had to speak sufficiently loud, so that everybody could overhear all negotiations.

We are very grateful to our associate Volker Häselbarth, who took down virtually complete protocols of all plays. These protocols contain the offers and counter-offers of the players. Tape-recordings were used to complement the protocols. (The protocols proved to be more valuable than the tape-recordings.)

After the explanation of the rules the big player was determined by lot; the players were told not to reveal their roles before the actual play began. They were asked to answer a questionnaire concerning their views of the game and their strategic intentions. This questionnaire was used in order to force the players to think about the game.

The players were told that they should try to get as much as possible for themselves. Each of them should maximize his individual profits.

After the game was played the sociometric measurements were repeated. Then the players received the money payoff from the game and the money rewards for the Raven test. The session was closed by a short discussion about the game.

III. OBSERVED COALITIONS AND GAME-THEORETICAL PREDICTIONS

Table 1 contains the sequence of registered coalitions for all plays. The payoffs are listed in the same order as the members of the coalitions. The registered coalition which is last in a play is of course the final one which remained stable for ten minutes. Under the heading 'time' the duration of each registered coalition is given. The first entry in the time column for each play indicates how long it took until the first intermediary coalition was registered.

It never occurred that a player left a registered coalition without immediately forming a new one with other players. This would have been allowed by the rules, but members of a registered coalition want to be sure to be in the next registered coalition when they leave the present one, and isolated players are also motivated to rush into a new registered coalition.

Eight final coalitions were type-1 coalitions; in five of these the payoff distribution was 15 for the small player and 25 for the big player. There were only two type-4 coalitions, both with asymmetrical payoff distributions (8·66, 8·66, 8·66, 14 in play 5 and 7, 7, 19, 7 in play 6). The symmetrical type-4 coalition with payoff distribution 10, 10, 10, 10 occurred nine times, but never remained stable. The final coalition of play 8 was a type-3 coalition, where the big player received 25 and each of his three small partners received 5. Play 12

TABLE 1

REGISTERED COALITIONS

Play No.	Big player	Coalition	Payoff distributions	Time		
				hr.	min.	sec.
1	3				2	15
		1, 2, 4, 5	10, 10, 10, 10		3	25
		2, 3	16, 24		4	10
		3, 4	25, 15		5	00
					14	50
2	5				35	00
		1, 5	10, 30		2	30
		1, 2, 3, 4	10, 10, 10, 10		5	00
		2, 3, 4, 5	4, 4, 4, 28		7	10
		1, 2, 3, 4	10, 10, 10, 10		3	45
		4, 5	15, 25		8	10
		3, 5	1, 39		9	05
		4, 5	15, 25		10	00
				1	20	40
3	3					45
		3, 5	15, 25		10	00
					10	45
4	2				23	15
		1, 3, 4, 5	10, 10, 10, 10		9	25
		2, 3	20, 20		8	25
		2, 3	25, 15		10	00
					51	05
5	4				10	30
		1, 2, 3, 5	10, 10, 10, 10			50
		4, 5	25, 15		3	55
		1, 2, 3, 5	8·66, 8·66, 8·66, 14		10	00
					25	15

TABLE 1

REGISTERED COALITIONS (*continued*)

Play No.	Big player	Coalition	Payoff distributions	Time	
				hr. min.	sec.
6	4			7	20
		2, 3, 4	12, 12, 16	8	45
		2, 3, 4	10·5, 10·5, 19	4	40
		4, 5	25, 15	8	10
		3, 4	13, 27	9	20
		1, 2, 3, 5	7, 7, 19, 7	10	00
				48	15
7	4			3	05
		1, 4	11, 29	5	40
		1, 2, 3, 5	10, 10, 10, 10	9	35
		4, 5	18, 22	10	00
				28	20
8	1			6	20
		2, 3, 4, 5	17, 7·66, 7·66, 7·66	4	55
		1, 2	20, 20	6	55
		1, 3, 4, 5	25, 5, 5, 5	10	00
				28	10
9	3			6	45
		2, 3, 4	11·5, 17, 11·5	9	59
		3, 5	30, 10	1	30
		3, 5	27, 13	3	30
		3, 4	28, 12	10	00
				31	44
10	2			9	15
		2, 3	26, 14	9	20
		2, 3	23, 17	3	05
		1, 3, 4, 5	6·66, 20, 6·66, 6·66	3	45
		2, 4	20, 20	10	00
				35	25

TABLE 1

REGISTERED COALITIONS (*continued*)

Play No.	Big Player	Coalition	Payoff distributions	Time		
				hr.	min.	sec.
11	4				9	05
		1, 2, 3, 5	10, 10, 10, 10		5	15
		1, 4	15, 25		7	30
		2, 3, 4, 5	3·33, 3·33, 30, 3·33		6	00
		1, 2, 3, 5	10, 10, 10, 10		9	59
		1, 4	20, 20		3	15
		4, 5	25, 15		7	25
		1, 2, 3, 5	6·66, 6·66, 6·66, 20		2	20
		3, 4	15, 25		10	00
				1	00	49
12	3				23	00
		1, 2, 4, 5	10, 10, 10, 10		4	30
		1, 2, 3, 4, 5	8, 8, 8, 8, 8		10	00
					37	30

was ended by a type-5 coalition with equal payoff for all members.

We shall now discuss various game-theoretical solution concepts which seem to be applicable to our experimental set-up.

Main Simple Solution (von Neumann and Morgenstern, 1944)

Our game is equivalent to a homogeneous simple-majority game with weights of 3 for the big player and 1 for each of the small players. Therefore it has a main simple solution which consists of five imputations; one of these comes about if a type-4 coalition with symmetrical payoff distribution 10, 10, 10, 10 is formed; the other four imputations in the main simple solution correspond to type-1 coalitions, where the big player gets 30 and his small partner gets 10.

The payoff distributions prescribed by the main simple solution never occurred in final coalitions; it seems to be clear from the results of the plays that the big player has to give his partner in a type-1 coalition substantially more than 10, if he wants a stable coalition. The type-4 coalition with symmetrical payoff distribution does not seem to be very stable.

Shapley value (Shapley, 1953)

The Shapley value may be considered as an *a priori* assessment of the chances of a player. The Shapley value of the big player is 24 and that of a small player is 4. The average profit of the big player was 18·67 and that of a small player was 5·33. Students' *t*-tests may be used to test the difference between the mean payoff to the big player and his Shapley value; the level of significance is somewhat below 10 per cent (two-tailed). This result suggests that the small players are stronger than assumed by the Shapley value.

John C. Harsanyi said in his letter cited by Davis and Maschler (1963) that in a type-1 coalition both members should receive equal amounts above their Shapley values, thus the big player should get $24+6 = 30$ and his small partner should get $4+6 = 10$. This coincides with the payoff distribution prescribed by the main simple solution.

Ψ-*stability* (Luce, 1955)

The notion of Ψ-stability is based on the idea that in most real situations there are some transitions from one coalition structure to another which are not possible because of organizational, psychological, and/or sociological reasons. Such restrictions may have a stabilizing effect.

It seems to be natural to apply this idea to the transitions between registered coalitions. We can think of only one class of transitions which maybe was excluded by our experimental set-up; we may call this class the class of 'exclusions'. An exclusion would be a transition from one winning coalition C_1 to a smaller winning coalition C_2 with $C_2 \subset C_1$. Such exclusions never occurred in our experiment.

On the other hand it cannot be said that the possibility of exclusions was not present in our experiment. In play number 12 the big player tried to destroy the type-5 coalition by forming a type-1 coalition. The small players reacted to this with the threat to exclude the big player if he continued these 'disloyal' offers. This threat proved to be so efficient that there was no further discussion.

The only coalition type which could be stabilized in the sense of Ψ-stability by the impossibility of exclusions would be type 5. For the other types there are always transitions which are not exclusions and which lead to a dominating imputation.

Bargaining Set (Aumann and Maschler, 1964)

The bargaining set $\mathscr{M}$ proposed by Aumann and Maschler suggests a payoff distribution for the type-1 coalition with a payoff between 20 and 30 for the big player and between 10 and 20 for his small partner. The payoff distribution which gives 25 to the big player and 15 to his small partner was the most frequent one in our experiment; this payoff distribution is exactly in the middle of the region prescribed by the bargaining set.

If a type-4 coalition is formed, the bargaining set $\mathscr{M}$ does not allow other payoff distributions than 10, 10, 10, 10.

A payoff distribution for a winning coalition is 'stable' in the sense of the bargaining set if no subcoalition has a 'justified objection'. An 'objection' is always an objection of one subcoalition against another subcoalition of the winning coalition. An objection consists in the possibility of forming a winning coalition containing the objecting subcoalition but not the subcoalition against which the objection is directed; the objection must be such that all members of the new winning coalition receive more than they get now. (Our definitions are not general, they are tailored to the special case analysed here.) An objection is justified if the subcoalition against which it is directed has no 'counter-objection'. A counter-objection consists in the possibility of forming a winning coalition which contains the subcoalition against which the objection is directed and which in a sense refutes the objection. This winning coalition must give to its members at least as much as they get now; the counter-objecting players can propose a coalition which contains some of the objecting players but not all of them; in doing this, they use the tactics of 'divide and rule'. Objecting players who are incorporated into the counter-objection must be promised at least as much by the counter-objection as by the objection.

The definition of the bargaining set $\mathscr{M}$ contains the additional requirement of 'coalitional rationality'; a winning coalition which is not minimal in the sense that it does not contain a smaller winning coalition is not 'coalitionally rational'. This excludes types 2, 3, and 5. The requirement of coalitional rationality is not an essential part of the bargaining-set concept and hence may be dropped without any loss of intuitive appeal (cf. Aumann and Maschler, 1964, pp. 471–2).

Even if coalitional rationality is abandoned, the final payoff distributions of play 8 and play 12 are not stable in the sense of the bargaining set $\mathscr{M}$. In the case of play 8 one small player in the type-3 coalition may object against the other two that he can form a type-1 coalition with the big player which gives 6 to him and 34 to the big player. The two small players against whom the objection is directed have no counter-objection by which they could defend their payoffs; they cannot promise more than 30 to the big player. The bargaining set $\mathcal{M}$ requires that the two attacked players are able to defend themselves *jointly*. Aumann and Maschler weaken this requirement in their definition of the bargaining set $\mathcal{M}_1$ (cf. Aumann and Maschler, 1964, p. 470). The final result of play 8 is stable in the weaker sense of $\mathcal{M}_1$, but the type-5 coalition of play 12 remains unstable also under this definition; the big player obviously has justified objections against the type-5 payoff distribution 8, 8, 8, 8, 8.

It is remarkable that eight of the twelve final results are compatible with the Aumann–Maschler theory. On the other hand it is also important that the asymmetrical payoff distributions in the final coalitions of play 5 and play 6 and the type-5 coalition of play 12 are serious deviations from that theory.

Kernel (Davis and Maschler, 1963)

The kernel is a subset of the bargaining set. It is based on the idea of 'equal excess'. The 'excess' of a new winning coalition relative to the payoff distribution within an existing one is the surplus of the value of the new winning coalition over the payoffs which its members receive now; it may be interpreted as an index of the attraction of that coalition. In our case the kernel may be described as the set of payoff distributions which are such that all new minimal winning coalitions (those of type 1 and type 4) have equal excess. (This is no general definition; the kernel concept is more complicated.)

If a type-1 coalition is formed, the kernel prescribes 20 for the big player and 20 for his small partner; relative to this payoff distribution the other three type-1 coalitions and the type-4 coalition have equal excesses of 20. If a type-4 coalition is formed, the kernel prescribes the symmetrical payoff distribution 10, 10, 10, 10. According to the kernel the big player receives 20 in type-2 and type-3 coalitions; his partners divide equally. In the type-5 coalition the big player receives $\frac{120}{7} = 17\cdot14$ and each of the small players gets $\frac{40}{7} = 5\cdot71$.

A final result which was in the kernel occurred only once (play 10).

IV. OBSERVED COALITIONS AND PSYCHOLOGICAL
VARIABLES

In this paper we shall concentrate on three topics : [1]

(1) Are there any psychological attributes characterizing the small players who get into a final type-1 coalition ?

(2) Are there any social-psychological factors influencing the success of the big player ?

(3) Is there any connection between the players' aspiration levels and their chance of getting into a coalition ?

Topics (1) and (3) are treated with the help of a non-parametric statistical test which we call the 'mean rank test'. This test is applicable to the following situations. There are n groups of k subjects. Within each group the subjects are ranked with respect to some variable v. In each group there is one and only one subject who is 'successful' in a certain sense. Let s_i be the rank of the successful subject in group i; then

$$S = \sum_{i=1}^{n} s_i$$

is the rank sum and

$$\bar{s} = \frac{S}{n}$$

is the mean rank of the successful subjects. The mean rank test determines whether s is significantly different from

$$\bar{s} = \frac{1}{k} \sum_{i=1}^{k} i = \frac{k+1}{2} \, ;$$

s is the expected value of s under the null-hypothesis that all ranks have the same probability to belong to the successful subject. The probability distributions of the s_i have the generating function

$$g(z) = \frac{1}{k} \sum_{i=1}^{k} z^i = \frac{1}{k} z \frac{1 - z^k}{1 - z}.$$

Therefore the generating function of the distribution of S is

$$f(z) = \frac{1}{k^n} (1 - z^k)^n (1 - z)^{-n}.$$

---

[1] These topics do not exhaust our material. Further investigations are planned.

$f(z)$ may be computed with the help of the following expansions

$$(1 - z^k)^n = \sum_{i=0}^{n}(-1)_i \binom{n}{i} z^{ki}$$

$$(1 - z)^{-n} = \sum_{i=0}^{\infty}(-1)^i \binom{-n}{i} z^i.$$

Table 2 contains exact cumulative probabilities for the case $n = 8$ and $k = 4$.

TABLE 2

CUMULATIVE PROBABILITIES FOR THE MEAN RANK TEST
$n = 8$ and $k = 4$ (one-tailed) [1]

Rank sum S	Cumulative probability
8	0·00002
9	0·00014
10	0·00069
11	0·00252
12	0·00743
13	0·01843
14	0·04033
15	0·07805
16	0·13638

The Small Player in the type-1 coalition

We may first ask some very obvious questions. Does sympathy influence the chance of getting into the coalition ? If in each of the eight plays ending with a type-1 coalition the four small players are ranked according to the sympathy scores they received from the big player before the game was played, we get a rank sum of $S = 15$ for the small players in the final type-1 coalition (high scores correspond to low ranks); it can be seen from Table 2 that the one-tailed level of significance is 10 per cent. This suggests that the big player tends to choose a small player whom he finds likeable. The sympathy scores given by the small partner to the big player do not seem to be so important ($S = 16\cdot5$).

Analogous applications of the mean rank test to pre-play ratings on

---

[1] We are indebted to Reinhard Tietz, who computed exact probabilities for $n = 12$ and $k = 16$; these are needed for topic (3).

trust and perceived fairness give insignificant results.

Problem-solving ability as measured by our Raven test modification does not seem to have any relation to the chance of a small player to get into the type-1 coalition ($S = 19$). On the other hand the small partners of the big players risk relatively few points for correctly-answered Raven items; if the mean rank test is applied to the mean number of points chosen for correctly-answered Raven items we get $S = 12.5$, which is significant at the 5 per cent level (two-tailed). This may be interpreted as risk aversion or alternatively as low self-confidence.

The small players in the final type-1 coalitions have relatively high scores on our ethical conformism scale; if high scores are ranked low we get $S = 12.5$, which is significant at the 5 per cent level (two-tailed).

Maybe fear of social disapproval is a factor which contributes to ethical conformism. Risk aversion in a competitive intelligence test situation may also be related to fear of social disapproval. Therefore it seems natural to conjecture a connection between our C-scores and our Raven measure of risk aversion. We computed the Spearman rank correlation for all sixty subjects between C-scores and mean points for correctly-answered Raven items. The correlation coefficient is $r_s = -0.218$, which is in the expected direction and significant at the 5 per cent level (one-tailed). The correlation is very weak, however, and therefore it is not possible to explain our result on ethical conformism by our result on risk aversion or vice versa.

It is difficult to explain these findings. Why should ethical conformism and risk aversion influence the chance of a small player to get into a final type-1 coalition? In order to answer this question we may look at the behaviour of the successful small players in the course of the game.

These small players make relatively few offers. The mean rank test gives $S = 13.5$, which is significant at the 10 per cent level (two-tailed). Another interesting variable is the 'isolation mean demand'; this is the average of the payoffs which a player demands in his coalition proposals while he is not in a registered coalition. The small players in final type-1 coalitions have relatively high isolation mean demands! If these means are ranked from above we get $S = 12$, which is significant at the 5 per cent level (two-tailed).

At first glance it seems to be unreasonable that such behaviour should be connected to risk-aversion. If a small player is isolated he should be content to get a small payoff, if he does not like the risk of getting nothing. We think that this is quite right, but that a small player who does not like risk may nevertheless prefer to demand relatively high payoffs because he is aware of the need for stability which may induce the other players not to accept offers which are too advantageous for them. If for example a small player proposes a type-1 coalition, where he only gets 11, the big player has good reasons not to accept this offer because he must fear that this coalition will not be stable against the possibility of a type-4 coalition with asymmetrical payoff distribution. Those small players who do not like risk are maybe most sensitive to the other players' need for stability.

There were nine small players in the twelve plays who at least once left a type-4 coalition to form a type-1 coalition with the big player. These players were with one exception among those two small players of their group who showed more risk aversion than the other two. This suggests that these players did not leave the type-4 coalition primarily because of the additional profit promised to them but mainly because of the risk that another small player may do so before them.

The fact that the small players in final type-1 coalitions made relatively few offers may be due to a certain reluctance to commitments. A small player may fear — and perhaps rightly so — that the big player will never accept him into a type-1 coalition if he speaks too much in favour of a type-4 coalition. It is our impression from the observation of the plays that this fear is justified. Naturally, an isolated big player will direct his offers primarily to those small players who are not the 'leaders' of the type-4 coalition.

If a small player does not want to be disapproved of by other players (including the big one), he may choose to remain passive and not to reveal his preferences for specific coalitions. This may be related to the lack of frankness which is expressed by high scores on ethical conformism.

The Success of the Big Player

The most natural measure of the success of the big player is his final payoff. But this measure is a very crude one which does not differentiate between the six big players who got 25. We may define a refined measure as follows. If two players received 25, that one was more successful who received this amount in less time. Similarly we may say that the big player in play 5 was less successful than the one in play 6 because he was defeated earlier. In this way we get 'success ranks' 10, 6, 11, 8, 1, 2, 4, 9, 12, 5, 7, 3 for the big players in plays 1 to 12 (successful players are ranked high).

The sum of the sympathy scores received by the big player before the game may be called his 'popularity'. The popularity of the big player is correlated with his payoff ($r_s = -0{\cdot}65$; $p = 0{\cdot}05$) and with his success rank ($r_s = -0{\cdot}61$; $p = 0{\cdot}05$). Here and in the following pages r_s stands for the Spearman rank correlation coefficient and p for its one-tailed level of significance.

The sum of the trust scores received by the big player before the game is also correlated negatively with his payoff ($r_s = -0{\cdot}54$; $p = 0{\cdot}05$) and his success rank ($r_s = -0{\cdot}43$).

It does not seem sensible to suppose that the big player is more successful if he is less popular and less trusted. It will be shown later that we have good reasons to think that these correlations are spurious.

The sum of trust scores given by the small players to all other players before the game may be thought of as an index of their readiness to trust others. This is negatively correlated to the payoff ($r_s = -0{\cdot}69$; $p = 0{\cdot}05$) and to the success rank of the big player ($r_s = -0{\cdot}55$; $p = 0{\cdot}05$). The sum of trust scores received by the small players from all other players before the game constitutes a collective judgement of their trustworthiness and therefore may be interpreted as an index of the (perceived) trustworthiness of the small players. This is also correlated negatively to the payoff ($r_s = -0{\cdot}69$; $p = 0{\cdot}05$) and to the success rank of the big player ($r_s = -0{\cdot}60$; $p = 0{\cdot}05$). If we add both sums of trust scores we get a combined index of readiness to trust and perceived trustworthiness. Correlations between this index and the payoff of the big player ($r_s = -0{\cdot}79$; $p = 0{\cdot}01$) and his success rank ($r_s = -0{\cdot}64$; $p = 0{\cdot}05$) are better than those for the component indices.

These correlations are very plausible. It is in harmony with our impressions from the observation of the plays that readiness to trust and trustworthiness are necessary for stable type-4 and type-5 coalitions. A lack of inner stability may be compensated by strong trust relations between the small players. The rules of the game do not give the small players any commitment power; the possibility of effective commitments must be based on trust. Therefore it is advantageous for the big player if trust relations are not easily established between the small players.

Our combined index of trustworthiness and readiness to trust correlates with the popularity of the big player ($r_s = 0.68$; $p = 0.05$). At the time of the ratings the players did not know their roles as big and small players. Therefore this correlation could only be explained by a general interdependence between the group mean scores on sympathy and trust, but there is no such connection ($r_s = 0.14$). Therefore we think that the correlation between the big player's popularity and our trust index is spurious. The negative correlations between the big player's popularity and his payoff and success rank can be explained by this correlation and consequently are likely to be spurious too.

The trust scores received by the big player correlate with the total sum of trust scores given by the small players ($r_s = 0.76$; $p = 0.01$). The trust scores received by the big player express the small players' readiness to trust. This explains the negative correlations with the big player's payoff and success rank.

There is a positive correlation between the C-score of the big player and his payoff ($r_s = 0.52$; $p = 0.05$). This seems to fit in with our analysis of the small players in final type-1 coalitions, but nevertheless we cannot accept it. The C-score of the big player is correlated with his popularity ($r_s = -0.53$; $p = 0.05$). This correlation is spurious because it does not hold for all 60 subjects ($r_s = -0.14$). The connection between the big player's C-score and his payoff can be explained by this spurious correlation and is therefore highly suspicious.

It is our impression from the observation of the plays that the big player should not be vague about his intentions; he should make a firm offer to say, 15, to that small player who will first accept it and he should make a firm statement that he does not want more. We may ask whether this impression can be validated statistically. The firmness of the big player can be measured by the variance of his payoff demands; in this variance we incorporated only those offers which were made when the big player was not in a registered coalition; it was calculated as the sum of squared deviations divided by the number of isolation demands minus one. The big player in play 3 made no offers but we feel that it is justified to give him rank 1 as if he would have the lowest variance because he was indeed very firm about his share in the type-1 coalition. The variance of demands is negatively correlated with the payoff of the big player ($r_s = -0.77$; $p = 0.01$) and his success rank ($r_s = -0.83$; $p = 0.01$).

We may conclude that trust among the small players and firmness of the big player are decisive for the success of the big player.

Our Raven measures of problem-solving ability and of risk aversion and the ratings on fairness and perceived bargaining ability are not significantly correlated with the payoff or success rank of the big player.

A Co-ordination Phenomenon

Lawrence E. Fouraker has proposed a theory of simple-majority games with an odd number of players which is based on the idea that the outcome of the game is determined by the aspiration levels of the players (Fouraker, 1964). Fouraker's theory suggests that a coalition may be stabilized by the fact that the excluded players have too high aspiration levels. Therefore the coalition with the lowest sum of aspiration levels for its members should have the best chance to become the final one.

This hypothesis, which we shall call the Fouraker hypothesis, cannot be tested directly if the aspiration levels are unknown, but an indirect test seems still to be possible if one is willing to accept the assumption that isolation mean demands reflect the aspiration levels.

There are sixteen winning coalitions: four type-1 coalitions, six type-2 coalitions, four type-3 coalitions, one type-4 coalition and one type-5 coalition. These sixteen coalitions can be ranked within each of the twelve plays according to the sum of their members' isolation mean demands. The mean rank test can be used to determine whether the sum of isolation mean demands is significantly low within the final coalitions. The rank sum is $S = 82$, which is not significant at the 10 per cent level (the exact probability for $S \leqslant 82$ is $0 \cdot 112$). The mean rank sum of $S = 82$ is influenced by the fact that ten of the twelve plays lead to minimal winning coalitions; minimal winning coalitions are obviously more likely to have low sums of isolation mean demands than other winning coalitions. If the five minimal winning coalitions are ranked within each of the ten plays with final coalitions of type 1 and type 4, we get a mean rank of 4 which indicates that the sum of isolation demand levels is significantly high for the final coalitions! ($S = 40$, $p = 0 \cdot 05$, two-tailed.) The only evidence for the Fouraker hypothesis contained in our data could be seen in the fact that minimal winning coalitions were more frequent than other ones; but this may be explained by many theories.

Our data suggests another hypothesis: the final coalition tends to have a sum of isolation mean demands for its members which is relatively near to 40. If the absolute values of the deviations from 40 are ranked for the sixteen winning coalitions we get a rank sum of $S = 69$, which is significant at the 5 per cent level (two-tailed). If only the minimal winning coalitions within the plays with final coalitions of type 1 and type 4 are ranked, we get $S = 17$, which corresponds to a cumulative probability of 0.0019 (one-tailed). These findings suggest that in order to reach a stable coalition the members must co-ordinate their aspiration levels as expressed by their isolation mean demands. In this sense we may speak of a 'co-ordination pheno-menon'. The isolation mean demands may or may not correspond to the real aspiration levels but it is plausible that the perceptions which the players have of each other's aspiration levels are strongly influenced by isolation mean demands. These perceptions are per-haps as important or even more important than the real aspiration levels of the players.

The co-ordination phenomenon may be explained as follows. The sum of isolation mean demands should not be too much above 40 because in order to have a stable coalition it is necessary that every-body in the coalition thinks that the other members are content with their shares. On the other hand nobody wants too high a share for himself because his subjective probability for the stability of the coalition depends on the shares of the other players in the coalition. Therefore, if the sum of isolation mean demands is too much below 40, it is very likely that the players' desire for stability cannot be satisfied within that coalition because everybody wants too *low* a share for himself.

REFERENCES

Aumann, R. J., and Maschler, M. (1964), 'The Bargaining Set for Coopera-tive Games', in Dresher, M., Shapley, L. S., and Tucker, A. W. (eds.), 'Advances in Game Theory', *Ann. Math. Stud.* 52, Princeton, N.J., pp. 443–76.

Davis, M., and Maschler, M. (1963), *The Kernel of a Cooperative Game*, Econometric Research Program Research Memorandum No. 58, Prince-ton, N.J.

Fouraker, L. E. (1964), 'Level of Aspiration and Group Decision-Making', in Messick, S., and Brayfield, A. (eds.), *Decision and Choice: Contribu-tions of Sidney Siegel*, New York–San Francisco–London–Toronto, pp. 201–39.

Guilford, J. P. (1954), *Psychometric Methods*, New York–Toronto–London.

Hoffmann, P., Festinger, L., and Lawrence, D. (1954), 'Tendencies towards

Group Comparability in Competitive Bargaining', in Thrall, R. M., Coombs, C. H., and Davis, R. L. (eds.), *Decision Processes*, New York–London, pp. 231–53.

Kalish, G., Milnor, J. W., Nash, J., and Nering, E. D., (1954), 'Some Experimental *n*-Person Games', in Thrall, R. M., Coombs, C. H., and Davis, R. L. (eds.), *Decision Processes*, New York–London, pp. 301–27.

Luce, R. D. (1955), 'Ψ-stability: a New Equilibrium Concept for *n*-Person Game Theory', in *Mathematical Models of Human Behavior, Proceedings of a Symposium*, Dunlap & Associates, pp. 32–44.

— and Raiffa, H. (1957), *Games and Decisions*, New York–London–Sydney.

Maschler, M. (1965), *Playing an* n-*Person Game, An Experiment*, Econometric Research Program Research Memorandum No. 73, Princeton, N.J.

Mills, T. M. (1954), 'The Coalition Pattern in Three-Person Groups', *Amer. Sociol. Rev.* 19, pp. 657–67.

Neumann, J. von, and Morgenstern, O. (1944), *Theory of Games and Economic Behavior*, Princeton Univ. Press.

Raven, J. C. (1960), *Guide to the Standard Progressive Matrices, Sets A, B, C, D and E*, London.

Siegel, S. (1956), *Nonparametric Statistics for the Behavioral Sciences*, New York–Toronto–London.

Shapley, L. S. (1953), 'A Value for *n*-Person Games', in Kuhn, H. W., and Tucker, A. W., (eds.), 'Contributions to the Theory of Games, II', *Ann. Math. Stud.* 28, Princeton, N.J., pp. 307–17.

Vinacke, E., and Arkoff, A. (1957), 'An Experimental Study of Coalitions in the Triad', *Amer. Sociol. Rev.* 22, pp. 406–14.

DISCUSSION OF THE PAPER BY DR. SELTEN AND DR. SCHUSTER

Professor Bühlmann : The authors report on the following experiment which they have performed :

A five-person characteristic function game is played with real money payoff. Before the actual game a group of five students come into a room and discuss a political subject for fifteen minutes. After this they are rated by each other with respect to sympathy, trust, perceived bargaining ability, and perceived fairness. Next some test is administered to measure their problem-solving ability as well as their risk aversion. Finally, they answer eighty-five questions and are rated for dominance, rigidity, and 'ethical conformism'.

Then the game is played as follows. One player is called 'big' ; all others 'small'. A winning coalition is any of these five types :

Type 1 : one big, one small player.
Type 2 : one big, two small players.
Type 3 : one big, three small players.
Type 4 : four small players.
Type 5 : all players.

A coalition is 'formed' when the players agree on the division of the payoff (DM 40) among the partners of the coalition. A coalition is final (and the game is over) when it has lasted at least ten minutes.

The game is of course very simple and one may ask what the solutions ought to be according to the various theories available. The authors then confront these theoretical solutions with their actual findings.

(a) von Neumann–Morgenstern

Main simple solutions :

(i) 1 big, DM 30 ; 1 small, DM 10 ;
(ii) 4 small, DM 10 each.

No simple solution occurred in a final coalition.

(b) Shapley

The Shapley value is an *a priori* assessment of expected payoffs to the players.

	Shapley value	Average observed payoff
Big player	24	18·67
Small players each	4	5·33

At a level of 10 per cent the differences are still significant under a two-tailed *t*-test.

(c) Luce ψ-stability

ψ-stability is reached through the exclusion of some transitions from one coalition to another. The theory of ψ-stability does not seem to be useful for the explanation of the results of this experiment.

(d) Aumann–Maschler Bargaining Set

If the big player forms a coalition with one of the small players the bargaining set suggests a payoff of between DM 20 and DM 30 for the big player and between DM 10 and DM 20 for the small player. Eight of the twelve final results are compatible with the bargaining-set theory, but three show serious deviations.

(e) Davis–Maschler Kernel

This kernel is a subset of the Aumann–Maschler Bargaining Set. It contained the final solution in only one out of twelve plays.

As these discrepancies with theory are observed one automatically asks the question 'Why?' The questions were specified by the authors as follows:

(1) Are there any psychological attributes characterizing the *small player* who gets into coalition with the big player?

(2) Are there any social-psychological factors influencing the success of the *big player*?

(3) Is there any connection between the players' aspiration levels and their chance of getting into a coalition?

The first question leads to the following answers. The player who gets into coalition with the big partner has the properties that he is sympathetic in the eyes of the big player, risk-averse, and relatively high on the ethical conformism score.

A final coalition partner has relatively high demands for getting into the coalition with the big player, and, further, he has made relatively few offers. The problem-solving ability does not seem to have any influence on the choice of the small partner.

Regarding the second question the following observations were made: The success of the big player (*a*) depends strongly on the small players' willingness to trust and their perceived trustworthiness, and (*b*) depends strongly on the big player's firmness in making offers.

The third question is related to a theory of Fouraker which says that for odd-person coalition games the outcome is determined by the aspiration levels of the players. No evidence to support this theory was obtained from the observations. There was, however, a very interesting finding made, namely, that the sum of isolation mean demands for the members of the final coalition tends to add up to nearly forty.

It must be pointed out that the answers under questions (1) and (3) were subject to a non-parametric test invented by the authors. This test seems reasonable, although I would conjecture that a test with higher power might be found. The proposed test essentially aims only at finding differences between the *average rank* of the successful players and the *average rank* of all players.

As a discussant of this paper I find it hard to criticize their findings since the results are based on actual observations. The only additional point I find to be debatable is the use of the correlation coefficients in making inferences under question (2). As the authors point out themselves, at least one of the correlations found is highly suspicious.

I find it most important to state, however, that the type of experiment made by the authors is pointing in a new direction which is very essential. They are pointing the way to empirical tests of whether game-theoretical solutions do conform with the actual world in which we live. The 'discovery' of the experiment in economics may prove as fruitful as the seventeenth-century 'discovery' of experiments in mechanics.

Professor Menges : The discussant of an empirical paper is always in a bad spot. He can hardly challenge experimental results, if results they are. So he voices criticism on the general experimental setting of inferences drawn. If he does, he is likely to produce the impression that he raises a point which is only of minor interest.

I do not wish to comment on the experiments reported, but on the background against which the authors seem to see them. To exaggerate a little bit, I doubt that results of experiments in the domain of the social sciences can be reliable indicators, at least I doubt that they can be as reliable as in the natural sciences. Their predictive value will only in part depend on the variables observed or taken into account. A large part depends on the assumption on which experimental evaluation rests. Crucial in this type of experiment are, in general, the circumstances considered 'normal'.

True, if one checks the list of variables analysed by the authors, an oversight is not easily detected, not even by the critical mind. Upon reflection it seems, however, that little or no attention has been paid to the already notorious chance–risk asymmetry in experimental situations.

That subjects can 'gain' without 'risking' even the slightest part of their fortune, cannot be disputed. On the other hand, we have every reason to suppose that in real life chance has its price ; you cannot gain without taking risks. As much as I agree with the admirable experimental set-up and the ably presented results, the intended degree of *generalization* of experimental results seems to me not entirely justified. The last situation provides no analogue to real-life conflicts — nor can there be much reliance on real-world hypotheses based on resultso btained in an experimental set-up.

Dr. MacCrimmon : An aspect of this study worthy of further elaboration is the *transition process* by which intermediary registered coalitions get superseded by other intermediary registered coalitions and ultimately by the final registered coalition. Particularly interesting are those cases in which the members of an existing coalition form a different coalition in which their payoffs are lower! Of the 34 coalition transitions shown in Table 1, 5 of the transitions take this form. (The 5 cases are as follows : in play no. 2, coalition 2 to coalition 3 ; in play no. 2, coalition 6 to coalition 7 ; in play no. 5, coalition 2 to coalition 3 ; in play no. 7, coalition 1 to coalition 2 ; and in play no. 12, coalition 1 to coalition 2.) As an example, let us take the transition from coalition 6 (players 3 and 5) to coalition 7 (players 4 and 5) in play no. 2. Player 5 was getting DM39 in the existing coalition and in the new coalition he gets only DM25. What was his motivation for breaking up the coalition with player 3 ? If player 5 did not break up the existing coalition, but rather it was broken up by player 3, this seems to conflict with the statement that 'it never occurred that a player left a registered coalition without immediately forming a new one with other players'. Further clarification of this process would seem to be desirable.

Mr. Bessière : (1) It may easily be seen that it would have been possible to get a similar structure for winning coalitions by taking groups of four players only with a weight of two for the 'big' player. I wonder if Dr. Selten can tell us why five-player groups were studied.

(2) It would be interesting to know which sort of use the players have made of their money. It is quite possible they met together after the end of the play to have a drink or a dinner, and if so the final coalition would in fact have been of type 5. Moreover, if they more or less implicitly agreed in advance on such a solution, then their bargaining would have been pure amusement, and not real gambling.

(3) The authors state that 'further investigations are planned'. Could I ask whether some of these planned investigations are concerned with the time during which a specific coalition remains stable ? I ask this because I have noticed that the distribution of these times seems to be *bimodal*. This can be seen from Table 1 where, leaving aside play no. 1, which is not homogeneous with the other plays, it is possible to select thirty-two *non-final* coalitions and study the distribution of their durations. This distribution seems to be bimodal, with a first maximum around four minutes, and a second just under ten minutes. We find seventeen times under 6 min. 30 sec., and fifteen above, among which seven longer than nine minutes. Two coalitions were broken after 9 min. 59 sec., really at the last second ; one of these is of type 4 with *symmetrical* payoffs (play no. 11) and the other one of type 2 (play no. 9) ; *these two types never figure among final coalitions*.

I am afraid that this reflects the fact that during the last seconds bargaining was particularly hard, which means that *the time limit of ten minutes gave a strong disturbance to the asymptotic behaviour* of the players. We can see that the plays had a total duration between ten and eighty minutes ; in any case, these times are not long enough for a five-person group to find its psycho-sociological stability. As I think that in fact we are most interested in the asymptotic behaviour of the group, I may suggest that it would be better if we could remove the disturbing effect of the time limit, possibly by saying that the play can be stopped in two ways : (*a*) *every* player, even those who are not members of the registered coalition, agree that there is nothing more to do ; (*b*) the experimenter stops it after an arbitrary time *unknown* by the players.

Professor Gordon : A unique contribution of this paper is to examine the correlation between an individual's effectiveness in participating in coalitions and his personality attributes. Psychological tests are made in industry to select successful managers. Hence, if ability to perform successfully in games played in these experiments is a measure of managerial ability, the tests he employed may be used to select managers.

Record of Discussion

Drs. Selten and Schuster found, for instance, that small players with aversion to risk and a high ethical conformity score were more effective. Of course, additional experimental work is needed to have confidence in the correlations obtained. Perhaps more important are questions on the correlation between performance in the game and managerial success. The game requires little or no problem-solving ability and involves no uncertainty as to the outcome of a coalition. It might be desirable to employ games where the payoff to a coalition is uncertain and varies among coalitions with their uncertainty.

Professor Hester : Do the authors believe that the character of the solutions would be significantly affected by altering the total payoff from DM40 to, say, 39 or 41 ? Were any experiments performed to test this possibility ?

Professor Siroyezhin : We all know that the sets of postulates developed for co-operative games have many points to be improved. Developing the line of thought brought to your attention by Professor Gordon, I should like to put a question. Would it be very difficult to extrapolate from such experiments to the development of a set of more rational and operational postulates and axioms for co-operative game theory and its more successful application to research and practical work in economic institutions ?

Dr. Selten : Professor Bühlmann has given a very good summary of our paper. In reply to his remark about the mean rank test I would like to say that it is the purpose of this test to detect influences which are due to the rank orders within the groups. I would be surprised if a test could be found which would be more powerful with respect to the specific set of alternative hypotheses indicated by that purpose. Professor Bühlmann seems to be disturbed by the fact that we have rejected some significant correlations as spurious. We had good reasons to do so. Errors of the first kind have to occur sometimes and we must be glad if they can be detected by causal arguments.

I do not agree with the opinion of Professor Menges that experiments in the social sciences are less generalizable than experiments in the natural sciences. In my opinion empirical work in both the natural and the social sciences must be guided by the same principles.

Professor Menges said further that our experiment does not provide an analogue to real conflict situations because in real life nobody can gain anything without the risk of losing a part of his fortune. I am somewhat surprised about this because it seems to be obvious that in many business negotiations the bargainers do not face a substantial risk of losing a part of their fortune. This does not mean that there is no risk involved because the risk to gain nothing is still there.

Dr. MacCrimmon has asked the very good question why some subjects leave a registered coalition in order to go into a new one where they get less. They do this because there is a danger that a new coalition will be formed without them and/or because they think that the new coalition is less profitable but more stable.

Mr. Bessière has asked why we have chosen this particular game structure. We have done so because of its notoriety among game theorists. I do not know what our subjects did after the experiment but it is my impression that the winners would not have wanted to give something to the losers and that most losers would have resented such generosity. The antagonistic atmosphere of the game does not establish harmonious inter-personal relations between winners and losers.

The distribution of registration times may be bimodal but it seems to be difficult to test this statistically. The registration times within the same play cannot be considered as statistically independent. It is not necessarily the case that last-second breakdowns of coalitions indicate hard bargaining; this conjecture does not correspond to our impression from the observation of the game. I think that last-second breakdowns come about because a player who is not sure whether he should leave the coalition may be undecided until the last possible moment and only then make his decision. If a play could only be terminated when every player agrees that there is nothing more to do, each individual player would have the power to block any coalition. This would drastically change the strategic situation. If the play is stopped after an arbitrary time unknown to the players, the stability of the last registered coalition is not really tested. Therefore I think that it is best to stick to our rule of a ten-minute registration time.

Professor Gordon has suggested that our experiment may be useful for the development of attitude tests for businessmen. I think that it would be dangerous to work along this line before very many experiments have been made. A personality factor which is correlated to success in one strategic situation may be a very bad asset in another strategic situation. Businessmen may also need psychological traits which are unimportant in experimental co-operative games.

Professor Gordon also mentioned the possibility of using 'risky' pay-offs for the coalitions. I think that it is better to explore the simpler case first.

Professor Hester has asked the question whether a slight change in payoff of the winning coalitions, say from 40 to 39 or 41, might not very much influence the outcomes. I cannot deny that this is a possibility. The (15, 25) payoff distribution in the type 1 coalition is very prominent in the sense of Schelling because 15 and 25 are round numbers; if we changed the payoff from 40 to 39 we would perhaps get (14, 25) or (15, 24) instead of $(14\frac{5}{8}, 24\frac{3}{8})$ which would correspond to (15, 25), because the payoff is divided in the same proportion.

Chapter 11

GENERAL EQUILIBRIUM IN THE ECONOMICS OF UNCERTAINTY

BY

KARL BORCH

I. INTRODUCTION

(1) Most of the papers presented to this Conference deal with various aspects of economic decisions under uncertainty. It is clear that such decisions present a number of very intricate problems. It is also clear that we can solve these problems only if we know the *objectives* of the decision-maker, and the *environment* in which the decisions are made.

The decision problems which we have discussed at the Conference can be considered as direct descendants of two central problems in classical economic theory:

(i) How should a *producer* use his resources in order to maximize his profits?

(ii) How should a *consumer* spend his income in order to maximize his utility?

When the problems are formulated in this way, the objectives of the decision-maker are implied. The environment is determined by the 'price situation'. The problems can be solved if the prices of all commodities are known to the decision-maker.

(2) The classical theory had no room for uncertainty. This element was ignored, or assumed away — often with a reference to insurance and the 'Law of Large Numbers'. It is, however, obvious that uncertainty exists, and this has led a number of authors to propose models which give a more realistic representation of the environment in which the decision is made — for instance by assuming that prices are known only in a stochastic sense. This assumption implies, however, that profit maximization becomes meaningless, so that one has to formulate the objective of the decision-maker in a more general manner.

The papers presented to this Conference illustrate the ingenuity which one can show when it comes to formulating decision problems with different objectives in different environments. It is, however, worth noting that the environments — in the classical case, the prices — are not given by nature. The environment which confronts one decision-maker is usually created by other decision-makers, who pursue their own objectives. It may be that the main source of uncertainty in economics is not the caprice of nature, but uncertainty about how other decision-makers will decide.

This argument is the real starting-point of the theory of games, created by von Neumann and Morgenstern (1944). It implies that we should not study isolated decision problems, but that we must study a whole set of interrelated decisions, if we want to penetrate the core of the real problem.

(3) The argument mentioned above can also be found in older economic literature — although not always clearly formulated. The two antecedents of the decision problems studied by contemporary economists were not considered as particularly interesting in themselves by Walras and Pareto. To them the interesting point was that the solution of these problems — for *all* decision-makers in the economy — would determine prices, i.e. the environment which an individual decision-maker might take as given and beyond his control.

This suggests that we should try to bring uncertainty into the classical theory of *general equilibrium*. In the following we shall indicate how this can be done.

The paper is expository in the sense that it contains very little which cannot be found in the pioneering paper by Arrow (1953). All results given in the present paper can be taken as special cases of more general theorems, proved in the book by Debreu (1959).

The need for a theory of the economics of uncertainty must have been obvious for quite a long time, and it is surprising that the problem was taken up in its full generality only fifteen years ago. It was then taken up simultaneously by Allais (1953) and Arrow (1953), and it led to the work of Arrow and Debreu (1954) and Debreu (1959), giving a theory which can handle uncertainty in a satisfactory manner.

(4) It appears that the significance of this work was not realized immediately by economists. I believe my own work on reinsurance premiums (Borch, 1960, 1962), was the first attempt to derive some practical conclusions from the rather abstract work of Arrow and Debreu.

During the last couple of years 'equilibrium under uncertainty' has become a very popular subject. A number of papers, e.g. Dreze (1965), Mossin (1966), Radner (1965), and Sharpe (1964), give results which are both elegant — and deceptively simple. These results may create the impression that the generalization from certainty to uncertainty is relatively easy, and that most of the familiar concepts from classical theory can be carried over with minor modifications. In this paper we shall demonstrate that the introduction of uncertainty really means a step from the finite to the infinite, and this is by no means a trivial generalization.

II. THE BASIC MODEL

(1) To illustrate our point, we shall consider the following simple model, which can be interpreted as a market with n persons and m commodities:

(i) There are m 'prospects'. Prospect i will give a monetary payment x_i, which is a variate with the distribution $F_i(x_i)$, $(i = 1, 2, \ldots, m)$. For the sake of simplicity we shall assume that these variates are independent, and that

$$F_i(x) = 0 \qquad \text{for } x_i < 0.$$

(ii) Person j is entitled to a fraction q_{ij} of the payment from prospect i:

$$\sum_{j=1}^{n} q_{ij} = 1 \qquad \text{for all } i,$$

$$q_{ij} \geqslant 0 \qquad \text{for all } i \text{ and } j.$$

(iii) Person j has a preference ordering over the set of all prospects, and this ordering can be represented by a Bernoulli utility function $u_j(x)$.

(2) To give the model concrete interpretation, we can think of the prospects as m firms, whose ordinary shares are held by n persons.

Person j will then assign the following utility to his initial portfolio of ordinary shares:

$$U_j(q_{1j}, \ldots, q_{mj}) = \int_0^\infty \ldots \int_0^\infty u_j(\sum_{i=1}^{m} q_{ij} x_i) dF_1(x_1), \ldots, dF_m(x_m). \qquad (1)$$

We have not introduced cash explicitly in the model. We can do this by assuming that, say, prospect m is degenerate, i.e. that

$$F_m(x_m) = 0 \qquad \text{for } x_m < c$$
$$F_m(x_m) = 1 \qquad \text{for } c \leqslant x_m.$$

We can then interpret c as the total amount of cash in the initial situation, and cq_{mj} as the initial cash holding of person j.

(3) The initial allocation of ordinary shares is given by the matrix $\{q_{ij}\}$. If the n persons can trade shares among themselves, it may be possible to reach another allocation $\{\bar{q}_{ij}\}$ which will give all persons a higher utility. Since we consider a closed model, we must have

$$\sum_{j=1}^{n} (q_{ij} - \bar{q}_{ij}) = 0 \qquad (i = 1, 2, \ldots, m). \tag{2}$$

It is natural to attack this problem in the classical manner, and introduce a price vector $p = \{p_1 \ldots p_m\}$, where p_1 is the price of firm i.

If shares can only be traded at these prices, we must have

$$\sum_{i=1}^{m} p_i(q_{ij} - \bar{q}_{ij}) = 0 \qquad (j = 1, 2, \ldots, n). \tag{3}$$

(4) By now we have obtained a completely classical model, and we can proceed in the classical manner.

We can assume that person j takes p as given, and maximizes his utility (1), subject to the budget constraints (3).

Under the usual regularity assumptions there exists a vector of equilibrium prices, so that the market relations (2) are satisfied, i.e. there exists a *competitive equilibrium* in our market for shares. It is easy to prove that this equilibrium represents a *Pareto-optimal* allocation of shares among the n persons.

It thus appears that one of the central theorems of classical economic theory can be generalized to include uncertainty with very little trouble.

III. PARETO-OPTIMAL ARRANGEMENTS

(1) By attacking our problem in the classical manner, we have ignored some essential aspects of uncertainty. It is clear that the real problem of our n persons is to find some arrangement which gives an optimal distribution of the conditional payments from the m prospects. It is obvious that an arrangement which consists of an

exchange of ordinary shares is very special. It would be surprising if it should turn out to be optimal.

Let us, therefore, consider a general arrangement which will give person j a payment of

$$y_j(x_1, x_2, \ldots, x_m) \qquad (j = 1, 2, \ldots, n)$$

if payments from the m prospects are $x_1 \ldots x_m$.

This arrangement is determined by n functions $y_1 \ldots y_n$. Only if these functions are all linear will the general arrangement become an exchange of ordinary shares.

(2) Since we consider a closed model, we must have

$$\sum_{j=1}^{n} y_j(x_1 \ldots x_m) = \sum_{i=1}^{m} x_i.$$

It may be desirable to impose some other restrictions on the functions y_j. We can require:

$$y_j > 0 \qquad \text{for all } j$$

or

$$y_j > -cq_{mj},$$

where the right-hand term is the amount of cash held by person j in the initial situation. In the following we shall, however, ignore such additional restrictions.

(3) The arrangement we have described will give person j the following utility:

$$U_j(y) = \int_0^\infty \ldots \int_0^\infty u_j(y_j) dF_1(x_1), \ldots, dF_n(x_n).$$

The Pareto-optimal arrangements are then given by the n-tuple of functions y_j, which maximize

$$\sum_{j=1}^{n} k_j U_j(y) = \int_0^\infty \ldots \int_0^\infty \{\sum_{j=1}^{n} k_j u_j(y_j)\} dF_1(x_1), \ldots, dF_n(x_n)$$

subject to the condition

$$\sum_{j=1}^{n} y_j = \sum_{i=1}^{m} x_i = z.$$

Here $k_1 \ldots k_n$ are arbitrary positive constants.

It is obvious that the solution we seek must maximize the integrand for every value of z. Hence the problem is reduced to finding the vector $y = \{y_1, \ldots, y_n\}$ which gives

$$\max \sum_{j=1}^{n} k_j u_j(y_j)$$

subject to

$$\sum_{j=1}^{n} y_j = z. \tag{4}$$

This means that y_j will be a function of a single variable $z = \sum x_i$. (4) To solve the problem we form the Lagrangian function

$$\sum_{j=1}^{n} k_j u_j(y_j) + \lambda \left(z - \sum_{j=1}^{n} y_j \right).$$

Differentiating, we obtain the first-order conditions for a maximum

$$k_j u'_j(y_j) = \lambda,$$

which we shall write in the form

$$k_j u'_j(y_j) = k_1 u'_1(y_1) \qquad (j = 1, 2, \ldots, n) \tag{5}$$

If the utility functions are of the conventional form, i.e. $u'_j(x) > 0$ and $u''_j(x) < 0$ for all j, conditions (4) and (5) will determine a unique n-tuple $\{y_1 \ldots y_n\}$ for given $k_1 \ldots k_n$. If we let z vary, the conditions will give us an n-tuple of functions, which represent Pareto-optimal arrangements. We obtain all such arrangements by letting $k_1 \ldots k_n$ vary. The functions $y_1(z) \ldots y_n(z)$ will depend on the utility functions of our n persons, but not on the distributions defining the m prospects.

(5) It is easy to see that the n-tuple of functions defined by (4) and (5) will not in general be linear. Hence a Pareto-optimal arrangement can be reached by an exchange of ordinary shares only if the n utility functions satisfy some very special conditions.

It is clear that the functions $y_j(z)$ defined by (4) and (5) are linear, if the defining relations themselves are linear, i.e. if $u'_j(x) = a_j + x$ $(j = 1 \ldots n)$.

It is easy to see that this will hold also when

$$u'_j(x) = (a_j + x)^{\alpha}.$$

In the latter case (5) becomes

$$k_j(a_j + y_j)^{\alpha} = k_1(a_1 + y_1)^{\alpha}$$

or

$$y_j = \frac{h_1}{h_j}(a_1 + y_1) - a_j$$

where $h_j = k_j^{\frac{1}{\alpha}}$.

Summing this equation over all j, we obtain by (4)

$$z = (a_1 + y_1)h_1 \sum_{j=1}^{n} h_j^{-1} - \sum_{j=1}^{n} a_j.$$

From this we can find y_1, and in general

$$y_j(z) = \frac{z + \sum_{t=1}^{n} a_t}{h_j \sum_{t=1}^{n} h_t^{-1}} - a_j.$$

(6) In general, $y_1(z)$ and $y_j(z)$ will be linear only if

$$k_j u'_j(a_j z + b_j) = k_1 u'_1(a_1 z + b_1)$$

or by a linear transformation of the variable

$$u'_j(az + b) = ku'_1(z). \tag{6}$$

Here a and b are independent of z, but may depend on k. Differentiating (6) with respect to z, we obtain

$$au''_j(az + b) = ku''_1(z).$$

Differentiating (6) with respect to k gives

$$(a'z + b')u''_j(az + b) = u'_1(z)$$

where $a' = da/dk$ and $b' = db/dk$.

Eliminating $u''_j(az + b)$ from the two equations, we obtain

$$k(a'z + b')u''_1(z) - au'_1(z) = 0.$$

The solution of this differential equation is

(i) For $a' = 0$

$$u'_1(z) = e^{\frac{a}{kb'}z}.$$

(ii) For $a' \neq 0$

$$u'_1(z) = \left(z + \frac{b'}{a'}\right)^{\frac{a}{ka'}}.$$

If the utility functions are not of one of these two forms, it will be impossible to reach a Pareto-optimal arrangement by trading in ordinary shares.[1]

IV. COMPETITIVE EQUILIBRIUM

(1) We can interpret our results to mean that a stock exchange, which is allowed to trade only in ordinary shares, will in general lead to a sub-optimal allocation of risk. If this is explained to our n persons, what will they do? We can think of at least three possible answers:

(i) Our persons may put aside the classical economic theory, and bargain their way to a Pareto-optimal arrangement — possibly with the help of game theory.

(ii) They may call on the government or some other *deus ex machina* for help to bring about a Pareto-optimal arrangement.

(iii) They may accept the sub-optimal arrangement out of sheer inertia, or because they fear or dislike the 'financial manipulations' or 'speculative transactions' which are necessary to reach a Pareto-optimal arrangement.

We could discuss these possibilities, and make some conjectures which might have some sociological interest. We shall, however, not take up these questions. Instead we shall show how Arrow was able to save the classical economic theory.

(2) The idea behind Arrow's paper (1953) is that the natural 'commodities' in the model are not ordinary shares in the firm, but claims to a certain part of the total amount available for distribution, i.e. of z. We can then assign a price to these claims. We do this by specifying a function $p(z)dz$ which we can interpret as the price of a certificate which promises to pay one unit of money if and only if total payments from the m prospects fall between z and $z+dz$. We shall refer to these 'commodities' as *Arrow certificates*.

Let $F(z)$ be the distribution of the variate z, i.e. the convolution of $F_1(x_1) \ldots F_n(x_n)$. To simplify our notation, we shall assume that a density function $f(z) = F'(z)$ exists. Let us assume that person j pays an amount $p(z)y_j(z)dz$ for a certificate, which will pay $y_j(z)$ if total payments from the prospects are z. The conditional payment promised by the certificate will make the contribution $u_j(y_j(z))f(z)dz$ to his expected utility.

[1] I am grateful to C. B. Winsten, who suggested this proof.

If we now in good classical fashion require marginal utility to be proportional to price, we obtain

$$u'_j(y_j(z))f(z) = \lambda_j p(z) \qquad (j = 1, 2 \ldots n).$$

This is substantially the same condition as (5), and we find

$$p(z) = k_j u'_j(y_j(z))f(z).$$

(3) Having determined the price function $p(z)$, our next task is to determine $y_j(z)$ so that the equivalent of relation (3) is satisfied. This relation says essentially that the market value of the holdings of person j is the same in the final situation as in the initial situation.

The market value of the initial holdings is

$$\int_0^\infty \left\{ \left(\int \cdots \int_{\Sigma x_i = z} \left\{ \sum_{i=1}^n q_{ij} x_i \right\} dx_1 \ldots dx_m \right) p(z) dz \right.$$

$$= k_j \int_0^\infty \frac{z^m}{m!} \left\{ \sum_{i=1}^m q_{ij} \right\} u'_j(y_j(z))f(z) dz.$$

The market value of the final holdings is:

$$\int_0^\infty \left\{ \left(\int \cdots \int_{\Sigma x i = z} dx_1 \ldots d_m \right) y_j(z) p(z) dz \right.$$

$$= k_j \int_0^\infty \frac{z^{m-1}}{(m-1)!} y_j(z) u'_j(y_j(z))f(z) dz.$$

The generalized version of relation (3) then becomes:

$$\int_0^\infty \left\{ \frac{z^m}{m} \sum_{i=1}^m q_{ij} - z^{m-1} y_j(z) \right\} u'_j(y_j(z))f(z) dz = 0 \qquad j = 1, 2 \ldots n. \quad (7)$$

The last factor of the integrand in (7), $u'_j(z)f(z)$, is the same for all j, apart from a constant factor. From (5) it follows that $y_j(z)$ depends on the constants $k_1 \ldots k_n$, of which $n-1$ can be chosen arbitrarily.

If we sum (7) over all j, and note that $\sum_{j=1}^n \sum_{i=j}^m q_{ij} = m$ and $\sum y_j(z) = z$, we see that there are only $n-1$ independent relations, so that (7) can be satisfied if $k_1 \ldots k_n$ are chosen appropriately.

(4) By this ingenious device Arrow is able to save the central result of classical economic theory, and show that a competitive

equilibrium is a Pareto-optimal allocation also when uncertainty is brought into the model.

This impressive result is obtained at a certain cost. In order to reach the result, we have to introduce an infinity — in the general case a continuum — of commodities and prices. This means that the simple model of Walras loses some of its common-sense appeal.

It seems natural to assume that people have a fair idea of the equilibrium prices of ordinary commodities, and that they figure out how much they want to buy or sell at these prices. It seems less natural to assume that people can figure out the equilibrium prices for 'Arrow certificates'.

There are additional complications. Unless the holdings of the n persons in the initial situation are spread over all the m prospects, they cannot honour the Arrow certificates they may sell, unless they are prepared to 'go short'. These short sales will be 'covered' on the way to a Pareto optimum, but this way can be blocked by any obstinate person. This indicates that game theory, and not classical economics, is the proper framework for analysing the situation.

(5) In Borch (1962), referred to above, another price concept was introduced. It was assumed that the price of a prospect was completely determined by its stochastic properties. Mathematically this means that the price of a prospect defined by $F(x)$ was a mapping $P\{F\}$ from the set of distributions to the real line.

The economic interpretation is that the price of a security is determined by its 'intrinsic value', or that the insurance premium of a risk depends only on the risk itself. This may appear an acceptable behavioural assumption, but it was proved that it is not compatible with a Pareto-optimal arrangement.

This should not be surprising, since the classical parallel to the assumption would be that the price of a commodity is determined by its qualities, and not by its scarcity.

(6) In the market considered in Section II (3), where it is only possible to trade in ordinary shares, we will have

$$\bar{q}_{1j} = \bar{q}_{2j} = \ldots = \bar{q}_{mj} = \bar{q}_j$$

in the equilibrium. This can be proved directly, and it follows from the considerations of Section II (2).

We can then assume that our n persons first reach an equilibrium under the condition that only trade in ordinary shares is permitted. When they have reached this point, they may realize that the arrangement is sub-optimal. As they are now all able to sell Arrow certificates, they may start the sequence of trades, which will lead to an optimal arrangement.

This means, however, that we have introduced considerations which are of dynamic nature in order to solve an essentially static problem. This is not satisfactory. If we want to bring in dynamic considerations — which will be a great step towards realism — we should do it at the start, and begin with a dynamic model.

V. AN EXAMPLE

(1) It may be useful to conclude by giving a simple example. Let

$$n = 2, \ u_1(x) = x^{1/2}, \text{ and } u_2(x) = x^{3/4}.$$

The Pareto-optimal payment functions are then given by

$$k_1 \{y_1(z)\}^{-1/2} = k_2 \{y_2(z)\}^{-1/4} \tag{5'}$$

or

$$\{y_1(z)\}^2 - \left(\frac{k_1}{k_2}\right)^4 (z - y_1(z)) = 0.$$

From this we obtain

$$y_1(z) = \sqrt{h^2 + 2hz} - h$$
$$y_2(z) = z + h - \sqrt{h^2 + 2hz}$$

where h is an arbitrary non-negative constant.

Further, let $m = 2$, $f_1(x) = f_2(x) = e^{-x}$ so that

$$f(z) = ze^{-z}.$$

The price function is then

$$p(z) = (\sqrt{h^2 + 2hz} - h)^{-1/2} ze^{-z}.$$

Let us assume that the initial allocation is:

$$q_{11} = 1, \quad q_{21} = 0, \quad q_{12} = 0 \quad \text{and} \quad q_{22} = 1.$$

The market equilibrium conditions then become:

$$\int_0^{\infty} \left\{ \frac{z^2}{2} - zy_j(z) \right\} u'_j(y_j(z)) f(z) dz = 0 \qquad (j = 1, 2) \tag{6'}$$

From these conditions it follows that h must be the unique real root of the equation:

Group Decisions and Market Mechanisms

$$\int_0^\infty \left\{ \frac{z^3}{2} - z^2(\sqrt{h^2+2hz} - h)\right\} \left\{\sqrt{h^2+2hz} - h\right\}^{-1} e^{-z}dz = 0.$$

(2) We have found a very complicated solution to an apparently simple problem. It would not be surprising if our two persons should put aside the ideas of perfect competition, and settle their *bargaining* problem by other principles, for instance by accepting the Nash (1950) solution.

If, however, two persons do this, the same thing may happen in a group of three or more persons. This will then mean that the introduction of uncertainty may lead to the abandonment of the familiar concepts of classical economic theory in favour of a more general bargaining theory.

The behavioural assumptions behind Arrow's model are attractive, but complicated. We should not be surprised if people settle for something simpler, though sub-optimal.

REFERENCES

Allais, M. (1953), 'Généralisation des théories de l'équilibre économique général et du rendement social au cas du risque', *Colloques internationaux du CNRS*, Paris, pp. 81–109.

Arrow, K. J. (1953), 'Le Rôle de valeurs boursières pour la répartition la meilleure des risques', *Colloques internationaux du CNRS*, Paris, pp. 41–8. English translation: 'The Rôle of Securities in the Optimal Allocation of Risk-Bearing', *Rev. Econ. Stud.* 1964, pp. 91–6.

— and Debreu, G. (1954), 'Existence of an Equilibrium for a Competitive Economy', *Econometrica*, pp. 265–90.

Borch, K. (1960), 'The Safety Loading of Reinsurance Premiums', *Skandinavisk Aktuarietidskrift*, pp. 163–84.

— (1962), 'Equilibrium in a Reinsurance Market', *Econometrica*, pp. 424–444.

Debreu, G. (1959), *Theory of Value*, New York: John Wiley & Sons.

Dreze, J. (1965), 'Market Allocation under Uncertainty', paper presented at the *First World Congress of the Econometric Society*, Rome.

Mossin, J. (1966), 'Equilibrium in a Capital Asset Market', *Econometrica*, 1966, pp. 768–83.

Nash, J. (1950), 'The Bargaining Problem', *Econometrica*, pp. 155–62.

Neumann, J. von, and Morgenstern, O. (1944), *Theory of Games and Economic Behavior*, Princeton Univ. Press.

Radner, R. (1965), 'Competitive Equilibrium under Uncertainty', paper presented at the *First World Congress of the Econometric Society*, Rome.

Sharpe, W. F. (1964), 'Capital Asset Prices: a Theory of Market Equilibrium under Conditions of Risk', *J. Finance*, pp. 425–42.

Record of Discussion

DISCUSSION OF THE PAPER BY
PROFESSOR BORCH

Dr. Winsten : I have the pleasure of opening the discussion on an interesting and elegantly presented paper.

My main concern about the paper is what I believe to be a confusion between points given for apparently mathematical reasons, and those given for reasons of economic analysis.

In the first section Professor Borch discusses the achievement of Pareto optima when n persons bargain about m 'prospects', i.e. shares in an uncertain gain. These are judged by their expected utilities before they yield their return. They are therefore mathematically closely akin to the goods usually considered in the theory of markets, and so the deterministic theory carries over to this case, and a suitable market can give a Pareto optimum.

Professor Borch now moves to a more general problem. But here I find myself in some confusion.

In Section III he states that what the n persons will wish to find is some arrangement which will give an optimal arrangement of the *conditional payments* of the m prospects (random yields). He then goes on to consider that payments will be a non-linear function of yields. But the yield for a particular person can be taken ('without loss of generality') as a function of the total money yield to that person, irrespective of the origin of any part of that yield.

After setting up the equations for the utility functions of the n people, Professor Borch states that 'it is obvious that the solution we must seek must maximize the integrand for every value of z'. z is the total payment from all the prospects. Now this seems to be not so much a mathematical condition as a formulation of the economic problem. In the first case considered it was considered desirable to have a Pareto optimum of the *expectations* of yield. In this latter case it is considered desirable to have what will be acknowledged to be a Pareto optimum *after* the total yield has been divided.

Professor Borch now goes on to discuss 'Arrow certificates'. These involve the possibility of buying a share in a particular small range of the total yield of the entire market. Far from this device representing something by which 'Arrow was able to save the classical economic theory' it is, in fact, a proposal for a new form of economic organization. But Professor Borch is more concerned with a mathematical point, that this model makes for a market in an infinite number of goods (of infinitesimal ranges of total yield) rather than a finite one. Not, admittedly, only a mathematical one, for this leads to troubles in economic organization too, as is pointed out in the paper.

Professor Borch finishes by considering a simple two-person case with an (algebraically) complicated solution. These algebraic complications are of more concern to the people analysing the nature of such solutions, than to the people involved in bargaining. And, especially in this age of computers, we should not determine the nature of the real world by the algebraic difficulties of those who study it.

A word about Pareto optima. These are useful in cases (such as those of competing insurance firms) where we accept the distribution of assets as given, and are not concerned with redistributive effects, but the systems described here are very redistributive. Thus, if we were considering individuals, we would have to reassess the usefulness of Pareto optima in the long run; for then redistribution, apart from that achieved by these markets and by chance, may well be desirable.

Dr. Selten: This paper is a very good article about the state of the subject; I agree with the opinion of Professor Borch that Arrow's ingenious attempt to save the classical theory is somewhat unrealistic. If we look at the stock exchange we do not see anything similar to Arrow certificates; but I think that the stock market has some devices which may serve to reduce the gap between the competitive equilibrium and the set of Pareto-optimal points. I would like to point out some of these: bonds, preferred stock and investment certificates are claims to fixed amounts which are paid unless they must be reduced because of partial or total insolvency; therefore bonds of the firm i may be thought of as piecewise linear functions of the amount x_i. The same is true for preferred stock endowed with a guarantee of a certain minimum dividend. If a firm issues bonds or preferred stock, then the shares become claims to amounts which are piecewise linear functions of x_i. It seems to be plausible to conjecture that the introduction of bonds and preferred stock tends to push the competitive equilibrium nearer to the set of Pareto-optimal points. Investment certificates which combine shares of many firms could have a similar effect. Such certificates may be a reasonable approximation of securities depending on the random variable z; that seems to be theoretically important, because the dependence on z is a very prominent feature of the Arrow certificates. It is my feeling that a substantial gap between competitive equilibrium and the set of Pareto-optimal points will tend to be closed by profitable institutional innovations such as the invention of new kinds of securities. In order to formalize this argument we could try to prove a theorem that profitable innovations are always possible if the competitive equilibrium is not Pareto-optimal. This should not be too difficult.

Professor Bühlmann: It has been brought out in the discussion that unless the utility functions have special forms, the competitive equilibrium is not Pareto-optimal. This is due to the fact that the model provides only for the possibility of a *proportional* split of the payments of the individual prospect. Professor Borch, in his paper 'Equilibrium in a Reinsurance

Record of Discussion

Market', has proved that through *non-proportional* forms of sharing the payments Pareto optimality can be reached.

Professor Menges: I want to ask Professor Borch: Do you really think that the work of Arrow and Debreu led to a theory which can handle uncertainty in a satisfactory manner? In my view their theories leave out an important aspect, namely, the game-theoretical one. Pareto optimum for society means that no reallocation of resources can take place without making at least one member of society worse off. Presupposed is the existence of one best allocation. A maximum can then only be found under a number of very strong assumptions. The main one is that individual utilities are mutually independent.

Another point I should like to make is that Professor Borch's theory does not allow for the possibility of co-operation. Application of Pareto-optimum may perhaps be justified for a market of insurance companies, but for other types of firms it is much less appropriate. I appreciate, however, that by Borch's attempt the deterministic character of the classical model is overcome.

Dr. Selten: Professor Menges mentioned the possibility that the utility functions of the traders may not be independent. If one is willing to abandon the assumption of independence one may run into serious difficulties, which may be illustrated by the following 'utility paradox'. Let us assume that two subjects 1 and 2 have utility functions

$$u_1 = u_1(x_1, u_2)$$
$$u_2 = u_2(x_2, u_1),$$

depending not only on the commodity bundles x_1 and x_2 but also on the utility of the other subject. If x_1 and x_2 are assumed to be fixed at certain values x_1^0 and x_2^0, we may draw a diagram showing u_1 as a function of u_2 and u_2 as a function of u_1. There may be several points of intersection. Which point corresponds to the utilities u_1^0 and u_2^0 in the situation given by x_1^0 and x_2^0? The utility concept does not seem to remain meaningful if the utilities of the subjects are not uniquely defined.

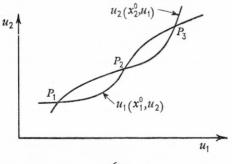

Group Decisions and Market Mechanisms

Professor Rosett : The paradox described by Dr. Selten may not be a paradox at all, but merely an accurate description of what the world is like.

Mr. Baudier : I do not believe that the whole contents of Professor Borch's paper can be considered as a simple application of the ideas of Debreu and Arrow. Some of the situations discussed cannot be put into their framework.

A different interpretation of the basic model may be proposed. Instead of payments of money it is possible to imagine that we are concerned with a part of the production of the enterprise and that the economy consists of only one kind of goods. It is produced by m enterprises but none of them knows in advance the quantity it will produce. The probability laws $F_i(x_i)$ reflect the level of confidence that consumers have in different enterprises. (We could also suppose that the F_i differ from one agent to another.)

The contracts which are traded seem to be of a totally new kind. According to Debreu and Arrow the amounts of the goods received depend on the different states of nature. These states depend only on variables which can be observed in an objective manner, and which are independent of the action of the parties to the contract. This is not the case here, as the production of an enterprise cannot be independent of the action of the enterprise itself. The contracts therefore imply that the consumers fully trust the producer or producers they have chosen. Debreu and Arrow in their theory require great trust and confidence, but every agent insists on his right to verify that the contract has been correctly executed. In Professor Borch's 'basic model' there is no such possibility.

In this framework it is not only the nature of the good which is in question, but also the debtor. He acquires an importance which the theory has not given him up to now. This naturally leads us to the following remark.

It does not seem possible to exclude the cases in which the origin of the payment is significant. Professor Borch's hypothesis leads to the result mentioned in Section IV. This implies that a consumer would take the same number of shares in a company which is certain to produce the goods as in a company which will produce nothing with certainty.

Professor Borch : In reply to Dr. Winsten's first point I should like to present a simple example.

Assume that two brothers are to divide their late father's business, which consists of two retail shops. They may consider the following three arrangements :

(i) The brothers get one shop each.
(ii) Each brother gets a 50 per cent interest on both shops.
(iii) One brother gets both shops, and gives the other brother an interest-bearing bond of say $100,000.

If the brothers have a 'risk aversion', they will probably prefer (ii) to (i).

It is also conceivable that both brothers will prefer (iii) to (ii). This may be the case if the brother who gets the bond has the stronger risk aversion.

In a more general context, (ii) will represent the case where it is permitted to trade only in ordinary shares. It may, however, be possible to increase the utility of all persons if they are allowed to create and to trade in other kinds of securities. This is illustrated by (iii). In a reinsurance market there are no obvious restrictions on the nature of 'new securities', which can be created in the form of reinsurance treaties. I therefore agree with Professor Bühlmann that such markets may be in a state near the absolute optimum.

All arrangements are considered *ex ante*, i.e. before the payoffs from the different prospects are known. It may be interesting, as Dr. Winsten suggests, to consider the situation *ex post*, but this will be a different problem.

The problem considered in Section III (3) of the paper can be formulated as follows :

For a particular value of z find the optimal allocation, i.e. the vector

$$y = \{y_1, \ldots, y_n\}$$

which maximizes

$$\sum_{j=1}^{n} k_j u_j(y_j) \tag{1}$$

subject to

$$\sum_{j=1}^{n} y_j = \sum_{i=1}^{m} x_i.$$

The variables $x_1 \ldots x_m$ occur only in the sum $\sum x_i = z$, hence the solution will give $y_1 \ldots y_n$ as functions of z.

This is a mathematical result, which can be interpreted as a proof that 'l'argent n'a pas d'odeur'.

The general maximum is then found by taking the weighted sum of (1), using $dF(z)$ as weights.

At a stock exchange brokers seem to have considerable imagination when it comes to creating new securities. This creativity will, as Dr. Selten points out, bring the market *closer to* a Pareto optimum. The conclusion follows from the simple observation that some people are usually willing to buy the new securities. It is, however, not certain that the market will *reach* a Pareto optimum. This may require unlimited computation facilities.

Dr. Selten's 'utility paradox' may, as Professor Rosett suggests, give a realistic picture of the real world. If so, there are things between heaven and earth which are not dreamt about in economic science. Many economists have suggested, as Professor Menges did, that the utility functions should be

$$u_1 = u_1(x_1, x_2) \text{ and } u_2 = u_2(x_1, x_2).$$

This means that the utility which I assign to an allocation depends not only on my own commodity vector, but also on the commodities allocated to my neighbour. This is no paradox. Dr. Selten does, however, go one step further, and suggests that my utility should depend on how pleased my neighbour is with the allocation. How do I know this? Is it a step towards realism to assume that I have this knowledge?

The two-person zero-sum game is a special case of Selten's paradox. In this game we have to assume inter-person comparability of utility, but the solution is invariant under linear transformations of the utility scale. It seems that the 'solution' of a more general case of the Selten paradox will depend on the utility scale. I take this to mean that the paradox can exist only if we assume utility to be cardinal.

To Professor Menges I will reply that I find the Arrow–Debreu theory reasonably satisfactory. I agree that it would be desirable to relax the assumption that utilities are mutually independent. This will, however, mean that most of the classical economic theory must be sacrificed, and a new theory, based on game theory, put in its place. A Pareto-optimal set of allocations — 'imputations' — will exist also in this more general theory, and is in my opinion the natural starting-point for further studies.

Mr. Baudier suggests some interesting generalizations. I do not, however, agree with his last point. In the paper I consider a closed model. Somebody has to own the shares of the bad company in the initial situation, and somebody has to own these shares in a Pareto-optimal allocation. This will hold also as we proceed towards the limit. At the limit, where a prospect will pay zero with probability 1, the allocation of shares will obviously be undetermined.

Chapter 12

INDIVIDUAL, CO-OPERATIVE, AND COMPETITIVE PRICING OF RISKS

BY

HANS BÜHLMANN

I. RISK MANAGEMENT AND MEASURES OF RISK

IN pursuing any economic task, one is bound to find that 'success' or 'failure' are not only a consequence of the actions taken but also depend to a great degree upon uncontrollable chance factors. It therefore seems a most natural definition of 'risk' to identify it with those chance factors which may be (but not necessarily are) working against the 'economical zoon'. The terminology just used is misleading in as much as there is no absolute dichotomy between controllable and uncontrollable factors. In particular, every risk (equal uncontrollable chance factor) can still be *managed* in some way. It can be avoided, retained, reduced through preventive measures, transferred, neutralized or pooled (Williams and Heins, 1964). It is the task of risk management to choose which attitude to take towards a risk.

Decisions regarding risks can only be taken on a rational basis if there is a complete ordering of preferences among risks. I am referring to von Neumann and Morgenstern (1944), where it is shown that on the basis of this ordering one can define a real-valued operator $\mathcal{U}(X) = \int u(x)dF_X(x)$ which transforms preferences into corresponding inequalities of real numbers. Under very mild assumptions $u(x)$ turns out to be uniquely determined up to order-preserving linear transformations. I have made an attempt (Bühlmann, 1965) to define this operator $\mathcal{U}(X)$ through the notion of 'risk aversion', in which case $u(x)$ is obtained up to a linear difference function. Both the operator $\mathcal{U}(X)$ and the function $u(x)$ are usually called 'utility'.

In practice the 'premium' is the common yardstick to measure risks. This yardstick is obtained through the possibility of transferring or accepting risks against a monetary fee. Insurance companies do this professionally and have therefore developed a number of techniques to price risks. By no means do I want to discuss these techniques in this paper. The basic guideline which I want to follow is this. The 'utility' is one measure of risk depending exclusively upon the (subjective or objective) assessment of the dangers involved in the risk. The 'premium' is of course also dependent upon the assessment of the dangers inherent in the risk, but in addition is very strongly influenced by the *bargaining behaviour* of the partners involved in any possible transfer of risk. This can be illustrated in a model case, where utilities are always kept equal but where the bargaining behaviour is altered from an individualistic to a co-operative and finally to a competitive one.

II. THE MODEL

The following model case of risk exchange is the basis of our considerations:

'Two entities are willing to accept risks. A third entity wants to transfer a particular risk at best possible conditions.'

It may be more appealing intuitively if this model case is formulated in the terminology of the insurance world (without losing sight of a possible more general interpretation).

'There are two insurance companies A and B. A possible client of both wants to insure a risk X at the lowest premium.'

Bearing in mind the general outline mentioned in Section I, we define for

Company A: utility function $u_1(x)$

Company B: utility function $u_2(x)$

and state the problem to find this lowest premium:

(i) if A and B are pricing the risk only on their individual strength (individualistic bargaining behaviour);
(ii) if A and B co-operate (co-operative bargaining behaviour);
(iii) if A and B compete against each other (competitive bargaining behaviour).

It has to be borne in mind that as long as the utility function $u(x)$ only reflects the ordering of risks as perceived by the individual company, any result obtained only makes sense if it is invariant under order-preserving linear transformations of utility (see discussion in Section I). However, as soon as the utility is also used as a relative yardstick to find out the difference in preference as expressed by company A and B, invariance must only be postulated for the case where $u_1(x)$ and $u_2(x)$ are subject to *the same* (arbitrary) linear and order-preserving transformation.

Finally, in order to simplify the presentation, we shall in the following assume that the utility functions are of the form

$$u_1(x) = a + bx - cx^2 \qquad x \leqslant \frac{b}{2c} = \alpha$$

$$u_2(x) = d + ex - fx^2 \qquad x \leqslant \frac{e}{2f} = \beta,$$

where b, c, e, f are non-negative and a, d arbitrary constants.

Observe that α and β are invariant under order-preserving linear transformations of $u_1(x)$ and $u_2(x)$.

This particular choice of the type of utility function can be justified by the local properties of any utility function

$$u'(x) > 0$$
$$u''(x) < 0.$$

$u_1(x)$ and $u_2(x)$ in the above form are hence the second-order Taylor approximation of any more general utility functions. This approximation is valid if the variation in x is small in comparison to the whole range $[0, \alpha]$ or $[0, \beta]$ respectively. This latter condition, in more practical terminology, would mean that the amount exposed under any individual risk has to be small compared to the total amount of risk the company can accept.

III. THE INDIVIDUALISTIC CASE

Individualistic bargaining behaviour is called the attitude which derives the pricing principles only from its own standards. In our model case this means that A is only quoting on the basis of its utility function $u_1(x)$ and B uses $u_2(x)$ as its standard. Let us go through the arguments of company A (replacing $u_1(x)$ by $u_2(x)$ the reasoning of B is identical):

To A any price P for the risk X is acceptable as long as

$$\mathscr{U}_1(P - X) = \int u_1(P - x) dF_X(x) > u_1(o).$$

Hence we define the technical minimum premium P_1 as the solution of the equation

$$\mathscr{U}_1(P_1 - X) = u_1(o).$$

Owing to the continuity and monotone properties of any reasonable utility function this minimum premium is always uniquely defined. Assuming the particular quadratic form for $u_1(x)$ as given above we find

$$a + b \cdot E(P - X) - c \cdot E(P - X)^2 = \alpha$$

which yields

$$P_1 = E(X) + \alpha - \sqrt{\alpha^2 - \sigma^2(x)}; \quad \alpha = \frac{b}{2c}. \tag{1}$$

The price (minimum premium) concept as given by formula (1) is quite interesting. We observe:

(i) the minimum premium is invariant under order-preserving linear transformations of utility (since α has this invariance property);

(ii) the amount α has the intuitive meaning of 'capacity' of the insurance company A (i.e. a measure of the maximum total risk which the company may accept);

(iii) we have the following monotone properties of the 'loading'
$$L(\alpha, \sigma) = \alpha - \sqrt{\alpha^2 - \sigma^2}$$

with fixed $\sigma = \sigma_0$ $L(\alpha, \sigma) \downarrow$ as α increases, in particular
$$L(\infty, \sigma) = 0$$

with fixed $\alpha = \alpha_0$ $L(a_0, \sigma) \uparrow$ as σ increases, in particular
$$L(\alpha_0, \alpha_0) = \alpha_0;$$

(iv) with two risks X and Y identical and independent, we find according to formula (1), ($P_1(Z)$ = price of risk Z):

$$P_1(2X) > P_1(X + Y) > 2P_1(X). \tag{2}$$

The first part of this inequality derives from the fact that the loading increases with the standard deviation. The second part can be shown as follows:

$$P_1(X + Y) - 2P_1(X) = [\alpha - \sqrt{\alpha^2 - 2\sigma^2}] - 2[\alpha - \sqrt{\alpha^2 - \sigma^2}]$$
$$= \alpha[2\sqrt{1 - c^2} - 1 - \sqrt{1 - 2c^2}] \quad c = \frac{\sigma}{\alpha},$$

268

but $\quad H(c) = 2\sqrt{1-c^2} - 1 - \sqrt{1-2c^2}$ has the properties

$$H(o) = 0$$

$$H'(c) > 0 \text{ for } 0 \leqslant C < \sqrt{\frac{1}{2}}$$

from which follows the second part of the above inequality (2).

Remark 1: It is easy to give the proof of inequality (2) by only using the convexity property of the utility function $u(x)$, hence rendering this inequality independent of the particular choice of form of the utility function.

Remark 2: The inequality $P_1(X+Y) > 2P_1(X)$ may seem unrealistic at first sight. Is it not to be expected that with bigger 'volume' one could decrease the 'loading'? However, this inequality expresses the very realistic fact that with increasing volume the company must also increase its capacity. An increase of capacity means an increase of the constant α to $C\alpha$ $C > 1$, or — with the same effect — a reduction of the 'argument scale' x to $\frac{x}{C}$. Hence, if with doubled volume (from X to $X+Y$) the capacity is also doubled, one finds as price for $X+Y$, $2P_1\left(\frac{X+Y}{2}\right)$. The first part of inequality (2) then gives

$$P_1\left(\frac{X+Y}{2}\right) < P_1(X),$$

which expresses the intuitive concept of 'more safety in a bigger volume'.

IV. THE CO-OPERATIVE CASE

This case is characterized by the fact that A and B combine efforts to cover the risk X. Combined efforts mean that, in practice, under a possible variety of forms, each company assumes part of the risk; say, A takes γX, B takes $(1-\gamma)X$.

A sceptical reader might believe that some other form (than the proportional one!) of splitting the risk between A and B should also be considered. Even if this is true, in general we can restrict ourselves to the above proportional distribution in the assumed model case. Our safeguard is the theorem of Borch on optimal reinsurance treaties (Borch, 1960, 1961), which in the case of quadratic utility functions states that this optimal form of reinsurance is a proportional split of risks (called quota share treaty).

Co-operation between A and B can hence be regarded as the following operational behaviour:

(*a*) To split the risk X into γX for A and $(1 - \gamma)X$ for B.

(*b*) To determine γ such that the resulting total of minimum premiums quoted by A and B respectively is smallest.

We define $P_A(\gamma) = $ minimum premium acceptable to A for γX

$P_B(1 - \gamma) = $ minimum premium acceptable to B for $(1 - \gamma)X$.

The problem: Find γ such that $P(\gamma) = P_A(\gamma) + P_B(1 - \gamma)$ minimum. From Section III we take

$$P_A(\gamma) \quad = \gamma E(X) + \alpha - \sqrt{\alpha^2 - \gamma^2 \sigma^2}$$
$$P_B(1 - \gamma) = (1 - \gamma)E(X) + \beta - \sqrt{\beta^2 - (1 - \gamma)^2 \sigma^2}$$
$$P(\gamma) \quad = E(X) + (\alpha + \beta) - \sqrt{\alpha^2 - \gamma^2 \sigma^2} - \sqrt{\beta^2 - (1 - \gamma)^2 \sigma^2}$$

$P(\gamma)$ is minimum if and only if $\sqrt{\alpha^2 - \gamma^2 \sigma^2} + \sqrt{\beta^2 - (1 - \gamma)^2 \sigma^2}$ is maximum.

After some calculations one finds that this is obtained if $\gamma = \gamma_0$

$$\gamma_0 = \frac{\alpha}{\alpha + \beta} \qquad 1 - \gamma_0 = \frac{\beta}{\alpha + \beta}$$

and hence

$$P_A(\gamma_0) \quad = \gamma_0 E(X) + \alpha - \frac{\alpha}{\alpha + \beta} \sqrt{(\alpha + \beta)^2 - \sigma^2}$$

$$P_B(1 - \gamma_0) = (1 - \gamma_0)E(X) + \beta - \frac{\beta}{\alpha + \beta} \sqrt{(\alpha + \beta)^2 - \sigma^2}$$

$$P_0 = \min_\gamma P(\gamma) = E(X) + \alpha + \beta - \sqrt{(\alpha + \beta)^2 - \sigma^2}. \tag{3}$$

It follows immediately from the above formulae that

$$P_A(\gamma_0) \quad = \gamma_0 P_0$$
$$P_B(1 - \gamma_0) = (1 - \gamma_0)P_0. \tag{4}$$

These results are quite remarkable indeed.

(i) Formula (3) shows that, if co-operating, the companies A and B can be considered as one single company with 'capacity' $\alpha + \beta$.

(ii) The optimal value γ_0 found indicates that between A and B the risk should be split up proportionately to their capacities respectively.

(iii) As formulae (4) show, the split of minimum premium is to be effected in the same proportion as the risks are split; in other words the minimum rate quoted jointly by A and B for the risk X is the same as the internal rate for the split-up between A and B.

Formula (3) indicates very clearly that co-operation (as was to be expected) reduces the minimum premium below the individualistic level of both companies A and B.

Last but not least, we also observe that the above co-operative price concept P is of course not dependent upon the utility scale of either company A or B (since P_A and P_B are not). Such co-operation as envisaged is hence possible as soon as each company has established a preference ordering for all types of risks.

V. THE COMPETITIVE CASE

The two companies A and B are, in the competitive case, assumed to aim exclusively at rendering the difference between their utilities as favourable as possible without observing their own individualistic minimum premium. Operationally we state the problem as follows: A and B are playing a zero-sum game with payoff V

$$
\begin{aligned}
V(P_A, P_B) &= \mathcal{U}_A(P_A - X) - u_2(0) && \text{if } P_A < P_B \\
&= a[\mathcal{U}_A(P_A - X) - u_2(0)] \\
&\quad - b[\mathcal{U}_B(P_B - X) - u_1(0)] && \text{if } P_A = P_B (a + b = 1) \\
u_1(0) - \mathcal{U}_B(P_B - X) && \text{if } P_A > P_B,
\end{aligned}
$$

where $\mathcal{V}_A(Q - X) = \int u_1(Q - x) dF_X(x)$ and similarly for $\mathcal{V}_B(Q - X)$

$$
\begin{aligned}
P_A &= \text{premium quoted by } A \\
P_B &= \text{premium quoted by } B.
\end{aligned}
$$

It is easily seen that the above payoff function results as the difference of utility in the case where the person who wants to insure the risk X always chooses the company charging the lower price and in the case of equal prices chooses A with probability a, B with probability b. $\mathcal{U}_A(Q - X)$ is of course monotone and continuous in Q, similarly for $\mathcal{U}_B(Q - X)$. Company A wants the payoff to be as big as possible, company B has the opposite interest.

One then finds:

For company A:

$$\inf_{P_B} V(P_A, P_B) = \min \; [\mathscr{U}_A(P_A - X) - u_2(\text{o}), \; u_1(\text{o}) - \mathscr{U}_B(P_A - X)]$$

and

$$\sup_{P_A} \inf_{P_B} V(P_A, P_B) = V(P, P), \text{ where } P \text{ satisfies the equation (5)}$$

$$\mathscr{U}_A(P - X) + \mathscr{U}_B(P - X) = u_1(\text{o}) + u_2(\text{o}). \tag{5}$$

For company B:

$$\sup_{P_A} V(P_A, P_B) = \max \; [\mathscr{U}_A(P_B - X) - u_2(\text{o}), \; u_1(\text{o}) - \mathscr{U}_B(P_B - X)]$$

$$\inf_{P_B} \sup_{P_A} V(P_A, P_B) = V(P, P), \text{ where } P \text{ again satisfies the equation (5).}$$

The game thus has a pure value; the strategy to be chosen by both companies is to quote the same price (competition price) P satisfying equation (5). This price can be characterized by the property that one competitor is as much 'above' his utility-null-level as the other one is 'below' it. If, for example, $P_1 < P_2$ (in the individualistic case), it immediately follows that $P_1 \leqslant P \leqslant P_2$. Using the particular form of

$$u_1(x) = a + bx - cx^2$$
$$u_2(x) = d + ex - fx^2$$

we further find

$$P = E(X) + \frac{b+e}{2(c+f)} - \sqrt{\left(\frac{b+e}{2(c+f)}\right)^2 - \sigma^2(X)}. \tag{6}$$

The 'competitive' price can hence be again regarded as if it were an 'individualistic' price quoted by a company with 'capacity' Γ.

$$\Gamma = \frac{b+e}{2(c+f)} = \alpha\left(\frac{c}{c+f}\right) + \beta\left(\frac{f}{c+f}\right). \tag{7}$$

Hence this 'competitive capacity' Γ lies (as could have already been inferred from the inequality $P_1 \leqslant P \leqslant P_2$) between the individualistic capacities α and β. As a matter of fact it is obtained as the weighted mean of α and β. Regarding the 'weights', one observes that in the special case of quadratic utility functions the concept of 'risk aversion', as defined in Bühlmann (1965), yields

for company A: risk aversion $A(x, h) = c, h^2$,
for company B: risk aversion $A(x, h) = f, h^2$ independent upon x.

The weights used in formula (7) are hence exactly the 'risk aversions'; in other words Γ will be closer to the capacity of the company with higher risk aversion.

It must be observed that in the competitive case our definition of price and capacity is no longer invariant under arbitrary monotone linear transformations. In the special quadratic case the ratio $\dfrac{c}{f}$ is essential and in the general case invariance only holds if both utility scales of A and B are subject to the same monotone linear transformation. Intuitively this is clear, since we need to compare (in the competitive case) the utility attached by company A to a particular risk with the assessment made by company B for the same risk. Expressed in terms of risk aversions this intuitive statement translates into: One must know how much more (or less) company A is 'afraid of risks' than company B. (Only if individual linear transformations degenerate into a pure change of origin may they be different without altering the competitive price.)

VI. CONCLUSION

We have found in our model case:

company A with utility function $u_1(x) = a + bx - cx^2$ $\qquad x \leqslant \dfrac{b}{2c} = \alpha$

company B with utility function $u_2(x) = d + ex - fx^2$ $\qquad x \leqslant \dfrac{e}{2f} = \beta$

that the price depends upon the bargaining behaviour of the two partners, namely as follows:

(i) In all cases the formula

$P(X) = E(X) + Z - \sqrt{Z^2 - \sigma^2(X)}$, gives the price for the risk X (Z can be interpreted as 'capacity').

(ii) The particular results can be summarized:

	Price	Capacity
Individualistic		
Company A	P_1	α
Company B	P_2	β
Co-operative	$P \leqslant \min(P_1, P_2)$	$\alpha + \beta$
Competitive	$P_1 \leqslant P_0 \leqslant P_2$	$\dfrac{c\alpha + f\beta}{c + f}$

c, f are proportional
to the risk aversion

REFERENCES

Borch, K. (1960), 'Reciprocal Reinsurance Treaties seen as a Two-Person Cooperative Game', *Skandinavisk Aktuarietidskrift*, pp. 29–58.

— (1961), 'Reciprocal Reinsurance Treaties', *ASTIN Bulletin*, 1, pp. 170–91.

Bühlmann, H. (1965), 'Die Risikoaversion als Interpretation und Konstruktionsbasis der Utilitätskurve', *Metrika*, pp. 38–48.

Neumann, J. von, and Morgenstern, O. (1944), *Theory of Games and Economic Behavior*, Princeton Univ. Press.

Williams, A., Jr., and Heins, R. (1964), *Risk Management and Insurance*, New York : McGraw-Hill.

———

DISCUSSION OF THE PAPER BY
PROFESSOR BÜHLMANN

Professor Rosett : Professor Bühlmann examines three possible charges that any insurance company might ask for assuming a risk. The first is a price that will leave a single insurer indifferent between assuming the risk and not assuming it. The second is the price that will leave two co-operating companies indifferent between assuming the risk and not assuming it, given that they are going to divide up the risk so as to make this price a minimum. The third is the price that will be obtained if two companies regard themselves as engaged in a certain zero-sum game. He designates these three cases the 'individualistic' case, the 'co-operative' case, and the 'competitive' case.

Record of Discussion

Given these three means of evaluating risk, Professor Bühlmann obtains the following results :

(1) The charge for the assumption of risk decreases as the capacity of the insurer increases and increases as the variance of the risk increases.

(2) The charge for assuming two identical risks simultaneously is greater if they are perfectly correlated than if they are independent.

(3) Two co-operating companies will behave like one company with the combined capacity of the two companies and they will divide the risk between them in the same proportion as their capacities.

(4) Competing companies will charge a price that lies between their 'individualistic' prices and they will behave as though they have a combined capacity that is a convex combination of their individual capacities.

The first three results seem perfectly sensible, and they are probably exactly the same as the results that would be derived from a model of the sort economists usually work with. In any case they are more or less consistent with my understanding of the way in which insurance companies would actually behave. It is not the conclusions, but the assumptions from which they are derived, that I find odd. Economists usually assume that every competitive firm behaves as though it were the only firm in the market, and that it behaves in such a way as to maximize its profit. Unfortunately for the firm the operation of the market is such as to make this profit zero. The firm is then indifferent between operating at its profit-maximizing level and not operating at all.

Since an insurance company deals in risk, an analagous description of a competitive insurance company might be that it behaves as though it were the only insurance company, that it operates in such a way as to maximize its expected utility, and that market forces will lead to situations in which the firm is indifferent between selling the amount of insurance that maximizes its utility and not selling any insurance at all.

But this is very different from the model treated by Professor Bühlmann. His firm leaps directly to the equilibrium state. It chooses to behave in such a way as to make itself indifferent between selling and not selling an insurance policy even though it could behave in such a way as to increase its utility. Here is Professor Bühlmann's first case : The probability distribution $F(X)$ represents some risk to be evaluated. The premium is P so that if

$$U = X - \alpha X^2,$$

$$U(P-X) = \int_{-\infty}^{+\infty} [(P-X) - \alpha(P-X)^2] dF(X)$$

$$= P - \bar{X} - \alpha P^2 + 2\alpha P \bar{X} - \alpha \bar{X}^2 - \alpha \sigma^2.$$

Setting this equal to zero and solving for P we obtain

$$P = \bar{X} + \frac{1}{2\alpha} - \sqrt{\left(\frac{1}{2\alpha}\right)^2 - \sigma^2}.$$

In my representation of Professor Bühlmann's model I have normalized so as to reduce the number of parameters. The quantity $\alpha/2$, that is the value of x for which U is a maximum, Professor Bühlmann calls the firm's capacity.

If the insurance company charges this price for assuming the risk $F(X)$, it will be indifferent between assuming the risk and not assuming it. This is the minimum premium at which the insurance company will be willing to assume the risk $F(X)$. But this is not the price that would prevail in an ordinary market. In a competitive market P would be fixed and the insurance company would choose to sell some number of policies, N, so as to maximize its utility. In a monopolistic market the company would be faced with a demand curve for policies that would relate N to P. In this case it would choose N and P so as to maximize utility.

In the competitive case we would write

$$U(NP - \Sigma X) = \int_{-\infty}^{+\infty} [(NP - \Sigma X) - \alpha(NP - \Sigma X)^2 dF(\Sigma X)],$$

where we assume that the risks are all independent.

This becomes

$$\begin{aligned} U(NP - \Sigma X) &= NP - N\bar{X} - \alpha(N^2 P^2 - 2N^2 P\bar{X} + N\sigma^2 + N^2\bar{X}^2) \\ &= N(P - \bar{X}) - \alpha N^2(P - \bar{X})^2 - \alpha N\sigma^2. \end{aligned}$$

Taking the derivative with respect to N and setting it equal to zero we get

$$\frac{dU}{dN} = (P - \bar{X}) - 2\alpha N(P - \bar{X})^2 - \alpha\sigma^2 = 0,$$

so that

$$N = \frac{(P - \bar{X}) - \alpha\sigma^2}{2\alpha(P - \bar{X})^2}.$$

Now suppose the market operates to reduce P until the maximum of U with respect to N is zero. Substituting for N and solving for P we get

$$P = \bar{X} + \alpha\sigma^2,$$

which seems sensible enough. The market will establish an equilibrium price at which the expected claim, $\bar{X}$, is charged, plus a risk premium, $\alpha\sigma^2$. If the quadratic function is a good approximation of the utility function, σ^2 must be very small relative to $\frac{1}{2\alpha}$, and since α must also be very small, the product, $\alpha\sigma^2$, must be very small. This is consistent with the idea that an insurance company, in accepting a large number of independent risks, can calculate almost exactly what the average claim will be and is therefore running a much smaller risk per policy than the insured would be running without insurance.

But sensible as this result seems, it is nonsense. Note that the condition for market equilibrium,

$$P = \bar{X} + \alpha\sigma^2,$$

implies that the numerator of the expression that determines the utility-maximizing value of N,

$$N = \frac{(P - \bar{X}) - \alpha\sigma^2}{2\alpha(P - \bar{X})^2},$$

is zero. This anomaly is exactly analogous to the case of a competitive firm whose average cost is everywhere increasing. In equilibrium its profit-maximizing output is zero. In the present case this can be repaired by assuming a fixed cost, K. We then get

$$N = \frac{(P - \bar{X})(1 + 2\alpha K) - \alpha\sigma^2}{2\alpha(P - \bar{X})^2}$$

and

$$P = \bar{X} + \frac{\alpha\sigma^2 + 2K(1 + \alpha K)}{1 + 2\alpha K}.$$

Once again the charge for the assumption of risk is small. Of course this charge is also small in the expression that Professor Bühlmann derived,

$$P = \bar{X} + \frac{1}{2\alpha} - \sqrt{\left(\frac{1}{2\alpha}\right)^2 - \sigma^2},$$

provided σ^2 is very small relative to $\frac{1}{2\alpha}$ as it should, in fact, be. The difference between the two expressions for the price is that one flows from usual assumptions about the operation of a market and the other does not.

Although I have not done so I believe that results analogous to those of Professor Bühlmann's that I have numbered (1), (2), and (3) could be derived from the price expression I have obtained. I believe also that the remarks I have made so far apply to both the 'individualistic' case of Professor Bühlmann and the 'co-operative' case.

The 'competitive' case is very strange. Professor Bühlmann has described something very different from what is usually called competition by economists. He assumes that if two companies are competing they are engaged in a zero-sum game in which each company enjoys its own utility minus the utility of the other. From this he derives the result that they will choose a price between their two individualistic prices. I shall resort to a diagram to illustrate the argument.

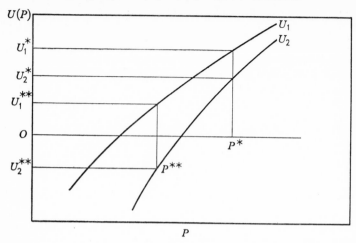

Suppose company 1 charges the price P^* and that is below company 2's price. Company 1's utility is U_1^* and company 2's utility is $-U_1^*$, since it is assumed that as 1's is lower, 1 will sell all the insurance. But by lowering its price to just below P^*, company 2 can increase its utility from $-U_1^*$ to a little less than U_2^*, which is greater. It will therefore do so. Now company 1 will have a similar incentive to lower its price. This will continue until the price P^{**} is reached at which $U_1^{**} = -U_2^{**}$. At that point company 1 will enjoy utility $aU_1^{**} + bU_2^{**} = U_1^{**}$ where $a+b=1$ and $0 < a < 1$, since it is assumed that when the two prices are equal, 1 will sell a proportion of the policies equal to a. Company 2 will enjoy utility $-U_1^{**}$. If either company changes its price its utility will decrease. All this follows from the assumptions, but why is it reasonable to assume that insurance companies suffer doubly from the loss of a sale, once when they lose it and once when someone else gets it?

There may be some context in which this 'competitive' case is of interest. As I said at the beginning of my remarks, they may be based on my ignorance rather than on any fault of Professor Bühlmann's paper. If this is so I hope that Professor Bühlmann and the rest of you will forgive me for wasting your time.

Professor Hester: Professor Bühlmann has studied the minimum premium which will be demanded by one and/or two life-insurance companies operating under three hypothetical market arrangements: (1) independence, where a firm is not cognizant of the existence of a rival, (2) cooperation, where the two firms operate together in order to minimize premiums, and (3) competition, where a firm tries to maximize the difference between his utility and that of his rival.

In his argument, he assumes the existence of a utility function of wealth which is unique up to an order-preserving linear transformation. Throughout the paper he uses a quadratic approximation to this utility function which is assumed to have a positive first derivative and a negative second derivative over the domain of definition.

I find his answers to his rather narrowly stated questions to be both plausible and accurate ; consequently my comments concern exposition and the relevance of his results for future research. My first complaint is with the concept of 'capacity' which Professor Bühlmann introduces. It disturbs me that this measure is a function of a parameter of a quadratic approximation to a utility function. Ordinarily one identifies capacity with net worth or total assets or some other balance-sheet variable ; his use of the word in an entirely different sense serves no good purpose.

Second, in order to obtain unique solutions, Professor Bühlmann has resorted to the ever-convenient quadratic utility function. This practice has become very widespread since Markowitz and Tobin exploited it successfully in the late 1950s. While unique solutions may be quite pleasant to report, they can be misleading if assumptions necessary for their derivation are unrealistic. This seems to be the case in the paper under discussion ; it is far from obvious that utility functions of insurance firms depart appreciably from linearity. As these functions approach linearity, Bühlmann's measure of capacity approaches infinity, his prices approach the expected value of gambles, and his analysis of co-operative and competitive markets degenerates towards indeterminacy. Some empirical evidence about the shape of the utility function should be reported.

Even in a world with no risk aversion one imagines that firms would succeed in dividing the market. Costs and revenues of lending and insuring must be introduced if a more general analysis of market shares is to result.

Professor Bühlmann has introduced some ingenious assumptions for solving the two-firm allocation problem with collusion. Ordinarily co-operation or collusion between two firms does not lead the firms to pass all benefits on to consumers in the form of lowered premiums. What features of the present model lead to this remarkable result ? Economics exist which are a function of industry size. So long as firms are risk-averters, pooling of risks lowers the opportunity cost of insuring. However, pooling is likely to lead simultaneously to monopolistic premium pricing ; Professor Bühlmann has assumed this possibility away. It would be very interesting to see gogopoly models combined with Professor Bühlmann's model and industry-size arguments.

The last section of his paper, which reports results of the two-firm competitive model, is not interesting to me. Reducing the problem to a zero-sum game seems very artificial. Firms maximize some function of their own earnings, not the difference between their expected utility and someone else's. Analysis of three- or four-firm markets would be most difficult with the zero-sum-game approach.

On the whole this paper reports some interesting results about the existence of industry-size economies arising in insurance when firms are risk-averse. It suffers from the author's failure to augment this analysis with elements from more conventional theories of firms and markets.

Mr. Bessière : (1) If we maintain the interpretation of your quadratic expression for utility as a local approximation of any utility function, the coefficient α which you call capacity appears as a characteristic of the local curve. This possible interpretation of α makes some of the objections which were submitted purposeless. However, it then seems to me that the word 'capacity' is misleading and that it would be preferable to choose another one, such as 'sensibility'.

(2) I think the 'co-operative' attitude which you define makes evident one of the main advantages people have from living in society : sharing a common risk.

Dr. Selten : Professor Bühlmann has been attacked because of his 'competitive case'. Maybe the behavioural assumption underlying this case is not so unrealistic as it seems to be at first glance. Managers of insurance companies could well be interested in a high relative standing of their own company within the world of insurance companies. Such motives may even serve the goal of long-run profit maximization, if the relative standing of a firm is correlated to its future business opportunities.

Professor Gordon : In Professor Bühlmann's model the random variable is the outcome of the particular policy. In this case the parameters of the utility function depend on the company's reserves and the outstanding policies. Hence the parameters change with each policy issued.

It might be more useful to have utility a function of total wealth with the existing utility (before selling the policy under consideration) depending upon the various possible values of wealth under the existing policy and reserves. The price of the policy that leaves utility unchanged may then be computed for successive policies without changing the parameters of the utility function.

Perhaps a more useful approach to the problem of our insurance company is to take the price of a policy as given by the market and to ask how much insurance it should sell at that price. The amount will depend on the utility function, wealth and outstanding policies. If the company cannot sell all the insurance it wants, the problem is how much advertising, or what price reduction, to offer.

Professor Bühlmann : I feel there have occurred some misunderstandings during the discussion. These may have arisen because some discussants seem to see the paper mainly from the angle of conventional economic theory and in particular from the point of view of the theory of the firm and the market.

The paper is intended to deal with 'forms of behaviour' in a 'risk laboratory' situation. Since — as Professor Borch mentions in one of his papers — the insurance world can provide us best with this laboratory, the terminology used is that of insurance, in particular that of the actuarial literature.

(1) *The Concept of Minimum Premium*

In a world of risk any 'rational' enterprise is assuming or transferring risks if *after this operation* utilities have not decreased compared with the situation *before the operation.*

Any situation which cannot be further improved through such operations is Pareto-optimal. It is easy to see that as long as each enterprise is accepting or transferring risks at least (respectively at most) at the minimum premium level as defined in my paper, then a Pareto-optimal solution is reached.

This minimum premium concept plays quite an important role in the insurance industry. Its main advantage lies in the fact that it is *independent* of the number and utilities of the other enterprises which are working in the same market and hence provides a universal yardstick for measuring the way into a Pareto-optimal situation.

On the other hand I realize that (as Professor Rosett is pointing out) economists usually assume that *market forces* tend to establish a price such that the firm is indifferent between selling its product and not selling at all. My *co-operative* case would indeed indicate that through the device of co-insurance such a price might be reached. It is interesting that whereas usually the forces of *competition* are made responsible for the reaching of such an equilibrium, it is exactly the forces of *co-operation* (sharing and/or reinsuring) which in a world of risks establishes this equilibrium. This might account for some difference in terminology.

In the paper I have avoided saying whether this minimum premium would be a *net premium* (i.e. not compensating the company for the costs of handling the risk) or *gross premium* (i.e. including a 'cost loading'). This point is immaterial when the *one-risk* case is treated. Professor Rosett finds in his discussion that the cost of handling becomes an essential factor when *many risks* are involved. This is certainly true but applies to a deterministic world (without risk) as well and hence offers nothing new. I am therefore thinking of the minimum premium (as is usual in the actuarial literature) as a *net premium.*

(2) *The Three Cases of Bargaining Behaviour*

I realize that the three cases as presented in the paper are idealizations. One might imagine that the actual cases of bargaining behaviour are some kind of weighted means of these extreme cases.

I also note that among my idealizations the 'competitive' case has stirred the greatest controversy as to its intuitive appeal. It is my belief that this form of bargaining behaviour — namely that of seeking to maximize the difference of utility over the opponent's — is a very plausible one. Whether it actually occurs in real life can only be decided on the basis of experiments. Fouraker and Siegel treat this form in their book on bargaining behaviour. They term it 'rivalistic' and also report on some very interesting experiments where people actually behave 'rivalistically'.

(3) 'Capacity'

Insurance companies ask for loadings (besides 'cost loadings') above the expected value of a risk in order to compensate for their risk aversion. There is, however, a point on their utility curve where no loading — however big — can induce them to accept a risk. This point I have termed the 'capacity' of the company. I agree that in this sense the capacity depends strongly on the form of the utility curve and I therefore understand Professor Hester's doubt as to the validity of this concept in the case of a quadratic approximation. I think that this doubt can be overcome if the notion 'capacity' which I wanted to introduce is entirely seen as a local approximation property depending on the curvature of the utility tunction in the region of approximation. However, it might be advisable fo replace the expression 'capacity' by some other term.

(4) General Background of the Paper

I say in the introduction to the paper that I intend it to be an attempt to describe possible types of 'behaviour under risk'. I am sorry if the paper was interpreted as applying to insurance exclusively (or — as Professor Rosett's discussion seems to imply — even to life insurance only). The reason for this regret is my feeling that we need a multitude of *theoretically possible* types of behaviour under risk which can serve as the basis for experiments on *actual behaviour*. I intended to give three models of *theoretical behaviour*.

Chapter 13

MINIMAX BEHAVIOUR AND PRICE PREDICTION

BY

EDMOND BAUDIER

THIS study is an attempt to describe an abstract economic universe whose agents are confronted with the problem of price prediction. The consequences of a particular behaviour in relation to this problem are examined. The behavioural hypothesis chosen is that each agent believes the unknown price pattern to be determined by an adversary whose aim is to minimize the agent's objective function. It follows that the forecasts made may differ from one agent to another. The purpose of the study is to show that the reactions generated by this method of prediction tend towards market equilibrium and price stability.

I. GENERAL DESCRIPTION OF THE MODEL

The main characteristics assumed are those of a resource-allocation model.

(1) Time-units

Discrete periods of time $1, 2, \ldots, t, \ldots$, are considered. They may extend to infinity, or as far as the economic horizon $\hat{t}$.

(2) Goods, Services, and Categories of Labour

It is assumed that the number of goods and services $(1, 2, \ldots, j, \ldots, \hat{j})$ is finite. In some paragraphs the labour inputs supplied by certain agents are considered as relating to either goods or services. There are $\hat{s}$ labour inputs, ranging over $1, 2, \ldots, s, \ldots, \hat{s}$.

An important point to observe is that the goods, services, and classes of labour considered are taken to be independent of time, i.e. the subscripts j and s do not implicitly define a value of time. This point may be specified further. The markets in which agents exchange these goods, services, and labour function during all the time-periods. They are all assumed to be spot markets, i.e. the purchase or sale of a good or service implies delivery of the good, or supply of the service, within the period during which the bargain was made. It will be shown that this assumption does not diminish the generality of the model.

The capital letters X and Y will be used to designate the quantities of goods and services and the volume of labour inputs respectively. They may carry subscripts defining the nature of the good, the class of labour input, the economic agent involved, and the period considered. When a forecast value is referred to, the symbols used are $\bar{X}$ and $\bar{Y}$.

(3) *Prices*

The prices attached to each good, service, or category of labour input are denoted by lower-case letters x (good or service) or y (labour). These letters may carry subscripts defining the good and the period considered.

(i) A system of prices for the period t defines the conditions of exchange of goods and services in the markets of that period. This system is defined, subject to a constant multiplicative factor, so that the need to consider the rise or fall of prices between one period and another does not arise.

(ii) It is assumed that market prices are the same for all agents. It will be seen that behaviour is influenced not only by prices but also by what economic agents believe will happen to prices, and these forecasts will differ among agents. In this study, only forecasts made in the first period will be taken into account. They are designated as $\bar{x}$ or $\bar{y}$, so that $\bar{x}_{i,\,j,\,t}$ denotes the forecast made in the first period by the economic agent i of what the price of good j will be in period t.

(4) *Consumers*

There are assumed to be $\hat{\imath}$ consumers, designated by a subscript from 1 to $\hat{\imath}$. Each consumer is characterized by a full pre-ordering with respect to the set of possible patterns of consumption goods (or, where the distinction is made, consumption of goods and supply of labour). Any one such pattern is a vector with $[(\hat{\jmath}+\hat{s})\hat{t}]$ components. The pre-ordering which characterizes consumers can be represented as a continuous, concave utility function of the $[(\hat{\jmath}+\hat{s})\hat{t}]$ variables.

Further, each consumer is assumed to have a certain (positive or negative) initial net wealth, subject to conditions to be defined below.

(5) Producers

There are $\hat{r}$ producers designated by the subscript r, which may vary from 1 to $\hat{r}$. A production pattern is a vector (X, Y) defining the production and consumption of goods and services and the volume of labour inputs for all periods. As in the case of the consumer, this vector has $[(\hat{\jmath}+\hat{s})\hat{t}]$ components. A given producer is characterized by the vector field Γr of the corresponding vector space. A production pattern is possible if the associated vector belongs to Γr, impossible otherwise. Γr is assumed to be convex and closed.

Each producer is assumed to have a (positive or negative) initial debt, subject to conditions which will be specified below.

(6) Saving and Financing

Since the system described above allows for spot-market transactions only, no procedure for arbitrage between the present and the future has been defined. Such a procedure is the essential feature of the model, and will now be introduced. In order to define their time-arbitrage, economic agents are assumed to use what will be called *indexed bonds*, or more briefly, bonds. These bonds have no equivalent in the real world, but have in many respects the qualities associated with interest-bearing securities. Their two main characteristics are:

(i) They do not entitle the holder to a voice in the management of the issuing firm (or of the assets of the issuing economic agent).

(ii) The income payments to which they give rise are systematically indexed to the price level obtaining at the due date.

This second characteristic should perhaps be amplified further. In each period, as well as the markets in goods and services, markets are assumed to exist for the $\hat{n}$ classes of bonds. $Q_{(n)}$ designates a quantity of bonds of category n, with n variable between 1 and $\hat{n}$. $Q_{(i, n, t)}$ denotes the quantity of bonds of category n bought by consumer i at period t, and $Q_{(r, n, t)}$ the quantity of bonds of category n issued by producer r at period t. It should be noted that Q can be negative. To each class of bonds there corresponds a price $q_{(n, t)}$, similar to the prices attached to goods, services, and labour. When underlined, these symbols relate to the forecasts of the corresponding value made in the first period.

The rights of the buyers of these bonds, and the obligations of the sellers, may now be defined. They consist of a transfer of value in favour of the buyer charged against the assets of the seller or issuer. These transfers (i) are proportional to the number of bonds, and (ii) occur in the period following that in which the purchase or sale took place, and (iii) are proportional to the level of an index of market prices ruling during the period in which the transfer occurs. This index is calculated as a linear combination of price readings. It is further specified that the price of the bonds themselves can and should be incorporated in the index formula. The weights given to the prices in the index formula are independent of quantities consumed, so that the level of prices and incomes is defined, subject to a constant multiplicative factor.

To illustrate the nature of the indexed bonds defined above, we consider a situation in which the holder of a bond desires to apply it to the purchase of goods and services. Here two components of the value of the bonds can be identified, namely, the transfer which may be imputed to the index formula, and the transfer reflecting the price of the bonds themselves. Clearly, the first component procures the quantities of goods and services indicated by the weighting coefficients in the index formula, and is independent of the state of the market. Its properties may therefore be considered as those of the interest coupon. By contrast, the second component only procures the quantity of goods and services indicated by the ratio of the price of goods to the price of bonds, a ratio which depends on market conditions.

The analogy between interest-bearing securities and indexed bonds is almost complete if the following definition of an interest-bearing security is adopted:

A debenture issued at a certain date t provides for a transfer of value in favour of its holder at date $t+1$. This transfer contains two components:

(i) A first component, the coupon, whose real value is indexed on the price of money (i.e. it entitles the holder to a fixed amount of money).

(ii) A second component, indexed on the value of the bond itself.

The notation to be used in connection with the index formula will now be specified. A single bond of class n bought in period $t-1$ gives rise to a transfer of value in period t whose amount is

$$R_{(n,\,t)} = \sum_j A_{(n,\,j)} x_{(j,\,t)} - \sum_s B_{(n,\,s)} y_{(s,\,t)} + \sum_m C_{(n,\,m)} q_{(m,\,t)},$$

where j denotes a good or service, s a category of labour, and n and m classes of bonds. The coefficients of the matrices are generally, but not necessarily, positive. If the quantities of labour inputs are considered as corresponding to goods and services, the transfer may be written

$$R_{(n,\,t)} = \sum_j A_{(n,\,j)} x_{(j,\,t)} + \sum_m C_{(n,\,m)} q_{(m,\,t)}$$

or, in a condensed form:

$$R = Ax - By + Cq \qquad \text{and} \qquad R = Ax + Cq.$$

Here A, B, C are matrices of dimensions $(\hat{n}, \hat{j})$, $(\hat{n}, \hat{s})$, and $(\hat{n}, \hat{n})$, and x, y, and q are vectors of dimension $\hat{j}$, $\hat{s}$, and $\hat{n}$ respectively.

The bonds may be expressed in terms of specific goods (e.g. those produced by the issuing enterprise). Again, the case in which the matrix C is diagonal or quasi-diagonal is one where the properties of the indexed bond approach those of an interest-bearing security. To see this, consider a group of classes of securities redeemable at 100 currency units and bearing a 5-unit interest coupon, and assume that at any given moment their prices depend on the length of their life to maturity. Let these prices be $p(1)$, $p(2)$, ..., $p(n)$. If an economic agent purchases a security of category n at a given date, he will in the following period be entitled to a transfer in his favour equal to

$$5M + p(n-1),$$

where M is the price of money and $p(n-1)$ the value of a security of category $n-1$. This formula is completely analogous to those applicable in the case of indexed bonds; there is no fundamental difference between the two cases. The index formula is based on the prices of goods and services, and excludes the price of money, which is not taken into account in the present model. By contrast, the value of an interest-bearing security is determined by the price of money, and is independent of prices of goods and services.

(7) *Budgetary Constraints*

A particularly significant element in the subsequent discussion is the examination of the budgetary equations of economic agents.

(i) *Consumer* i. This consumer's outlays consist of his purchases of goods and services and of indexed bonds. His income consists of wages, the income from bonds purchased in the preceding period, and any share of business profits to which he is entitled.

$$\left.\begin{array}{ll}
\sum_j X_{(i,\,j,\,t)}x_{(i,\,t)} & \text{Purchases of goods and services} \\[4pt]
\sum_n Q_{(i,\,n,\,t)}q_{(n,\,t)} & \text{Purchases of indexed bonds}
\end{array}\right\} \text{outlays}$$

$$\left.\begin{array}{ll}
\sum_s Y_{(i,\,s,\,t)}y_{(s,\,t)} & \text{Wages} \\[4pt]
\sum_n Q_{(i,\,n,\,t-1)}R_{(n,\,t)} & \text{Income from indexed bonds}
\end{array}\right\} \text{income,}$$

with

$$R_{(n,\,t)} = \sum_j A_{(n,\,j)}x_{(j,\,t)} - \sum_s B_{(n,\,s)}y_{(s,\,t)} + \sum_m C_{(n,\,m)}q_{(m,\,t)} + \sum_r \theta_{(i,\,r,\,t)}P_{(r,\,t)}.$$

$P_{(r,\,t)}$ stands for the profits made by producer r in period t (defined in the section below) and $\theta_{(i,\,r,\,t)}$ denotes the share of consumer i in the profits of producer r at period t.

The last term calls for some comment. For $t>1$, the value of $P_{(r,\,t)}$ requires to be forecast. This forecast will simply be $P_{(r,\,t)}=0$, so that the term need not be written for $t>1$. By contrast, for $t=1$, P is known, as is the system of prices of the first period, and therefore will not be forecast. It must be allowed for to ensure the existence of equilibrium if producers' profits in the first period are not zero. The budgetary equation for period t can then be written shortly as:

$$(EB1)\quad X_{(i,\,t)}x_{(t)} + Q_{(i,\,t)}q_{(t)} - Y_{(i,\,t)}y_{(t)} \leqslant Q_{(i,\,t-1)}\{\bar{A}x_{(t)} - By_{(t)} + Cq_{(t)}\}.$$

The terms in the left-hand member are scalar products. Those on the right are bilinear forms with respect to the components of $Q_{(i,\,t-1)}$ on the one hand and those of $x_{(t)}$, $y_{(t)}$, and $q_{(t)}$ on the other.

This budgetary equation can be cast in another form in which the price coefficients are shown explicitly:

$$(EB2)\quad \{\bar{X}_{(i,\,t)} - Q_{(i,\,t-1)}A\}x_{(t)} + \{Q_{(i,\,t)} - Q_{(i,\,t-1)}C\}q_{(t)} - \{\bar{Y}_{(i,\,t)} - Q_{(i,\,t-1)}B\}y_t \leqslant 0.$$

Considerable use will be made of this form in Section II.

The first period restraint is written

$$X_{(i,\,1)}x_{(1)} + Q_{(i,\,1)}q_{(1)} - Y_{(i,\,1)}y_{(1)} \leqslant$$
$$Q_{(i,\,0)}[Ax_{(1)} - By_{(1)} + Cq_{(1)}] + R_{(i,\,r,\,1)}P_{(r,\,1)},$$

with $Q_{(i,\,o)}$ denoting the consumer's initial net asset position.

The hypothesis concerning the consumer's behaviour can now be specified. The discussion below is in terms of the first period, but can be adapted to other periods.

The utility function is to be maximized subject to the following constraints:

(a) the budgetary constraint of the first period, for which prices and profits are known;

(b) the budgetary constraints of other periods for which prices and profits are unknown and are assumed to be so determined as to minimize satisfaction (whence it follows immediately that profits are zero).

The consumer's behaviour can then be written mathematically as follows. First maximize utility S subject to all the budgetary constraints:

$$\text{Max } S(X_{(1)},\, Y_{(1)};\, \ldots;\, X_{(t)},\, Y_{(t)};\, \ldots)$$

$X\ Y$ Budgetary constraints satisfied.

This result depends on prices, and in many cases may not be bounded. The next step is then to choose the system of prices for the periods $t = 2, \ldots, t$ which minimizes the function (the system of prices for the first period is known, and need not therefore be estimated)

$$\text{Min} \qquad \{\text{Max } S(X_{(t)},\, Y_{(t)})\}$$
$$\underset{\substack{x_{(t)}y_{(t)}q_{(t)} \\ t>1}}{} \qquad \underset{\substack{X_{(t)}\,Y_{(t)} \text{ subject to budgetary constraints.} \\ t\geqslant 1}}{}$$

(ii) *Producer* r. Income arises from the sale of goods and services and the issue of bonds. Outlays correspond to purchases of goods and services (intermediate consumption), wages, and transfers of value arising from the issue of bonds in the preceding period:

$\sum_{j} X_{(r,\,j,\,t)} x_{(j,\,t)}$ — Sales less intermediate consumption ⎫

$\sum_{n} Q_{(r,\,n,\,t)} q_{(n,\,t)}$ — Borrowing (issue or sale of indexed bonds) ⎬ Income

$\sum_{s} Y_{(r,\,s,\,t)} y_{(s,\,t)}$ — Wages ⎫

$\sum_{n} Q_{(r,\,n,\,t-1)} R_{(n,\,t)}$ — Redemption of earlier borrowing ⎬ Outlay

with

$$R_{(n,\,t)} = \sum_{j} A_{(n,\,t)} x_{(j,\,t)} - \sum_{s} B_{(n,\,s)} y_{(s,\,t)} + \sum_{m} C_{(n,\,m)} q_{(m,\,t)}.$$

Profits of the period t are written as follows:

$$P_{(r,\,t)} = X_{(r,\,t)}x_{(t)} + Q_{(r,\,t)}q_{(t)} - Y_{(r,\,t)}y_{(t)} - Q_{(r,\,t-1)}[Ax_{(t)} - By_{(t)} + Cq_{(t)}]$$

As for the consumer, the cash surplus can be written in an alternative form:

$$P_{(r,\,t)} = \{\bar{X}_{(r,\,t)} - Q_{(r,\,t-1)}A\}x_{(t)} + \{Q_{(r,\,t)} - Q_{(r,\,t-1)}C\}q_t - \{Y_{(r,\,t)} - Q_{(r,\,t-1)}B\}y_t.$$

In the first form, the profits of the initial period are written as:

$$P_{(r,\,1)} = X_{(r,\,1)}x_{(1)} + Q_{(r,\,1)}q_{(1)} - Y_{(r,\,1)}y_{(1)} - Q_{(r,\,0)}\{Ax_{(1)} - By_{(1)} + Cq_{(1)}\},$$

where $Q_{(r,\,0)}$ indicates the initial indebtedness of the producer.

The assumption concerning producers' behaviour to be used in the subsequent discussion is as follows:

The producer will select a production pattern which maximizes the profits of the first period (*for which prices are known*). This maximization is subject to the following constraints:

(*a*) The production pattern belongs to the vector field Γr defined above (production set).

(*b*) Profits in periods other than the first should be positive, given that the prices which define these profits *are unknown*, and are assumed to be so determined as to minimize the profits of the first period.

This behaviour can be described as follows:

As a first step, maximize the profits of period 1, subject to the constraints:

$$\text{Max } (x_{(1)}X_{(1)} + y_{(1)}Y_{(1)} + q_{(1)}Q_{(1)})$$
$$X_{(t)}Y_{(t)} \epsilon \Gamma_{(r)} \quad \text{and} \quad P_{(r,\,t)} \geqslant 0.$$
$$t > 1$$

Again, however, this result depends on prices and may not be bounded. The next step is again to choose the system of prices in periods $t = 2, \ldots \hat{t}$ which minimizes the function:

$$\underset{\substack{x_{(t)}y_{(t)}q_{(t)} \\ t > 1}}{\text{Min}} \quad \underset{\substack{X_{(t)}T_{(t)} \epsilon \Gamma \surd \\ t \geqslant 1}}{\text{Max }} (x_{(1)}X_{(1)} - y_{(1)}Y_{(1)} + q_{(1)}Q_{(1)})$$
$$\quad X_{(t)}T_{(t)} \epsilon \Gamma \surd \quad \text{and} \quad P_{(r,\,t)} \geqslant 0.$$

II. EQUILIBRIUM OF INDIVIDUAL ECONOMIC AGENTS

This section consists of two parts, one dealing with the consumer, the other relating to the producer. Given the analogies between the two cases, the detailed discussion of the first part will also apply in the second case.

(1) *The Case of the Consumer*

We shall first consider a special case, and then generalize it. Throughout the section, the subscript i which denotes the consumer is omitted, as the discussion relates to a single consumer.

Case 1. A single good, a single class of bonds, no labour categories. The form of the utility function is then

$$S = \sum_{t=1}^{\infty} \alpha^t \ \log X_{(t)} \qquad (\alpha < 1).$$

The budgetary equation of the first period is written

$$X_{(1)}x_{(1)} + Q_{(1)}q_{(1)} \leqslant Q_{(0)}\{Ax_{(1)} + Cq_{(1)}\},$$

where A and C are scalars.

The following sequence of calculation will be adopted:

(*a*) Define a family of consumption patterns which are budgetarily feasible for all forecasts of prices, ruling beyond the first period.

(*b*) Choose, within this family, the pattern which maximizes the utility function subject to the first-period budgetary constraint (the prices of this period are known).

(*c*) Show that there exists a development of prices such that any pattern preferable to that shown is budgetarily non-feasible. Since there is no labour, the condition:

$$X_{(t)} = AQ_{(t-1)} \quad Q_{(t)} = CQ_{(t-1)}$$

implies that the budgetary equation of period t is satisfied for all systems of prices.

Each pattern in this family is defined by its initial value $Q_{(1)}$, so that

$$\bar{X}_{(t)} = ACt^{-2}Q_{(1)} \quad \bar{Q}_{(t)} = Ct^{-1}Q_{(1)}.$$

$Q_{(1)}$ and $X_{(1)}$ are now chosen so as to maximize S while satisfying the first budgetary constraint

$$S = \alpha \log X_{(1)} + \sum_{t=2}^{\infty} \alpha t \log [AC^{t-2} Q_1].$$

The sought-for maximum is then

$$S = \alpha \log X_{(1)} + \alpha^2 \frac{\log Q_{(1)}}{1 - \alpha},$$

subject to the constraint

$$X_{(1)} x_{(1)} + Q_{(1)} q_{(1)} = Q_0 \{ A x_{(1)} + C q_{(1)} \}$$

and it is easily found that

$$\left.\begin{aligned}
X_{(1)} &= (1 - \alpha) \left(A + C \left\{ \frac{q_{(1)}}{x_{(1)}} \right\} \right) Q_{(0)} \\[2mm]
Q_{(1)} &= \alpha \left(A \left\{ \frac{x_1}{q_1} \right\} + C \right) Q_0
\end{aligned}\right\} \tag{1}$$

$$\left.\begin{aligned}
X_{(t)} &= AC^{t-2} Q_{(1)} \\
Q_{(t)} &= C^{t-1} Q_{(1)}.
\end{aligned}\right\} \tag{2}$$

The third element of the sequence is more delicate. It involves several phases:

(i) definition of a family of price developments;
(ii) taking account of (i), the deduction of two particular consequences of the budgetary equations;
(iii) maximization of the utility function subject to the two consequences defined at (ii);
(iv) complete determination of the system of prices by minimizing the utility function when the system belongs to the family (i), and comparison with the preceding result.

These phases are examined below.

(i) The sum of all the budgetary equations for all periods, except the first, is formed:

$$\sum_{t=3}^{\infty} (X_{(t)} x_{(t)} + Q_{(t)} q_{(t)}) \leqslant \sum_{t=2}^{\infty} Q_{(t-1)} [A x_{(t)} + C q_{(t)}].$$

The coefficient of $Q_{(t)}$ is then shown explicitly:

$$\sum_{t=2}^{\infty} X_{(t)} x_{(t)} + \sum_{t=2}^{\infty} Q_{(t)} \{ q_{(t)} - A x_{(t+1)} - C q_{(t+1)} \} \leqslant Q_{(1)} \{ A x_{(2)} + C q_{(2)} \}.$$

The following relation:

$$q_{(t)} = Ax_{(t+1)} + Cq_{(t+1)} \tag{3}$$

is then introduced for $t > 1$. This relation contributes to the definition of the family mentioned above. It has a simple economic interpretation: $q_{(t)}$, the purchase price of a bond in period t, is equal to the value transfer to which it gives rise in the following period.

It is important to take account of relation (3) in calculating $q_{(2)}$. Multiplying by C^t and summing from 2 to T, we find:

$$C^2 q_{(2)} = A \sum_{t=2}^{T} C^t x_{(t+1)} + C^{T+1} q_{(T+1)}.$$

The family described above may be defined by assuming that

$$\lim_{T \to \infty} C^{T+1} q_{(T+1)} = 0.$$

It follows that

$$q_{(2)} = A \sum_{t=3}^{\infty} x_{(t)} C^{t-3}.$$

(ii) The two consequences are:

The budgetary equation of the first period

$$X_{(1)} x_{(1)} + Q_{(1)} q_{(1)} \leqslant Q_{(0)} \{ Ax_{(1)} + Cq_{(1)} \}$$

and the sum of the other equations, which, taking account of the preceding relations, is

$$\sum_{t=2}^{\infty} X_{(t)} x_{(t)} \leqslant Q_{(1)} A \sum_{t=2}^{\infty} x_{(t)} C^{t-2}. \tag{4}$$

(iii) Taking λ and μ as Lagrange multipliers of the two constraints, we find by differentiating:

with respect to $X_{(1)}$: $X_{(1)} x_{(1)} = \dfrac{\alpha}{\lambda}$; $\tag{5}$

with respect to $X_{(t)}$: $X_{(t)} x_{(t)} = \dfrac{\alpha^t}{\lambda}$; $\tag{6}$

with respect to $Q_{(1)}$: $-\lambda q_{(1)} + \mu \sum_{t=2}^{\infty} x_{(t)} C^{t-2}. \tag{7}$

(iv) If the value of $X_t x_t$ obtained in (6) is carried into (4), the value of μ is found as

$$\frac{1}{\mu} = \frac{1-\alpha}{\alpha^2} Q_{(1)} \sum_{t=2}^{t=\infty} x_t C^{t-2} \tag{8}$$

and, combining (7) and (8):

$$\lambda = \frac{\alpha 2}{1-\alpha} \frac{1}{Q_{(1)}q_{(1)}} \tag{9}$$

From (9) and (5)

$$X_{(1)}x_{(1)} = \frac{\alpha}{\lambda} = \frac{1-\alpha}{\alpha}Q_{(1)}q_{(1)}. \tag{10}$$

Inserting the value of $X_{(t)}$ from (6) into the utility function leads to

$$\alpha \log X_{(1)} + \sum_{t=2}^{\infty} \alpha^t [\log \alpha^t - \log x^{(t)} - \log \mu],$$

and this expression is to be minimized with respect to the prices $x_{(t)}$. Omitting the constant, which is irrelevant to this operation, the expression to be minimized is

$$-\sum_{t=2}^{\infty} 2\alpha^t \log x_{(t)} - \frac{\alpha^2}{1-\alpha} \log \mu.$$

Deriving with respect to $x_{(t)}$, and equating to zero, we obtain

$$-\frac{\alpha t}{x_{(t)}} - \frac{\alpha^2}{1-\alpha} \frac{1}{\mu} \frac{\partial \mu}{\partial x_{(t)}} = 0, \tag{11}$$

or, taking account of (8),

$$x_{(t)} = \frac{\alpha^t}{\mu Q_{(1)}AC^{t-2}}, \tag{12}$$

we find:

$$X_{(t)} = Q_{(1)}AC^{t-2}, \tag{2 bis}$$

i.e. relation (2) above.

The preceding reasoning may be recapitulated as follows. A family of budgetarily feasible patterns under all price systems (except for the first period) was defined, and the pattern maximizing the utility function was selected from this family. In a second calculation, a specific development of the system of prices was assumed, and the utility function maximized on the assumption that this development was known. The confrontation of the results of the two procedures shows that both lead to identification of the same pattern.

If the behavioural hypothesis postulated at the outset is accepted, this is the pattern which will be adopted by the economic agent.

Case 2: A single good, two classes of bonds, with the index formulae:

Class 1 bonds $A_{(1)}x_{(t)} + C_{(1, 1)}q_{(1, t)} + C_{(1, 2)}q_{(2, t)}$

Class 2 bonds $A_{(2)}x_{(t)} + C_{(2, 1)}q_{(1, t)} + C_{(2, 2)}q_{(2, t)}.$

The budgetary equation of period t is satisfied whatever the subsequent development of prices if, and only if:

$$X_{(t)} = A_{(1)}Q_{(1, t-1)} + A_2 Q_{(2, t-1)}$$

$$Q_{(1, t)} = C_{(1, 1)}Q_{(1, t-1)} + C_{(1, 2)}Q_{(2, t-1)}$$

$$Q_{(2, t)} = C_{(2, 1)}Q_{(1, t-1)} + C_{(2, 2)}Q_{(2, t-1)}.$$

These recurrence equations define x_t, $Q_{(1, t)}$ and $Q_{(2, t)}$ as functions of $Q_{(1, 1)}$ and $Q_{(2, 1)}$, the quantities of bonds purchased in the initial period. If the values of X_t are substituted into S, a function of $X_{(1)}$, $Q_{(1, 1)}$,and $Q_{(2, 1)}$ is obtained which is to be maximized subject to the budgetary constraint of the first period.

The optimization calculation will not be undertaken here, as it is a great deal more complex than in the case of a single bond and offers nothing really new.

Case 3.   A single good, and an infinite number of categories of bonds.

The income accruing to the holder of a bond of category n purchased in period $t - 1$ is

$$R_{(n, t)} = q_{(n-1, t)},$$

where, in the notation already used, $q_{(n-1, t)}$ is the price in period t of a bond of category $n - 1$. Following this through to $n = 1$, the income is

$$R_{(1, t)} = x_{(t)},$$

where $x_{(t)}$ denotes the price in period t of the single good which exists.

This leads to the budgetary equation for period t:

$$X_{(t)}x_{(t)} + \sum_{n=1}^{\infty} Q_{(n, t)}q_{(n, t)} \leqslant Q_{(1, t-1)}x_{(t)} + \sum_{n=2}^{\infty} Q_{(n, t-1)}q_{(n-1, t)}.$$

This equation can be used to develop the recurrence relations which ensure that the resulting patterns are budgetarily feasible whatever the system of prices.

By the same procedure as in the previous two cases, we obtain:

$$X_1 x_1 + \sum_{n=1}^{\infty} X_{n+1} q_{n, 1} \leqslant Q_{(1, 0)}x_{(1)} + \sum_{n=2}^{\infty} Q_{(n, 0)}q_{(n-1 1,)},$$

and we are faced with the most classic of problems, namely, to maximize $S(X_{(1)}, X_{(2)}, \ldots, X_{(t)}, \ldots)$ subject to the single constraint above, but in which $q_{(n,\,1)}$ plays the role of the price of the good X available in the period $n+1$.

The summation of the budgetary equations for $t \geqslant 1$ results in

$$\sum_{t=1}^{\infty} X_{(t)} x_{(t)} + \sum_{t=1}^{\infty} \sum_{n=1}^{\infty} Q_{(n,\,t)} q_{(n,\,t)}$$

$$\leqslant \sum_{t=1}^{\infty} Q_{(1,\,t-1)} x_{(t)} + \sum_{t=1}^{\infty} \sum_{n=2}^{\infty} Q_{(n,\,t-1)} q_{(n-1,\,t)}$$

or, showing the coefficients of $Q_{(n,\,t)}$ explicitly,

$$\sum_{t=1} X_{(t)} x_{(t)} + \sum_{t=2} \sum_{n=2} Q_{(n,\,t)} [q_{(n,\,t)} - q_{(n-1)(t+1)}]$$

$$+ \sum_{t=1} Q_{(1,\,t)} q_{(1,\,t)} - x_{(t+1)} \leqslant Q_{(1,\,0)} x_{(1)} + \sum_{n=2} Q_{(n,\,0)} q_{(n-1,\,1)},$$

whence

$$q_{(n,\,t)} = q_{(n-1,\,t+1)}$$

$$q_{(1,\,t)} = x_{(t+1)},$$

and consequently

$$q_{(n,\,1)} = q_{(1,\,n)} = x_{(n+1)}.$$

The following considerations throw further light on these results.

(*a*) The two equalities

$$Q_{(t-1,\,1)} = X_{(t)}$$

$$q_{(n,\,1)} = x_{(n+1)}$$

imply that the consumer considers his purchase in period 1 of a bond of category $t-1$ as equivalent to purchase of the corresponding goods falling available in period t. The market for bonds of category n in period 1 is no more or less than a forward market for the single good envisaged, with delivery in period $n+1$. This implies that no purpose is served by incorporating forward markets in goods into the model. The bond markets fulfil this function.

This remark holds whatever the number of goods. In this case the categories of bonds must be defined in terms of two indexes, one specifying the date when the bond is redeemable in goods, the other the nature of the good in which payment is to be made.

(*b*) Two important conclusions follow from the assumptions made.

(1) The pattern established in the first period is considered as definitive. The economic agent envisages neither the resale of what

he has bought or the repurchase of what he has sold. This is equivalent to rejecting any notion of speculation.

(2) The system of prices is invariant from one period to the next. This statement should be interpreted appropriately. The prices to be compared are those of a given good, available at the same date. Since

$$q_{(n, t)} = q_{(n-1, t+1)} = q_{(1, t+n-1)} = x_{(n+t)},$$

all the prices in the equalities are those of the single good envisaged where the date of availability is $(n+t)$; $q_{(n, t)}$ is the price of the good when the transaction occurs in period t, $q_{(n-1, t+1)}$ the price when it occurs in $t+1$, etc.

These two consequences are not mutually dependent. The assumption that the pattern of the first period is considered as definitive does not entrain the invariance of prices as a necessary consequence, nor does it follow from the fact that prices are considered as independent of the date of the transaction that the pattern of the first period must be considered as definitive.

Case 4. The sole restrictive hypothesis is the assumption of a finite economic horizon beyond which economic activity is assumed to cease.

The method of exposition used above may be recalled here:

(i) In the first period, the consumer selects $X_{(1)} Y_{(1)}$, and $Q_{(1)}$ to satisfy the first-period budgetary constraint.

(ii) With $Q_{(1)}$ chosen there is a pattern $\bar{X}_{(t)}$, $\bar{Y}_{(t)} (2 \leqslant t \leqslant \hat{t})$ which can always be realized whatever the future development of prices.

(iii) To this pattern there corresponds a level of utility S.

(iv) There is a selection of X, Y, and Q, such that a system of price vectors $x_{(t)}$ $y_{(t)}$ $q_{(t)}$ $(t > 2)$ can be found which renders impossible any pattern for which $S > \bar{S}$.

The budgetary equation of period (t) is now

$$X_{(t)} x_{(t)} - Y_{(t)} y_{(t)} + Q_{(t)} q_{(t)} \leqslant Q_{(t-1)} [A x_{(t)} - B y_{(t)} + C q_{(t)}].$$

The terms on the left-hand side are scalar–vector products. A, B, and C being matrices, the expressions on the right are linear forms with respect to the components of $Q_{(t-1)}$, on the one hand, and the components of $x_{(t)}$, $y_{(t)}$, and $q_{(t)}$.

As before, we find:

$$X_{(t)} = Q_{(t-1)}A$$
$$Y_{(t)} = Q_{(t-1)}B$$
$$Q_{(t)} = Q_{(t-1)}C$$

are necessarily feasible for all systems of future prices.

These equations can be resolved applying the initial conditions

$$X_{(t)} = Q_{(1)}C^{t-2}A$$
$$Y_{(t)} = Q_{(1)}C^{t-2}B$$
$$Q_{(t)} = Q_{(1)}C^{t-1}.$$

Substitution of these values into the function S leads to

$$U(X_{(1)}, Y_{(1)}, Q) = S(X_{(1)}, Y_{(1)}; \ Q_{(1)}A, Q_{(1)}B, \ldots Q_{(1)}C^{t-2}A,$$
$$Q_{(1)}C^{t-2}B, \ldots),$$

and U is to be maximized subject to the constraint

$$X_{(1)}x_{(1)} + Y_{(1)}y_{(1)} + q_{(1)}Q_{(1)} \leqslant Q_{(0)}[Ax_{(1)} - By_{(1)} + Cq_{(1)}] + \sum_r \theta_{(r,\,1)}P_{(r,\,1)}.$$

This gives the consumption pattern, which will be denoted as $\bar{P}$, and to which there corresponds a level of utility which will be denoted as $\bar{S}$.

The last phase is carried out in the same way as earlier. The budgetary equations are summed over $t > 1$:

$$\sum_{t=2}^{t=t} X_{(t)}x_{(t)} - Y_{(t)}y_{(t)} + Q_{(t)}q_{(t)} \leqslant \sum_{t=1}^{t=t} Q_{(t)}[Ax_{(t+1)} - By_{(t+1)} + Cq_{(t+1)}],$$

and we find:

$$C^2 q_2 = \sum_{t=2}^{t=t-1} (C^t Ax_{(t+1)} - C^t By_{(t+1)} + C^{t+1}q_{(t+1)}).$$

It is assumed that prices beyond the economic horizon are zero. Using these results, the budgetary inequalities are given by the following system of inequalities, in which $Q_{(1)}$ has its optimal value $\check{Q}_{(1)}$.

$$X_{(1)}x_{(1)} - Y_{(1)}y_{(1)} \leqslant Q_0[Ax_{(1)} - By_{(1)} + Cq_{(1)}] - \check{Q}_{(1)}q_{(1)} + \sum_r \theta_{(r,\,1)}P_{(r,\,1)}$$
$$-\bar{X}_{(t)} + X_{(t)} \quad \leqslant 0$$

$$t > 1$$

$$\bar{Y}_{(t)} - Y_{(t)} \quad \leqslant 0$$
$$-S[\bar{X}_{(1)}, \bar{Y}_{(1)}; \ldots; \ x_{(t)}, y_{(t)} \ldots] + S[\bar{X}_{(1)}, \bar{Y}_{(1)}; \ldots; \ \bar{x}_{(t)}, \bar{Y}_{(t)} \ldots] \leqslant 0.$$

The symbols $\bar{X}_{(1)}$ and $\bar{Y}_{(1)}$ denote the optimalized values of $X_{(1)}$ and $Y_{(1)}$.

This system of inequalities cannot be solved. If $X_{(t)} = \bar{X}_{(t)}$ and $Y_{(t)} = \bar{Y}_{(t)}$, the first and last inequalities are incompatible; for otherwise $X_{(1)} = \bar{X}_{(1)}$ and $Y_{(1)} = \bar{Y}_{(1)}$ would not be optimum, in contradiction to what has been said. Not to maintain the assumption that $X_{(t)} = \bar{X}_{(t)}$ and $Y_{(t)} = \bar{Y}_{(t)}$ only renders the situation worse if the second and third inequalities are to be respected, for to diminish the quantities consumed while increasing labour input can only diminish the utility function, or at best leave it unchanged.

On the other hand, the system of inequalities

$$X_{(1)}x_{(1)} - Y_{(1)}y_{(1)} \leqslant Q_{(o)}[Ax_{(1)} - By_{(1)} + Cq_{(1)}] - \bar{Q}_{(1)}q_{(1)}$$

$$+ \sum_r \theta_{(r,1)}P_{(r,1)} - \bar{X}_{(t)} + X_t \qquad \leqslant 0$$

$$+ \bar{Y}_{(t)} - Y_t \qquad \leqslant 0$$

admits of the solution

$$X_{(1)} = \bar{X}_{(1)}, \; Y_{(1)} = \bar{Y}_{(1)}$$
$$X_{(t)} = \bar{X}_{(t)}, \; Y_{(t)} = \bar{Y}_{(t)},$$

for, if the function S is assumed concave, the conditions in which the Farkas–Minkowski theorem [1] is applicable are respected. According to this theorem, there are positive or zero, but not all zero, numbers λ, $\bar{x}_{(t)}$ $\bar{y}_{(t)}$ $(t>2)$, such that

$$S[\bar{X}_{(1)}Y_{(1)}; \ldots; X_{(t)}, Y_{(t)} \ldots] - \bar{S} + [Q_o[Ax_{(1)} - By_{(1)} + Cq_{(1)}]$$

$$+ \sum_r \theta_{(r,1)}P_{(r,1)} - \bar{Q}_{(1)}q_{(1)} - X_{(1)}x_{(1)} + Y_{(1)}y_{(1)}]$$

$$+ \sum_{t=2}^{t=i} \bar{x}_{(t)}[\bar{X}_t - X_{(t)}] - \bar{y}_{(t)}[\bar{Y}_{(t)} - Y_{(t)}] \leqslant 0.$$

But this inequality translates the fact that the utility function cannot be improved if the budgetary constraint for the first period and the sum of the budgetary equations for the remaining periods, for which $x_{(t)}$ and $y_{(t)}$ have been respectively taken as equal to $\bar{x}_{(t)}$ and $\bar{y}_{(t)}$, are both to be satisfied simultaneously.

(2) *The Case of the Producer*

We shall examine only the case corresponding to Case 4 above.

---

[1] See C. Berge and A. Ghoulia Houri, *Programmes, jeux et réseaux de transport*, Paris, Dunod, 1962, p. 66.

There are a finite number of goods, of categories of labour and of periods. The economic horizon is at $\hat{t}$, and economic life is assumed to cease thereafter.

Using the notation already employed above, the profits for period t are

$$P_{(t)} = X_{(t)}x_{(t)} - Y_{(t)}y_{(t)} + Q_{(t)}q_{(t)} - Q_{(t-1)}[Ax_{(t)} - By_{(t)} + Cq_{(t)}].$$

This expression is certainly non-negative if

$$X_{(t)} = Q_{(t-1)}A$$
$$Y_{(t)} = Q_{(t-1)}B$$
$$Q_{(t)} = Q_{(t-1)}C.$$

These relations define a set of production patterns whose intersection with the production set should not be empty. This will be assumed.

Within this intersection, the producer will choose the production pattern which maximizes profits in the first period. The definition of the production pattern to be selected is then complete.

It remains to be shown that there indeed exists a system of prices (for $t > 1$) for which no higher profit can be made. The same procedure as employed earlier leads to

$$q_2 = \sum_{t=2}^{t=\hat{t}-1} C^{t-2}[Ax_{(t+1)} - By_{(t+1)}],$$

and, making use of the definition of $\bar{X}_{(t)}$ and $\bar{Y}_t$,

$$P = \sum_{t=2}^{t=\hat{t}} [X_{(t)} - \bar{X}_{(t)}]x_t - \sum_{t=2}^{t=\hat{t}} [Y_t - \bar{Y}_t]y_t.$$

The symbols $\bar{X}_{(1)}$ and $\bar{Y}_{(1)}$ will be used to designate the values of X_1 and Y_1 which correspond to the optimum defined earlier.

The production set may be represented by a concave function F, and is defined by

$$F(X_{(1)}, Y_{(1)}; \ldots; X_{(t)}, Y_{(t)}; \ldots) \geqslant 0.$$

The following system of inequalities

$$
\begin{aligned}
&X_{(1)}x_{(1)} - Y_{(1)}y_{(1)} \quad \bar{X}_{(1)}x_{(1)} - \bar{Y}_{(1)}y_{(1)} \\
&F(X_{(1)}, Y_{(1)}; \ldots; X_{(t)}Y_{(t)}; \ldots) \quad 0 \\
&\left.\begin{aligned} X_{(t)} - \bar{X}_{(t)} &\geqslant 0 \\ \bar{Y}_{(t)} - Y_{(t)} &\geqslant 0 \end{aligned}\right\} t > 1
\end{aligned}
$$

has no solution.

On the other hand, the relations

$$F(X_{(1)}, Y_{(1)}; \ldots; X_{(t)} Y_{(t)}; \ldots) > 0$$
$$\left. \begin{array}{l} X_{(t)} - \bar{X}_{(t)} \geqslant 0 \\ \bar{Y}_{(t)} - Y_{(t)} \geqslant 0 \end{array} \right\} t > 1$$

are compatible. Taking first $X_{(t)} = \bar{X}_{(t)} Y_{(t)} = \bar{Y}_{(t)} X_1 = \bar{X}_{(1)}$ and $Y_{(1)} = \bar{Y}_{(1)}$, the last two inequalities are verified and $F = 0$. A decline in the variables $X_{(1)}$ or an increase in the variables $Y_{(1)}$ results in a positive value of F (i.e. brings the pattern within the range of possible production patterns).

Then, applying the Farkas–Minkowski theorem cited above, one can show that there exist non-negative numbers λ, $\bar{x}_{(t)}$ $\bar{y}_{(t)}$ $(t\ 1)$ so that the inequalities are satisfied.

This implies that any higher level of profits in the first period is incompatible with the condition of non-negative future profits.

III. THE GENERAL EQUILIBRIUM OF THE ECONOMY

The existence of individual equilibria for all economic agents does not imply the existence of an overall equilibrium.

The situation in the first period is:

Each consumer attempts to maximize a utility function

$$U(X_{(1)}, Y_{(1)}, Q_{(1)}) = S[X_{(1)}, Y_{(1)}; \ldots; Q_{(1)}C^{t-2}A, Q_{(1)}C^{t-2}B; \ldots],$$

subject to the first-period budgetary constraint.

Each producer attempts to maximize his profits:

$$X_{(1)}x_{(1)} - Y_{(1)}y_{(1)} + Q_{(1)}q_{(1)} - Q_{(0)}[Ax_{(1)} - By_{(1)} + Cq_{(1)}]$$

subject to the constraint

$$F[X_{(1)}, Y_{(1)}; \ldots; Q_{(1)}C^{t-2}A, Q_{(1)}C^{t-2}B; \ldots] \geqslant 0.$$

Here again we find the classic case in which it is sought to determine a system of prices in a purely static framework.

If the preference systems and the production sets satisfy appropriate hypotheses of convexity[1] there exists a system of prices which will implement the equilibrium of supply and demand for goods and services and for indexed bonds.

There is therefore a system of prices such that

---

[1] See G. Debreu, *Theory of Value*, New York, Wiley (1959).

$$\sum_{i=1}^{i=\hat{\imath}} X_{(i,\ j,\ 1)} = \sum_{r=1}^{r=\hat{r}} X_{(r,\ j,\ 1)} \tag{1}$$

$$\sum_{i=1}^{i=\hat{\imath}} Y_{(i,\ s,\ 1)} = \sum_{r=1}^{r=\hat{r}} Y_{(r,\ s,\ 1)} \tag{2}$$

$$\sum_{i=1}^{i=\hat{\imath}} Q_{(i,\ n,\ 1)} = \sum_{r=1}^{r=\hat{r}} Q_{(r,\ n,\ 1)}. \tag{3}$$

This market equilibrium of the first period has as a consequence the compatibility of the patterns for the subsequent period, for

$$X_{(i,\ t)} = Q_{(i,\ 1)} C^{t-2} A$$
$$X_{(r,\ t)} = Q_{(r,\ 1)} C^{t-2} A$$

and

$$\sum_i X_{(i,\ t)} = \sum_i Q_{(i,\ 1)} C^{t-2} A$$
$$\sum_i X_{(r,\ t)} = \sum_r Q_{(r,\ 1)} C^{t-2} A,$$

while, as a result of the equality (3) above,

$$\sum_i X_{(i,\ t)} = \sum_r X_{(r,\ t)}$$

with similar equations in $Y_{(i,\ t)}$ and $Y_{(r,\ t)}$, and of $Q_{(i,\ t)}$ and $Q_{(r,\ t)}$.

Thus there is an equilibrium position of the economy under study. But is it an optimum equilibrium? In general, the answer to this question must be in the negative, except for the case in which the variety of indexed bonds is such that each category corresponds to a future good becoming available at a fixed date.

The proof that the result is not optimal is that better results will in general be obtained in the periods following the first. The relation which defines the predicted consumption of goods,

$$\bar{X}_{(t)} = Q_{(1)} C^{t-2} A,$$

includes $\hat{\jmath}(\hat{t}-1)$ variables which specify the quantities of the different goods, and $\hat{n}$ variables specifying the quantity of bonds. When $\hat{\jmath}(\hat{t}-1) > n$, there are restrictions on the choice of the $X_{(t)}$, although they may be eased to some extent when there are distinct markets for the different goods.

It may be noted that $\hat{\jmath}(\hat{t}-1)$ is the number of forward markets which would have to exist in the first period for a Pareto optimum to be obtained. Limiting oneself to $\hat{n}$ markets will doubtless facilitate the organization, but it involves abandoning the Pareto optimum.

At the same time, it is also possible to consider that the need for a large number of markets represents a major obstacle on the way to a Pareto optimum. The reduction of the number of markets in practice can be thought of as an attempt to obtain an optimal situation when the organization of markets represents an essential constraint.

Clearly, the choice of the formulae for bond indexation is an essential factor in the attempt to reach an optimum. This choice may be considered as falling in the purview of planning techniques.

It should also be observed that while each agent's price predictions are personal, certain relations between these predictions are common to all agents. These are

$$q_{(t)} = Ax_{(t+1)} - By_{(t+1)} + Cq_{(t+1)}.$$

Thus despite the individualistic nature of price forecasting, the existence of markets for indexed bonds implies certain relations between these forecasts.

IV. CONCLUSIONS

Before stating the conclusions, it is well to specify that the model makes no pretence of corresponding to reality. Despite the analogies drawn between real interest-bearing securities and our 'indexed bonds', there is no question of their identity. It is even less possible to claim that economic agents in real life make price predictions based on a minimax strategy.

In the absence of any claim that the model corresponds to the real world, what then is its interest?

It may first be noted that our assumption about price forecasting involves the same behaviour as the assumption of perfect competition. In the latter case, the economic agent proceeds to maximize his objective function (utility or profit), treating the system of prices as a datum. The agent who predicts prices using our hypothesis arrives at the same result. If he does not maximize his objective function, he obtains a less favourable outcome, beyond which he cannot hope to go — for there is always a system of prices which can prevent him from doing so, and he is led to postulate that this will be the ruling system.

The economic agent is therefore induced to forsake speculation completely, i.e. to give up all hope of making profit by purchasing products with the intention of reselling them. Naturally, this is tantamount to suggesting that money serves no useful purpose, since any money received in the course of the exchanges undertaken is not definitively acquired, but merely leads to the performance of further exchange transactions. Thus, money could be introduced into the model only at the cost of abandoning its main hypothesis.

To clarify the situation described, it is of interest again to take up some of the ideas already presented, and discuss them in marginalist terminology. The proportionality of prices and marginal utilities results from the maximization of the utility function subject to a budgetary constraint. The assumption concerning price prediction leads to the same relation, but with a different interpretation. It is known that exchange is always advantageous, since there is no compulsion to exchange. The advantage may be more or less important: it is a function of the system of prices. The least advantage is available when no exchanges occur, that is, in the case where there is proportionality between prices and the marginal utility of the quantities possessed. This proportionality defines prices as functions of quantity, whereas in the classical case it is quantity which is defined as a function of price. In this case the economic agent is in the same position as if he had no access to the market.

The standpoint adopted in our model is a compromise between the two positions. The economic agent has full access to the market for present goods, but the indexed bonds offer only partial access to the markets for future goods. This is the root of the non-optimal nature of the solution. The model is in an intermediate position between the real world in which forward markets (other than for money) exist only sporadically, and the extended theory of equilibrium as expounded by Debreu in his *Theory of Value*, where forward markets are assumed to exist for all goods.

The pessimism concerning price developments which has been postulated may appear unjustified in practice. The same holds for the assumptions which imply absolute confidence that all engagements undertaken will be duly honoured. In other words, the total distrust existing prior to signature of a contract is equalled only by the degree of confidence which replaces it immediately afterwards. In practice the shift between these two attitudes is much more gradual.

The economic agent is confronted in the first instance with markets whose ruling prices may change before he has made any purchase. In a subsequent stage he agrees with the seller on both the price and quantity involved in the transaction, and finally he accepts delivery.

As this process is carried forward, his opinion of the probability of obtaining what he desires evolves gradually. In the model proposed here, by contrast, the economic agent holds no hope as long as there has been no transaction, but once the transaction has been undertaken, he completely ignores any possibility that the seller may fail to deliver.

——

DISCUSSION OF THE PAPER BY MR. BAUDIER

Dr. Thore : I am happy to be the first to get the opportunity to congratulate Mr. Baudier on a most stimulating and original paper. In his paper Mr. Baudier outlines a general equilibrium model under uncertainty, and his model has no doubt a great deal of attraction in that he avoids the rather monstrous assumptions of Debreu of infinitely many future markets. The economic agents of Mr. Baudier's model have only partial access to the markets for future goods, and this access is provided by means of a very particular kind of indexed bond, which plays a crucial role in Mr. Baudier's analysis. Very roughly speaking, these bonds can be compared with ordinary interest-bearing securities, issued by firms and bought by households. Mr. Baudier's indexed bonds are no doubt a very particular construct, but they do simulate the properties of financial assets in the real world, and I think it is beyond question that Mr. Baudier has managed to acquire a good deal of increased realism in his model in this respect as compared with Debreu's wildly dreamed-up world. Mr. Baudier has to pay a very high price for this increased realism, however. For one thing, and I shall return to this point, Mr. Baudier's world is pretty unrealistic in some other regards, because he is forced to introduce some very specific assumptions. For another thing, Mr. Baudier's equilibrium is of course in general not a Pareto optimum.

Every agent in Mr. Baudier's world is supposed to play a kind of game against nature, and the agent is supposed to believe that this 'nature' will be unfriendly enough to announce future prices which will minimize his utility level (for households) or his profits (for firms). Using Mr. Baudier's notation, every household is expected to be forced down to the utility level

$$\underset{\substack{\text{all future} \\ \text{prices}}}{\text{Min}} \quad \underset{\substack{X, Y \text{ subject to} \\ \text{budget constraints}}}{\text{Max}} \quad S(X, Y) \qquad (1)$$

and similarly for firms.

Then there is a theorem, and the theorem says that the solution to (1), say (X_1, Y_1), could alternatively have been obtained along the following route of reasoning : The household maximizes utility S subject to the budget constraints and further subject to the added condition that these budget constraints hold *identically* for all possible future prices. In symbols

Max $S(X, Y)$ (2)
X, Y subject to budget constraints, and further that
these constraints hold *identically* for all future prices.

The theorem says that the solution to (2), say (X_2, Y_2), is equal to (X_1, Y_1). And there is a corresponding theorem for firms.

The modest criticism that I should now like to direct against Mr. Baudier's treatment is that there is a good deal of repetition in his paper, and the mentioned theorem is proved not less than four times, at increasing levels of complication. I wonder if it would not be possible to prove the theorem right away, once and for all, on a quite general level. I shall try to outline the main steps of such a proof. In order to do that, I propose to consider a kind of intermediary procedure, viz. :

Value   Max $S(X, Y)$ (3)
independent of X, Y subject to
future prices in   budget constraints.
an infinitesimal
region.

That is, the household is first supposed to maximize utility in the ordinary manner, and thus there would be one solution for every possible expected constellation of future prices. Then pick that particular solution for which in an infinitesimal region around it one would obtain identically the same utility level, independent of future prices. That is, rather than, as in (2), narrowing down the solution to be chosen subject to budget constraints which are independent of future prices, one would in (3) first maximize utility without this special condition being imposed, and then afterwards pick that solution for which the obtained maximized utility level were in an infinitesimal region around it independent of future prices. It is clear that the order of the two mentioned procedures is immaterial, and hence the solution to (3), say (X_3, Y_3), must coincide with (X_2, Y_2). But it must also coincide with (X_1, Y_1), because the value of

Max $S(X, Y)$
X, Y subject to
budget constraints

considered as a multi-dimensional surface in the space of all future prices can at any point be replaced by the value of a tangent plane, and hence the constellation of future prices for which this value is minimum coincides with the constellation of future prices for which this value is independent of prices in an infinitesimal region around it.

Let me now discuss the implications of this theorem. It has very strong implications. It means that both consumers and producers will choose very particular, and very specific, plans for the future. In order to describe this, the characteristics of Mr. Baudier's indexed bonds must be remembered. Essentially, the coupons on these bonds can be thought of as consisting of two parts, one positive part indexed on the prices of goods, and one negative part indexed on the wage level. The plans of the consumers and of the producers can then be described as follows : The consumers plan to be a kind of *rentier* in all future periods, consuming in each period an amount exactly equal to the goods part of the coupon on their holdings of bonds. And they plan to offer a supply of labour in each period exactly equal to the labour part of the coupon on their holdings of bonds. The producers, for their part, plan to produce in each future period an amount of goods equal to the goods part of the coupon they have to pay on their outstanding debt (of issued bonds). And they plan to demand a quantity of labour in each future period equal to the labour part of the coupon they have to pay on the same outstanding debt. Surely Mr. Baudier's world is a very particular world.

At the same time, the equilibrium properties of the whole market are immediately apparent. For since the total amount of coupons received by consumers is the same as the total amount of coupons paid out by producers, it follows that the planned total demand for goods in each period will equal the total planned supply of goods. And since the total amount of (negative) labour parts of coupons received by consumers is the same as the total amount of (negative) labour parts of coupons paid out by the producers, it follows that the planned total supply of labour in each period will equal the total planned demand for labour. And by Walras's law, then, there will also be equilibrium in the bond market.

A final remark. At the end of his paper, Mr. Baudier discusses the role of money in his model, and he states that 'money serves no useful purpose' in his model. I should just like to point out that this is of course an assumption of his, not a conclusion. The situation would have been different if money, or real balances, had been included as an argument in the utility function S.

Without going to any formal analysis, I should like to submit that money is indeed one of the most important media of the real world by which the economic agents acquire partial access to the markets for future goods.

Professor Borch : (1) In Mr. Baudier's model there is a well-defined equilibrium, but this is in general not a Pareto optimum. Mr. Baudier states that in order to make the equilibrium optimal, he would have to introduce far more — virtually an infinity — of future markets in the model.

This is an important conclusion, which in a more general form could be one of the final conclusions of our conference. Several of the papers we have discussed indicate that the introduction of risk and uncertainty in economic theory really implies a step from the finite to the infinite.

In my own paper I had to introduce an infinite number of commodities and prices in order to make sure that the economic equilibrium also was a Pareto optimum. This is just a paraphrasing of Mr. Baudier's conclusion. In Professor Marschak's paper the same result is formulated as a need for unlimited computational facilities. Other papers stress that 'attitude to risk' cannot be described by a few parameters, but requires a function — a utility function — defined for an infinite number of values.

Infinity cannot be satisfactorily handled by elementary mathematics. Our conclusion may, therefore, be that to master risk and uncertainty we shall need mathematical tools of a more advanced nature than those used in classical economic theory.

(2) I find it difficult to accept an economic equilibrium which is not Pareto-optimal.

In an economic system one usually specifies an *initial situation*, and makes some assumptions as to how people — or the economic agents — will behave in this situation. These assumptions will in general lead to some transactions between the agents, which will bring the system to a *final situation*. Since no further transactions will take place, it is natural to say that the system then has reached an equilibrium.

If this equilibrium is not Pareto-optimal, there will exist situations which all people consider as better than the equilibrium. It is only our behavioural assumptions which prevent the system from reaching one of these more attractive situations. It is then natural to revise these assumptions, as they obviously contradict the basic traditional assumption that economic agents are rational people.

If all people can gain by the creation of a new market, we must assume that somebody takes the initiative to create that market. If everybody stands to gain if new securities are created, we must assume that some enterprising broker understands the situation, and creates these securities — and makes a profit.

If we have to choose between equilibrium and Pareto optimality, I will opt for Pareto optimality. If, however, we can reach a Pareto optimum only through an infinite number of markets and after infinite computations, we may never reach it at all. This may mean that both concepts will have to be dropped in a theory for the 'economics of uncertainty'. I think, however, that the forces which drive the system towards a Pareto optimum are more fundamental than the forces — essentially the inertia of conventional behaviour — which tend to keep the system in a sub-optimal state of equilibrium.

(3) The essential element of the classical behavioural assumptions is probably the *decentralized decision-making*. This inevitably brings uncertainty into the model, since one economic agent does not know how the others will decide.

Record of Discussion

It is obvious that decentralized decision-making cannot always lead to a Pareto optimum. This is demonstrated by a simple two-person game, illustrated by the payoff matrix

		Strategies of Player 2	
		1	2
Strategies of	1	(1. 1)	$(-1, 2)$
Player 1	2	$(2, -1)$	(0, 0)

If each player has to choose his strategy in ignorance of what the other will do, it is likely that both will choose strategy 2, and arrive at a sub-optimal situation. Strategy 2 dominates strategy 1, in the sense that it will give a player the higher payoff, no matter what the opponent does. It is, however, clear that the only sensible thing the two players can do is to agree on joint use of strategy 1.

The game is known as the 'prisoners' dilemma', and has a considerable interest. However, decision-makers in an economic system are not prisoners unable to communicate with each other. If decentralization obviously leads the system to a sub-optimal situation, we must assume that rational people somehow — sooner or later — find a way to co-ordinate their decisions and arrive at an optimal situations.

Professor Hester: I should like to bring up a problem which was discussed also in connection with Professor Borch's paper. That is the question of the costs of collecting and processing information. Just as in most other equilibrium models, Mr. Baudier's models disregard these costs, although we know that they are of great importance: in particular, they may represent a practical obstacle to a Pareto-optimal situation.

Dr. Selten: I am very surprised to hear that Mr. Baudier looks at minimax strategies as instruments of co-operation. It is true that in two-person constant-sum games there is no need for secrecy if minimax strategies are used; the players can announce these strategies honestly. But this property does not carry over to more general games. If the market is interpreted as a co-operative game it would seem better to use one of the approaches available in co-operative game theory. I have nothing to say against a sub-optimal solution, but why should it be reached by means of a minimax strategy?

The argument of Professor Borch that behavioural limitations will not prevent a Pareto optimum being reached (at least approximately) by adaptation has considerable force, if the market or bargaining situations involve only one period of time. If all kinds of futures are introduced the situation is no longer a purely static one and I should hesitate to rely on Professor Borch's argument in that case. Some degree of sub-optimality would have to be expected in such markets.

Mr. Bessière : I think that we have to accept situations which are not optimal in the Pareto–Debreu meaning, for these optimal situations imply an unlimited computing ability in every economic agent, *and* a perfect knowledge of what is going on at present and of anything which may happen in the future, *and* a perfectly efficient organization of the society. These are of course quite unrealistic assumptions, and the difference between practical optimal situations and ideal situations should measure the cost we have to pay for all these real inefficiencies in economic life. This proves that it would be a useful effort to analyse this cost.

Anyway, what I most appreciate in Mr. Baudier's paper is that it presents us with an intermediate situation between Debreu's idealized optimum and real situations where the only term-market is, in practice, the money market.

Mr. Baudier : I want to thank Dr. Thore most sincerely for his interesting comments on my paper, and I have very little to add.

In my paper I have indicated that money could naturally be brought into the model as an argument in the utility functions, but that this would not lead to a very satisfactory monetary theory. From this I concluded that the assumptions behind my model were not suitable for a theoretical analysis of monetary problems.

The minimax criterion was developed by von Neumann and Morgenstern in connection with the two-person constant-sum game, but can obviously be used in other situations. I think the minimax criterion has three interesting properties :

(i) *Liberty*, i.e. it enables a player to secure a certain payoff, regardless of what the others do.

(ii) *Honesty*, which in my model means that an economic agent will always be able to fulfil his commitment, even in the most improbable circumstances.

(iii) *Co-operation*, in the sense that a player does not seek to exploit possible mistakes made by others.

I hope these remarks will also answer some of the questions raised by Dr. Selten.

I shall make two remarks in reply to Professor Borch's observations on the importance of the Pareto optimum :

(i) The real world seems very far from a Pareto optimum. A model with a limited number of forward markets may therefore give a good representation of reality, even if — or because — it does not lead to a Pareto optimum.

(ii) The Pareto optimum is not unique, and it is certainly desirable to determine which particular Pareto optimum the economy will reach — or approach. If the economy can reach a Pareto optimum only after some adjustment, we can look for the optimal adjustment process, which will probably have to be described in stochastic terms.

Chapter 14

COMPUTATION IN ORGANIZATION
COMPARISON OF PRICE MECHANISMS
AND OTHER ADJUSTMENT PROCESSES[1]

BY

T. A. MARSCHAK

I. INTRODUCTION

WE shall be concerned in this paper with the good design of a team (Marschak and Radner) — the design of an organization whose members share certain preferences and are to respond in a desirable way to a changing environment. The discussion is partly motivated by economists' continuing interest in the formulation of decentralized 'price' mechanisms to be used by planned economies, firms, and other organizations which it is helpful to view as teams. The current work on such mechanisms [2] seems aimed mainly at generating more of them so as to permit previously excluded conditions such as increasing returns and certain externalities. The very difficult question of choice between alternative decentralized mechanisms or between a decentralized mechanism and a centralized alternative— the question of what characterizes a 'good' mechanism — has received little attention.

One may be able to formulate several extremely general problems of good design for a team. But if one wants to say something of interest about the comparative performance of alternative designs, especially designs that have something in common with price mechanisms, then in familiar fashion generality has to yield to tractability and arbitrary specializing assumptions have to be made.

[1] This research was supported by a National Science Foundation Grant, GS-71.
[2] Recent efforts (all of which have some roots in the classic discussions of Barone (1935), Lange (1938), Hayek (1945), and others) include : Arrow and Hurwicz on gradient methods (1962) ; Malinvaud on decentralization in national planning (1961) ; Marglin on decentralized water-resource planning (1963) and on decentralized adjustment processes for certain kinds of increasing returns (1964) ; A. Whinston on some more general aspects of decentralization (1962) ; and Dantzig and Wolfe on decomposed linear programming (1961), with a national-planning interpretation by C. Almon (1962).

Thus in a very general formulation one might consider a team composed of n members. Each member repeatedly chooses an action and in addition sends and receives messages and stores and retrieves information. The team faces an environment which changes, say, according to a known stochastic process. A design for the team specifies precisely what happens within the team at each point of time for every possible realization of the stochastic process: what messages each member sends to every other, what action each member takes, what information each member stores or retrieves, what computations each member performs. At some points of time a member may be continuing his previous action but computing his next one, using the information he then has; at other moments he may be reading or writing a message or preparing (by performing certain computations) messages to be shortly written and sent; or he may be in the midst of reading or writing messages or storing and retrieving information. At certain moments his action will change.[1]

The sequence of communication, computing, and storage-retrieval tasks which a design implies for each succession of environments has to be carried out with certain equipment, which we may call 'information-handling equipment'. One version of the general problem of optimal design would require the equipment to have sufficient computing, communication, and storage capacity so that for each environment sequence each task is completed at the time assigned to it by the chosen design. The cost of alternative 'sufficient' equipments, together with the sequence of actions generated by the design for each environment sequence, determine the desirability of a given design. One might suppose in particular that the team's preferences as between designs are given by a payoff function defined on the set of all possible action–environment–equipment cost 'histories'; for a given environmental stochastic process one design is preferred to another if its expected payoff, using the best possible 'sufficient' equipment, is higher.

Studying such a problem of optimal design in its full generality is unlikely to be worthwhile for at least two reasons. In the first place the general formulation imposes no stability at all on the team's successive responses to its environment. Hence many suggestive properties of both real organizations and fictitious organizations studied by economists (organizations using price mechanisms) are not exploited; for in these cases the successive responses remain

---

[1] In a still more general formulation, the distinction between 'action-taking' and the other activities just mentioned (e.g. 'message-writing') can be dropped.

similar in important ways. In the second place, in such a general formulation the technology of communication, computation, and storage-retrieval, still so little understood and so difficult to characterize, must enter the problem in an extremely detailed and unwieldy fashion. For each design, all possible equipments meeting the design's requirements have to be considered and the best one found.

We shall accordingly consider here a problem of good design whose generality is greatly curtailed. It is relevant, however, to the comparative study of price mechanisms and alternative schemes. And it is a design problem in which the missing technological information is of a *relatively* modest sort, so that there may be some hope that specialists in information technology can eventually supply it.

The price mechanisms which have so far been proposed for teams have at least the following important properties in common:

(1) The team using the mechanism wants to achieve a high value of a many-valued payoff function (profit, planners' utility, National Product) whose arguments are the actions taken by the members (e.g. production decisions, local plans) and the team's environment (market price, resource availabilities, technical coefficients). In important cases the action must also lie in a constraint set determined by the environment (e.g. resource requirements must not exceed resource availabilities).

(2) The members who participate in the operation of the mechanism (managers of production units, custodians of resources, local planners) observe part of the environment (the technology of a particular production unit, the prices in a particular market, the availability of a particular resource), but they are never required to transmit this specialized knowledge to anyone else. Instead, through a sequence of very limited information exchanges, each followed by an adjustment of 'tentative' actions, they achieve final actions approximating those which a complete pooling of information could achieve.

(3) The information that is transmitted between members consists partly of signals which it is natural to think of as 'prices'.

(4) Formally the mechanism may be written as a difference-equation system in which, at each iteration, each member's vector of tentative actions and of messages to be sent to others is given as a function of his information — his knowledge of the environment, his previous actions, and the messages previously sent to him by others. The number of the iteration may enter the function as well or it may

not — the case of 'temporally homogeneous' mechanisms. The system may be a first-order system or it may not. The main price mechanisms proposed appear to be, when appropriately formulated, both temporally homogeneous and first-order. In any case, the path of the system is well defined once initial values of all the variables are specified and it attains, in time, high values of the payoff function.

The mechanisms are also frequently labelled 'decentralized' and are proposed as alternatives to 'centralized' schemes which are, indeed, sometimes held to be totally infeasible. The advantages of the decentralized mechanisms are presumed to lie in the small amount of information transmitted, in the spreading of the computational burden among many members, possibly in desirable incentive properties, and — at least for temporally homogeneous schemes — in the routine nature of the tasks repeatedly performed.

For a thoroughgoing study of these advantages one must doubtless begin with a much more precise definition of the class of decentralized schemes than the rough sketch above. Some attempts in that direction were made in Marschak (1959). In addition, L. Hurwicz has studied (Hurwicz, 1960) decentralization in a different but related context — that of an economy whose members successively adjust their trades by means of a temporally homogeneous difference-equation system that achieves Pareto-optimality at equilibrium. He has developed a complete definition of a decentralized class of such schemes.

We shall consider (below) only one, rather arbitrary, definition of decentralization and will loosely use the term 'centralized' to apply to certain schemes in need of convenient labelling. This will suffice for the main purpose, which is simply to illustrate some issues that arise in the limited choices of schemes open to the team we consider. The same issues must also be faced in any attempt to compare price mechanisms or to compare decentralized and centralized classes of schemes when these terms are given a more complete definition.

II. A SPECIAL FRAMEWORK

It is a very helpful simplification to suppose that the team's environment changes only at discrete points of time, that it is instantly observed at those points of time, and that the environment does not change while the scheme is in operation. When the scheme has come to a halt, it has generated a set of actions that are a response to the environment. These actions are put into effect and they remain in force at least until the next environment occurs. Only once during its operation — when it terminates — does the scheme generate a new set of actions actually taken by the organization in response to the new environment; the scheme generates a whole sequence of *tentative actions*, but only the terminal one is put into effect.

One scheme is better than another if, very roughly speaking, it reaches appropriate new actions more quickly, when the information-handling capacity at the disposal of the participants is chosen to be equally costly in both schemes. Speed is generally desirable because until actions that are a good response to the new environment have been generated, the actions in force are inferior (for example, they may be a response to the preceding environment, which may be only very weakly correlated with the current one). In some tasks — e.g. once-and-for-all long-range planning — one could argue that speed is desirable even though the relevant environment never changes, simply because of the opportunities that have to be foregone until the plan is ready.

We proceed now to restrict the schemes considered, and to formulate more precisely the problem of choice between schemes. We consider an organization of n members which chooses actions a out of some unchanging set of actions and faces environments μ. Both a and μ are vectors; they have components $a_i, \ldots, a_n$ and $\mu_1, \ldots, \mu_n$, respectively. The components a_i, μ_i, $i = 1, \ldots, n$, are real column vectors. The vector μ_i, $i = 1, \ldots, n$, is a random variable; each of its components has a finite mean. The vector μ always lies in a set M. Its successive values are generated by a stochastic process which is known to the organization.

At an instant of time during which μ obtains and a is in force, *payoff* is given by $W(a, \mu)$. Of two pairs (a, μ) prevailing at some instant of time the one with higher payoff is preferred, and of two alternative actions to be taken, at some instant of time, in the face of an unknown μ, the one with the higher value of $EW(a, \mu)$ is preferred. We assume in addition that there is an interval of time called a *time unit* and a discount factor ρ $(0 < \rho)$ such that the following is true. Consider any two sequences of action-environment pairs (a^{11}, μ^{11}), $\ldots, (a^{1r}, \mu^{1r}), \ldots, (a^{1k_1}, \mu^{1k_1}), (a^{21}, \mu^{21}), \ldots, (a^{2r}, \mu^{2r}), \ldots, (a^{2k_2}, \mu^{2k_2}), (a^{31}, \mu^{31}), \ldots, (a^{3r}, \mu^{3r}), \ldots, (a^{3k_3}, \mu^{3k_3}), \ldots$ and $(\tilde{a}^{11}, \tilde{\mu}^{11}), \ldots, (\tilde{a}^{1r}, \tilde{\mu}^{1r}), \ldots, (\tilde{a}^{1\tilde{k}_1}, \tilde{\mu}^{1\tilde{k}_1}), \ldots, (\tilde{a}^{21}, \tilde{\mu}^{21}), \ldots, (\tilde{a}^{2r}, \tilde{\mu}^{2r}), \ldots, (\tilde{a}^{2\tilde{k}_2}, \tilde{\mu}^{2\tilde{k}_2}), (\tilde{a}^{31}, \tilde{\mu}^{31}), \ldots, (\tilde{a}^{3r}, \tilde{\mu}^{3r}), \ldots, (\tilde{a}^{3\tilde{k}_3}, \tilde{\mu}^{3\tilde{k}_3}), \ldots$, where the first co-ordinate of each pair is a value of a and the second a value of μ. Each subsequence $(a^{s1}, \mu^{s1}), \ldots, (a^{sr}, \mu^{sr}), \ldots, (a^{sk_s}, \mu^{sk_s})$ or $(\tilde{a}^{s1}, \mu^{s1}), \ldots,$ $(\tilde{a}^{sr}, \mu^{sr}), \ldots, (\tilde{a}^{s\tilde{k}_s}, \mu^{s\tilde{k}_s})$ is completed in one time unit and the members of the subsequence prevail, respectively, for periods of length $c_{s1}, \ldots, c_{sr}, \ldots, c_{sk_s}$ and $\tilde{c}_{s1}, \ldots, \tilde{c}_{sr}, \ldots, \tilde{c}_{s\tilde{k}_s}$, where

$$\sum_{r=1}^{k_s} c_{sr} = \sum_{r=1}^{\tilde{k}_s} \tilde{c}_{sr} = 1.$$

Then the organization prefers the first sequence to the second if and only if the total discounted payoff is higher, i.e. if and only if

$$\sum_{s=1}^{\infty} \rho^j \left[\sum_{r=1}^{k_s} c_{sr} W\left(a^{sr}, \mu^{sr}\right) \right] > \sum_{s=1}^{\infty} \rho^j \left[\sum_{r=1}^{\tilde{k}_s} \tilde{c}_{sr} W\left(a^{sr}, \mu^{sr}\right) \right].$$

Given two gambles whose outcomes are such action-environment sequences the organization prefers the first to the second if and only if the expected discounted total payoff is higher.

Note that perhaps the most drastic implication of our assumptions so far is that current actions have no influence on the desirability of alternative future actions. This simplification seems essential, however; even when we make it, the problem of choice we consider will be quite complex enough.

The successive environments occur, and are instantly observed, at discrete points of time. We assume these points to be evenly spaced, *one time unit* occurring between them. In response to a new μ the organization starts to carry out a scheme, or, as we shall call it, an *adjustment process*, defined by the first-order system of difference equations

$$a_i(t) = f^i[a(t-1)\mu, t], \qquad i = 1, \ldots, n, \, t = 1, 2, 3, \ldots \quad (1)$$

For an initial value of a, say $a(0) = a_0$, the system has the solution vector $a(t, \mu, a_0) = [a_1(t, \mu, a_0), \ldots, a_n(t, \mu, a_0)]$. The vector $a_i(t, \mu, a_0)$, $i = 1, \ldots, n$, has the same dimension as a_i; $a(t, \mu, a_0)$ is the organization's *tentative action vector* at iteration t. We now specify that member i observes μ_i; is responsible for adjusting the tentative action $a_i(t)$ at each iteration t; and is also responsible for seeing that the action a_i has at any instant of time the value the organization wants it to have at that instant. Then specifying f also specifies precisely the information that each member must have at iteration t about the parts of the environment observed by other members and about the previous tentative actions of other members. The messages that must be exchanged following an iteration t in order to make the adjustment process function are therefore also implied.

There are a number of appealing properties that one could require an adjustment process to display, given a payoff function W. One could require that $W[a(t, \mu, a_0)]$ be for each μ a strictly increasing function of t — that for any fixed environment operating the process longer yields a better action. If W is maximized at a unique value of a for each μ, one could require that the process be at equilibrium only at this value. One could require that for each μ the process converge — in a sense that has to be made precise — to its equilibrium value.

Though at least one of these properties characterizes each of the proposed price mechanisms, exactly why these properties should be valuable has not been made very clear. It is certainly possible that a process which does not converge to the maximizing action but eventually oscillates around, or converges to, some other 'good' action, performs better than one displaying the last two of the above properties, according to some reasonable measure of performance. In much of what follows we shall nevertheless adopt the traditional bias in favour of convergence to maximizing actions. The study of processes displaying this property, and the property's precise definition, will be given priority and a possible reason for the superiority of such processes, as well as a disadvantage of the convergence requirement, will emerge.

Now consider the interval between two successive environments μ and μ^*. At some *terminal iteration T*, but not later than the occurrence of μ^*, the process will be halted and the action vector actually in force will at that instant be given the value $a(T, \mu, a_0)$. Between the observation of μ and the achievement of the Tth iteration the organization has in force some *interim action* ã. Let us assume now that f does not contain t as an argument — so that the computational operations performed by each participant i between any iterations $t-1$ and t remain the same for all t, as do the dimensions of the messages sent by i. The adjustment process is temporally homogeneous. It is then reasonable to assume that given the organization's information-handling equipment it requires a time $C(C>0)$ to complete each iteration (to pass from $a(t-1, \mu, a_0)$ to $a(t, \mu, a_0)$).[1] Hence (since the interval between successive environments is one

---

[1] The assumption that it is the dimension of a message that determines the time required to send it over a given transmission line is valid only under certain further assumptions about the transmission technology. We later return to this point very briefly.

time unit), our condition that the operation of the process must be stopped before the environment changes can be stated as

Assumption 1: The terminal iteration T chosen by the organization must satisfy $0 \leqslant T \leqslant 1/C$, where C is the time required to complete an iteration.

Between the two successive environments μ and μ^*, the organization's total payoff is then given by

$$W(\tilde{a}, \mu)CT + W[a(T, \mu, a_0), \mu](1 - CT).$$

For a given probability distribution over the possible sequences of environments, and a given rule for choosing (after each new environment) the terminal iteration T, the interim action $\tilde{a}$, and the initial value a_0, the expected stream of total payoffs that the organization enjoys depends only on C. If we know precisely the relation expressing this dependence for two adjustment processes f and f^*, we can then make what we shall call a 'technology-free' statement about which process is better. A technology-free statement says that *if* the costs of alternative information-handling capacities are such that the best choice of C for adjustment process f yields a larger expected stream of net payoffs than the best choice of C for adjustment process f^*, then f is better than f^*.

But note that for two adjustment processes f and f^*, different rules for choosing terminal iteration, interim action, and initial value — different *arrangements*, as we shall call them — lead to different technology-free statements about f and f^*.

III. THE ADJUSTMENT PROCESSES TO BE STUDIED

To illustrate these matters more concretely, we shall consider still further restricted classes of payoff functions and adjustment processes.

First, however, we make more precise the term *decentralized* as applied to the adjustment processes (1), since the term will frequently be used.

Definition. An adjustment process defined by the first-order temporally homogeneous difference-equation system $a(t) = f[a(t-1), \mu]$ will be called a *decentralized process for an n-member team whose payoff function is* $W(a, \mu)$ *and whose ith member observes* μ_i, *is in charge of the action* a_i, *and adjusts the tentative action* $a_i(t)$ if the following is true for at least $n-1$ of the team's members i:

(i) the action a_i, in the charge of member i, effectively enters the payoff function W,

(ii) the adjustments which the process requires for member i are given by

$$a_i(t) = f^i[a(t-1), \mu_i].$$

This definition is one way (perhaps a rather drastic one) of capturing the main classical property of decentralized schemes — the privacy accorded each participant with respect to his knowledge of the environment — while still solving the rather delicate problem that any definition of decentralization must solve : how to rule out schemes which formally are decentralized according to the definition but which seem clearly centralized in the popular sense. If one did not rule out temporal non-homogeneity, systems of more than first order, or extra 'dummy' variables not effectively entering the payoff function, one could disguise as 'decentralized' schemes, in which member i needs to know no other environment component than μ_i, schemes in which all the μ_i are in fact made known to one or more persons. Allowing conditions (i) and (ii) to be violated for one of the n members permits one member to be a legitimate 'price-setter' in a decentralized price mechanism : a member whose action (and tentative action) is a price vector that does not effectively enter the payoff function.

We shall assume that each component a_i of a and μ_i of μ is a scalar and that for each μ in M, $W(a, \mu)$ is strictly concave and differentiable with respect to all co-ordinates of a. For each μ, then, W is maximized at a unique value, $\hat{a}(\mu)$ of the action vector a. We consider the *gradient-method* adjustment process wherein each co-ordinate of a is adjusted at a rate proportional to the partial derivative of W with respect to that co-ordinate. The process is the difference-equation system

$$a_i(t) - a_i(t-1) = hW_i[a(t-1), \mu], \qquad i = 1, \ldots, n, \qquad (2)$$

where W_i denotes $\partial W / \partial a_i$ which has the equilibrium value $\hat{a}(\mu)$ and solution vector $a(t, \mu, a_0)$.

If W has the form

$$W(a, \mu) = \sum_{i=1}^{n} \mu_i a_i + S(a), \qquad (3)$$

where $S(a)$ is strictly concave, then the decision process (2) has the form

$$a_i(t) - a_i(t-1) = h\mu_i + S_i[a(t-1)], \qquad i = 1, \ldots, n, \qquad (4)$$

and so has the principal property of decentralized schemes: no participant i is required to communicate μ_i, his knowledge of the environment, to anyone else. Each participant may be required, however, to know the preceding tentative actions of all other participants. If W does not have the form (3) the decision process (2) may still have computational advantages, stemming partly from the fact that it 'decomposes' the problem of finding a good value of a into a sequence of n simultaneously computed 'small' problems.

We shall be particularly interested in a special payoff function having the form (3). The function, studied in a related context by R. Radner (1962), is quadratic:

$$W[a, \mu) = \mu'a - a'Qa,$$

where $Q = (q_{ij})$ is a positive definitive symmetrical matrix. The matrix Q is, in fact, a matrix of 'interactions'[1] in the sense that q_{ij} is equal to the second partial derivative $\partial^2 W / \partial a_i \partial a_j$. For every μ the action maximizing W is, $\hat{a}(\mu) = \frac{1}{2}Q^{-1}\mu$. The adjustment process (2) becomes

$$a_i(t) - a_i(t - 1) = h\mu_i - 2h\sum_{j=1}^{n} q_{ij}a_j(t - 1)$$

or, in matrix notation:

$$a(t) = h\mu + (I - 2hQ)a(t - 1). \tag{5}$$

It may appear at first sight that the general adjustment process (1) and the special decentralized adjustment processes (2) and (4) are quite remote from the decentralized price mechanisms which have been discussed and hence their study can shed little light on the virtues of these mechanisms. For in the first place the aim of all mechanisms proposed is to achieve a high payoff subject to *constraints* on the actions; a distinctive property of the mechanisms is that they either continuously maintain feasibility of the tentative actions or they reverse departures from feasibility. In the second place, the participants in a number of the schemes, unlike the participants in (1), (2), and (4), never need to announce their tentative actions to anyone else.

[1] A payoff function of this form would characterize, for example, a firm with branch plants, each producing the same output (sold at a local price which is a random variable) and each using the same input; the total input required is bought by the firm as a whole in the face of an unchanging rising linear supply curve. The interaction q_{ij} is the effect on the ith branch's marginal cost of an incremental increase in the jth branch's output.

With respect to the first point, we remark that if the original payoff function in a price mechanism is replaced by one that preserves the ranking of feasible pairs (a, μ), while assigning an extremely low payoff to infeasible pairs, it might well be possible to approximate the new payoff function by a strictly concave function, perhaps the quadratic one. If the payoff assigned to infeasible pairs is sufficiently small, the gradient-method decision process corresponding to such an approximating function would yield a feasible action at any terminal iteration.

With respect to the second point we remark that in at least one of the important 'price' mechanisms (the Dantzig–Wolfe scheme for decomposing linear programming problems) the tentative actions *are* communicated. Moreover, in all the price mechanisms certain information other than knowledge of the environment is communicated — namely, prices and, in some cases, each participant's tentative demand for one or more commodities.

On the other hand if the processes (2), (4), and (5) are to provide, like the price mechanisms, an appealing alternative to complete centralization of information and computation, then it may seem reasonable to require that the *number* of actions communicated at each iteration should at least be less than the dimension of the vector μ (which could be centrally collected and the action $\hat{a}(\mu)$ then computed directly). Reasonable as the requirement seems, it yet rests on arbitrary assumptions about the technology of information handling, a point we return to in Section IV.7 below. If one accepts these assumptions then it is worth observing that in the quadratic case there are certain suggestive forms of the matrix Q for which the number of 'costly' action transmissions *is*, under a suitable interpretation, less than the dimension of μ.

Consider, for example, a matrix $Q = Q^* = (q_{ij}^*)$ of order mv by mv. The mv components of the action vector a are divided up among m 'blocks' of members, and so are the mv components of the environment vector μ. Any two members of a block, say members i and j, interact with each other in the sense that the second partial derivative $\partial^2 W / \partial a_i \, \partial a_j = q_{ij}^*$ has a non-zero value, say q, for $i \neq j$ and equals 1 for $i = j$. But between every member of a block except the vth member and every member of any other block there is no interaction (the relevant second partial derivative is zero). Between the vth members of every two blocks there is interaction: the relevant second partial derivative is equal to $r \neq 0$.

To summarize: for $k = 0, \ldots, m-1$, $q_{kv+v,\, kv+v}^* = r$ and for i,

$j = kv + 1, \ldots, kv + v - 1$, $q^*_{ij} = q$ when $i \neq j$ and 1 when $i = j$; q and r are such that Q^* is positive definite. To carry out the process (5) at an iteration t, each member of a block needs to know the actions of every other member of the block at $t - 1$, but only the vth member needs to know the previous actions of members outside the block (namely the action of the vth member of every other block). A reasonable assumption is that the gathering of the actions in a block is much less costly than transmission of actions from one block to all the others. A centralized process, with direct computation of

$$\hat{a}(\mu) = \frac{1}{2} Q^{*-1} \mu$$ in a central place, would require the transmission of

all mv components of μ; there is no simple and reasonable techno-logical assumption under which it dominates the process (5), since the number of costly (intra-block) action transmissions in (5) is less than the dimension of μ.

The principal reason for considering the processes (2), (4), and (5) is, of course, that they are far easier to study than the price mechan-isms that have been formulated.

What are the convergence properties of the difference-equation system (2)? In the first place one does not generally have strict global convergence; it is not true for all $W(a, \mu)$ strictly concave in a that there exists an h such that for all a_0 and all μ

$$\lim_{t \to \infty} a(t, \mu, a_0) = \hat{a}(\mu). \tag{6}$$

As we shall see it is true, however, in the quadratic case — i.e., in the process (5). Nor is it generally true that for each μ and each initial value a_0 there exists a number $h(\mu, a_0)$ such that (6) holds for $h = h(\mu, a_0)$. The difficulty is that one cannot rule out

(1) the possibility of *overshooting*, i.e. the possibility that at some iteration $t = t^*$, and for some i, the difference $a_i(t) - \hat{a}_i(\mu)$ changes sign;

(2) when this happens, the possibility that at some iteration the variable in question may start fluctuating about its equilibrium value without converging to it.

A limited convergence property — that the neighbourhood in which such fluctuation occurs can be made arbitrarily small — was found by Uzawa (1958). The argument was given for the case of a gradient-method difference-equation system which converges, not to the unconstrained maximum of W with respect to a, but to its maximum subject to the constraints $a \geqslant 0$, $g_j(a) \geqslant 0$, g_j concave,

$j = 1, \ldots, m$. Removing the constraints leaves the relevant parts of the argument intact (after suitable reinterpretation), but does not appear to strengthen the conclusion with respect to convergence. The convergence property shown by the argument is (for any fixed μ) as follows :

For any a_0 and any $\epsilon > 0$, there exists a number $\bar{h}(\mu, a_0, \epsilon) > 0$ such that for $0 < h < \bar{h}(\mu, a_0, \epsilon)$ there is an integer $t_0 > 0$ with the property

$$D[a(t+1)] \leqslant D[a(t)] \qquad \text{for } 0 \leqslant t \leqslant t_0 \text{ and}$$
$$D[a(t)] \leqslant \epsilon \qquad \text{for } t \geqslant t_0, \qquad (7)$$

where $D[a(t)]$ is the distance from $a(t)$ to the equilibrium value $\hat{a}(\mu)$; i.e.

$$D[a(t)] = \sqrt{\sum_{i=1}^{n} [a_i(t) - \hat{a}_i(\mu)]^2}.$$

By the strict concavity of W, (6) also implies that

$$W[a(t+1), \mu] \geqslant W[a(t), \mu] \qquad \text{for } 0 < t < t_0. \qquad (8)$$

For a given μ and a_0 there are in general, then, two iterations at which the path followed by $a(t)$ displays an important change : the iteration t^* at which overshooting first occurs, and the iteration $t_0 \geqslant t^*$ at which $a(t)$ begins to fluctuate about $\hat{a}(\mu)$ without getting closer to $a(\mu)$. It seems reasonable to suppose that the organization, knowing the above convergence property, prefers not to iterate beyond t_0. A difficulty is, however, that the t_0 and the $\bar{h}(\mu, a_0, \epsilon)$ are functions of the equilibrium point $\hat{a}(\mu)$. Thus there is no known way at present for the organization to choose an $\bar{h}(\mu, a_0, \epsilon)$ and a terminal iteration prior to which fluctuation about $\hat{a}(\mu)$ does not occur, without sacrificing both the decentralized property of the adjustment process, and the computational justification for using the process in the first place.

The determination of t^*, however, presents no such difficulty, for strict concavity implies that :

For two values of a, say a^* and a^{**}, the sign of $a_1^* - \hat{a}_i(\mu)$ is the same as the sign of $a_1^{**} - \hat{a}_i(\mu)$ for all i, if and only if sign of $W_i(a^*, \mu) = $ sign of $W_i(a^{**}, \mu)$ for all i. $\qquad (9)$

Thus t^* can be detected to have occurred as soon as some one member of the team, say the member in charge of a_i, observes that $W_i[a(t), \mu]$ has changed sign. If W is of the form (3), t^* can therefore be detected while preserving decentralization. (The action

$a(t^* - 1)$ can then be taken as the action to be put into force if it is desired to carry the process until the last possible iteration prior to overshooting.) Moreover, by taking $|h|$ sufficiently small, one can, for a given μ and a_0, either eliminate overshooting altogether or, if this is not possible, make t^* as large as desired. Finally, if the organization is constrained to choose the terminal iteration T from the interval $0 \leqslant T < \min (t^*, 1/C)$, when overshooting occurs, and $0 \leqslant T \leqslant 1/C$ otherwise, then, as we shall see, (9) implies some results about the uniqueness of the best terminal iteration.

The choice of h is certainly one of the important choices facing the organization. A small $|h|$ has the advantage of postponing over-shooting, as well as shrinking the size of the region about $\hat{a}(\mu)$ in which fluctuation occurs. A small $|h|$ has the disadvantage that it increases the number of iterations required to reach a given value of W. While we shall concentrate here on varying the arrangement, as defined above (different rules for choosing interim action, terminal iteration, and initial value), some changes in h will also be discussed.

IV. THE CASE OF SERIALLY INDEPENDENT ENVIRONMENTS

We shall now concentrate on the processes just presented for the case in which the successive environment vectors facing the organization are independently distributed. The vector μ is always a drawing from the same set M, according to the same probability measure. We shall also assume that each component μ_i of μ has mean zero and variance 1 and is uncorrelated with any other component. The latter conditions comprise

Assumption 2: $E\mu_i = 0$, $E\mu_i^2 = 1$, $E\mu_i\mu_j = 0$, $i \neq j$, $i, j = 1, \ldots, n$.

The assumption of serial independence is a strong one, but seems an essential starting-place; moreover, it renders Assumption 1 quite innocuous, for it is easy to see that if there is serial independence there can be no advantage in continuing to operate a process when a new environment, subsequent to the one which initiated the process, prevails.

We consider a number, but by no means all, of the possible arrangements — the possible choices of interim action, terminal iteration, and initial value — that the organization can make. Each arrangement seems worth examining, for, as we shall see, there may be sound reasons why the organization is constrained to choose it. For the arrangements considered the discussion deals partly with any adjustment process $a(t) = f[a(t-1), \mu]$, partly with any decentralized process, and partly with the specific processes (2), (4), and (5).

Throughout this section we shall assume that for a given process the iteration time C is held at the same level for all arrangements considered. In comparing different arrangements, then, the cost of the information-handling equipment used plays no role.

IV. 1. *Arrangement A: Constant Interim Action, Constant Terminal Iteration, Constant Initial Value*

A highly routine response to a new environment is always to switch instantly to the same interim action $\tilde{a}$, and always to generate a new action by operating the chosen adjustment process for precisely T iterations, starting always at the same initial value $a_0 = (a_{0,}, \ldots, a_{0n})$, all of whose components are known to all members. If routine is sufficiently important to the organization, this may be the preferred arrangement and we shall examine it at some length. The organization's expected total payoff between two successive environments is then, for $0 \leqslant T \leqslant 1/C$,

$$\pi_1(C, T) \equiv E\{W(\tilde{a}, \mu)CT + W[a(T, \mu, a_0), \mu](1 - CT)\}.$$

Since the environment always has the same expected value, the expected value of the discounted sum of future total payoffs is greater for one process than for another if and only if π_1 is greater. We can therefore ignore the discount factor altogether and may take π_1 as the measure of the process's performance.

If W is strictly concave in a, and if the adjustment process is (2), then for fixed μ, T, and a_0 the first term of the expression in braces is strictly concave in $\tilde{a}$. Moreover, the second term, $W[a(T, \mu, a_0), \mu]$ $(1 - CT)$, does not depend on $\tilde{a}$. It follows that $\pi_1(C, T)$ is strictly concave in $\tilde{a}$ and therefore that *there exists a unique best constant interim action $\tilde{a}$, independent of T and a_0.* The best interim action is the action maximizing $EW(\tilde{a}, \mu)$; in the quadratic case this is $a(E\mu) = 0$.

We shall not investigate the existence and uniqueness of a best initial value a_0, for fixed T and $\tilde{a}$, except in the quadratic case. Here the best a_0 is readily seen [1] to be independent of T and $\tilde{a}$; it is always zero.

We turn now to the question of a best constant terminal iteration T, given an a_0 and an $\tilde{a}$. This is a considerably more difficult matter,

---

[1] From the solution to (5), which is given below.

especially as T must be an integer, constrained by Assumption 1 and perhaps by additional assumptions, to fall in a certain interval. Suppose the interval is $0 \leqslant T \leqslant T^*$, where $T^* \leqslant 1/C$, and let W_t denote $W[a(t, \mu, a_0), \mu]$. Let ΔW_t denote the first difference $W_t - W_{t-1}$ (defined for $t \geqslant 1$), and $\Delta 2W_t$ the second difference $\Delta W_t - \Delta W_{t-1}$ (defined for $t \geqslant 2$). It is easily seen that if

$$\Delta W_t > 0 \text{ and } \Delta^2 W_t < 0 \text{ for all integers } t, \ 2 \leqslant t < T^*, \qquad (10)$$

then there is a unique integer T maximizing $\pi_1(C, T)$ on the interval $0 \leqslant T \leqslant T^*$. For if (10) holds we have

$$W_t - 2W_{t-1} + W_{t-2} < 0, \qquad 2 \leqslant t < T^*.$$

Multiplying by the number $1 - Ct + C$, which is positive for $2 \leqslant t \leqslant T^*$, rearranging, and using $\Delta W_t > 0$, we obtain

$$W_t(1 - Ct) - W_{t-1}[1 - C(t-1)] < W_{t-1}[1 - C(t-1)] -$$
$$W_{t-2}[1 - C(t-2)], \qquad 2 \leqslant t \leqslant T^*.$$

Hence

> $W(a, \mu) \ CT + W[a(T, \mu, a_0), \mu](1 - CT)$ has a negative second difference with respect to T for $2 \leqslant T \leqslant T^*$.

It follows that $\pi_1(C, T)$ has a negative second difference with respect to T for all T, $2 \leqslant T \leqslant T^*$, so that a unique integer T maximizes $\pi_1(C, T)$ subject to $0 \leqslant T \leqslant T^*$.

This argument makes no use of the strict concavity of W; it establishes the following theorem about any decision process $a(t) = f[a(t-1), \mu]$:

> *Theorem* : If successive environments are independent, if the organization always uses the same interim action $\tilde{a}$ and the same initial value a_0, if the terminal iteration T must lie in the interval $0 \leqslant T \leqslant T^*$, where $T^* \leqslant 1/C$, and if $\Delta W_t > 0$ and $\Delta^2 W_t < 0$ for integers t in this interval, then $\Delta^2 \pi_1(C, T) < 0$ over this interval and there is a unique best terminal iteration.

The main practical interest of the theorem is that it permits the organization to approximate the best terminal iteration by treating the function $\pi_1(C, T)$ as continuous and differentiable in T, using the fact that $d^2\pi_1/dt^2 < 0$ to find $\hat{T}$, the value of T maximizing π on the given interval, and taking the best terminal iteration to be the nearest integer to T^*.

Now we have from (9) that prior to overshooting all partial derivatives W_i keep the same sign. It follows immediately from equation

(2) that prior to overshooting $\Delta W_t > 0$. It is also a consequence of the equation (2) and of strict concavity (i.e. of the negative definiteness of the matrix of second partial derivatives of $W(a, \mu)$) that prior to overshooting

$$D[a(t)] - D[a(t-1)] > D[a(t+1)] - D[a(t)], \qquad t \geqslant 1,$$

where $D[a(t)]$ is the distance $\sqrt{\sum_i [a_i(t) - \hat{a}_i(\mu)]^2}$. Strict concavity further implies that for three values of a, say a^*, a^{**}, a^{***} such that $W(a^*, \mu) < W(a^{**}, \mu) < W(a^{***}, \mu)$ and $D(a^{**}) - D(a^*) > D(a^{***}) - D(a^{**}) > 0$,

$$W(a^{***}, \mu) - W(a^{**}, \mu) < W(a^{**}, \mu) - W(a^*, \mu).$$

Hence it is also the case that $\Delta^2 W_t < 0$ prior to overshooting. By the theorem we have that if h is chosen so small that overshooting does not occur prior to $T^* \leqslant 1/C$, then on the interval $0 \leqslant T \leqslant T^*$ there is *a unique best constant terminal iteration for the organization that uses the process* (2).

It is now seen why the avoidance of overshooting is helpful for the uniqueness of the best T: for iterations t *subsequent* to the first overshooting it may be that W_t *temporarily drops*, so that $\Delta W_t > 0$, $\Delta^2 W_t < 0$ no longer hold.

We next investigate the possibility of overshooting in the quadratic case.

The solution of (5) is, for an initial value a_0,

$$a(t, \mu, a_0) = [I - (I - 2hQ)^t](2hQ)^{-1}h\mu + (I - 2hQ)^t a_0$$
$$= 1/2[I - (I - 2hQ)^t]Q^{-1}\mu + (I - 2hQ)^t a_0. \qquad (11)$$

Let $\hat{W}$ denote the maximum of W; i.e. $\hat{W} = W[\hat{a}(\mu), \mu] = 1/4\mu'Q^{-1}\mu$. After suitably rearranging we can write the path followed by the payoff W in the form

$$W[a(t, \mu, a_0), \mu] = \hat{W} - 1/4\mu'H_t\mu + R_t, \qquad (12)$$

where $H_t = Q^{-1}(I - 2hQ)^t Q(I - 2hQ)^t Q^{-1}$ and $R_t = a'_0(I - 2hQ)^t Q(I - 2hQ)^t(Q^{-1}\mu - a_0)$. If $a_0 = 0$, $R_t = 0$. Because of the symmetry of Q, we can diagonalize; i.e. we can write $Q = BDB'$, where D is the diagonal matrix of characteristic roots of Q and B is a matrix of characteristic vectors forming an orthonormal basis. Then $(I - 2hQ)^t$ can be written $B(I - 2hD)^t B'$ and $W[a(t, \mu, a_0), \mu]$ can be written

$$W[a(t, \mu, a_0), \mu] = \hat{W} - 1/4\mu'BD^{-1}(I - 2hD)^t D(I - 2hD)^t D^{-1}B'\mu + R_t$$
$$= \hat{W} - 1/4\mu'B(I - 2hD)^{2t}D^{-1}B'\mu + R_t. \qquad (13)$$

Now $\lim_{t \to \infty} a(t, \mu, a_0) = \hat{a}(\mu)$ if and only if the characteristic roots of $I - 2hQ$ are less than 1 in absolute value. Since the roots of Q are all positive, this means that for convergence we must have

$$0 < h < 1/\lambda, \tag{14}$$

where λ is the largest characteristic root of Q. If (14) is satisfied, overshooting is still possible for some a_0 and μ. As far as the uniqueness of the best terminal iteration is concerned, however, overshooting is of no consequence in the quadratic case as long as (14) is satisfied. To show this we investigate the second difference $\Delta^2 W_t$, after observing first that (14) implies

the diagonal elements of $I - 2hD$ are >0 and <1. (15)

For the case $a_0 = 0$ we have

$$\Delta W_t = \frac{1}{4}\mu' B(I - 2hD)^{2t-1} D^{-1} B' \mu - \frac{1}{4}\mu' B(I - 2hD)^{2t} D^{-1} B' \mu$$

$$= \frac{1}{4}\mu' B(I - 2hD)^{2t-1} 2hD B' \mu,$$

which, by (15), is positive. Then

$$\Delta^2 W_t = \frac{1}{4}\mu' B(I - 2hD)^{2(2-2)}[(I - 2hD)^2 - I]^2 2hB' \mu,$$

so that, by (15), $\Delta^2 W_t < 0$. The extension of this result to the case $a_0 \neq 0$ is straightforward.

Thus if the organization picks h once and for all so as to satisfy (14), there is, for any a_0, strict convergence to $\hat{a}(\mu)$ and no fluctuation in W_t. There is also, for any a_0 and any interim action $\tilde{a}$, a unique best constant terminal iteration T in the interval $0 \leqslant T \leqslant 1/C$. One advantage of the convergence property is well illustrated: it may make determination of best terminal iteration much easier. The best constant T depends on the choice of $\tilde{a}$ and a_0. Since, as we saw above, the best choice of $\tilde{a}$ and of a_0 is zero for the quadratic case, the best T in the quadratic case is, under Assumptions 1 and 2, the T maximizing the function

$$\pi_1(C, T) = EW[a(T, \mu, 0)](1 - CT) = 1/4(1 - CT)\sum_{i=1}^{n}(\bar{q}_{ii} - h_{Tii}),$$

on the interval, where $\bar{q}_{ii}$ and h_{Tii} are the ith diagonal elements of Q^{-1} and H_T, respectively.

We make three further observations about Arrangement A. First, consider any adjustment process $a(t) = f[a(t-1), \mu)]$ such that for all (μ, a_0), $\Delta W_t > 0$, $1 \leqslant t \leqslant 1/C$. As one decreases C, the terminal iteration T which uniquely maximizes $\pi_1(C, T)$ on an interval contained in $0 \leqslant t \leqslant 1/C$ becomes an earlier and earlier iteration.

Secondly, as long as $EW(\tilde{a}, \mu) < EW[a(T, \mu, a_0), \mu]$, a decline in C increases $\pi_1(C, T)$ *for a fixed T*, and does so at a constant rate; i.e. $\partial \pi_1(C, T)/\partial C$ is a positive constant. If, however (under the same condition), T is always taken to be an optimal T, $0 \leqslant T \leqslant 1/C$, for each C then the rate of the increase in expected total payoff as C decreases is generally not a constant, i.e. $d\pi_2/dC$ is not a constant, where

$$\pi_2(C) = \max_{0 \leqslant T \leqslant 1/C} \pi_1(C, T).$$

An organization which uses an arbitrary constant terminal iteration benefits from increases in its information-handling capacity in a manner quite different from that of an organization using the same adjustment process but using the best terminal iteration for each C. The condition $EW(\tilde{a}, \mu) < EW[a(T, \mu, a_0), \mu]$ is met for the process (2) when a_0 is taken to equal $\tilde{a}$.

Our third observation about Arrangement A is a lengthy one. We shall consider the quadratic case for a particular matrix Q, namely the 'identical-interaction' matrix for which $q_{ij} = q$, $i \neq j$, and $q_{ii} = 1$, $i, j = 1, \ldots, n$, where, to preserve positive definitiveness, $-1/(n-1) < q < 1$. In this case the process (5) displays a degenerate sort of decentralization. Since the initial actions a_{0i} are known to all, it is possible for each member to use the information he receives at iteration 1 to compute the μ_is of all other members and thereupon to compute his optimal action. It is hard (though not impossible) to visualize an information technology for which it would be more costly to achieve the optimal action in this way, in a given time interval, than to complete two iterations of the process (5). But the issues which we wish to examine are much more easily studied for the equal-interaction matrix than for any other.

We shall therefore investigate the performance of process (5) under Arrangement A *as one varies the interactions q while preserving the convergence of the process*. We are to preserve, that is to say, the property $\lim_{t \to \infty} a(t) = \hat{a}(\mu)$ which implies $\Delta W_t > 0$, $\Delta^2 W_t < 0$, and hence determines a best terminal iteration. For simplicity of exposition we consider the case $n = 2$; the generalization of the results to any n is tedious but straightforward.

The characteristic roots of the given matrix Q are the root $1 - q$ and the root $1 + (n - 1)q$, which has multiplicity $n - 1$. An orthonormal matrix of characteristic vectors is $B = (b_{ij})$. Since $H_t = 1/4\mu'B(I - 2hD)^{2t}D^{-1}B'\mu$, one obtains after some calculation:

$$\pi_1(C, T) = \tfrac{1}{4}(1 - CT)\sum_{i=1}^{n}(\bar{q}_{ii} - h_{T_{ii}}) = \frac{1}{4}(1 - CT)\left[\sum_{i=1}^{n}\bar{q}_{ii} - \theta(n, q, h, T)\right],$$

where

$$\theta(n, q, h, T) > \sum_{i=1}^{n} h_{T_{ii}} = [1/(1 - q)]\{1 - [1 - 2h(1 - q)]^{2T}\} +$$

$$\{1/1 + (n - 1)q\}\{1 - [1 - 2h + (n - 1)q]^{2T}\}$$

$$\cdot \sum_{k=2}^{n}[1 + (n - k + 1)^2]/[(n - k + 2)(n - k + 1)].$$

In order to compare the performance of process (5) with that of a centralized scheme for different values of q, it suffices to study the behaviour of θ, the expected distance left to go, as q changes for a fixed T, $1 \leqslant T \leqslant 1/C$. For as we shall see θ determines the expected 'penalty' suffered in the period between successive environments due to the imperfect information of the decentralized process (5). More precisely, this is the penalty due to computing for T iterations and then taking the non-optimal action $a(T, \mu, 0)$ for the rest of the period rather than operating a centralized process for just the iterations required to collect all μ_is and to compute and disseminate the optimal action $\hat{a}(\mu)$ which is thereupon in force for the rest of the period.

Now for each q in the interval $-1/(n - 1) < q < 1$, there is a different upper bound for the values of h which yield convergence. Since $1 + (n - 1)q$ is the largest root of Q the convergence requirement (14) becomes [1]

$$0 < h < 1/[1 + (n - 1)q]. \tag{16}$$

It is easily verified that for each q, the higher the value of h satisfying (16) the higher the value of the payoff $W[a(T, \mu, 0), \mu]$ achieved at the terminal iteration T. We shall therefore examine the variation with respect to q of the expected distance left to go when h is chosen to be 'best' (largest) for each q while still preserving con-

---

[1] It may be noted that one could consider varying n (the size of the organization) under the assumption that increasing n by one increases the dimension of μ by one and increases by one the order of Q. Then the larger the organization the smaller must be h, if convergence is to be preserved, and hence the smaller the value of W attained at any iteration T.

vergence. We examine the expected distance left to go, that is to say, for $h = 1/[1 + (n-1)q] - \epsilon(q)$, where $\epsilon(q)$ is small.

Suppose, however, that we establish that over the qs lying in some closed interval the function $\theta(n, q, 1/[1 + (n-1)q], T)$ has a derivative of a certain sign with respect to q. Then the continuity with respect to q and h of θ and its partial derivatives also imply that there exists an ϵ^* such that, for each positive $\epsilon < \epsilon^*$, the partial derivative of $\theta(n, q, 1/[1 + (n-1)q] - \epsilon, T)$ with respect to q has the same sign over the same interval. Accordingly it suffices to investigate the derivative of $\theta(n, q, T) = \theta(n, q, 1/[1 + (n-1)q], T)$ with respect to q over the closed interval $-1/(n-1) + \delta \leqslant q \leqslant 1 - \delta$, where $\delta > 0$ is arbitrarily small.

In particular,

$$\bar{\theta}(2, q, T) = \frac{(3q-1)/(1+q)^{2T}}{1-q} + 1/(1+q).$$

Its derivative with respect to q can be written

$$\frac{1}{(1+q)^2}\left\{\left(\frac{3q-1}{1+q}\right)^{2T-1}\frac{1}{(1-q)^2}[8T(1-q) + (3q-1)(1+q)] - 1\right\}. \qquad (17)$$

This becomes infinite as q approaches one but is negative for $-1(n+1) \leqslant q \leqslant 1/3$. Moreover

$$\frac{\partial^2\bar{\theta}(2, q, T)}{\partial q^2} = \frac{1}{(1+q)^2}\left[\frac{d\varphi}{dq} - \frac{2\varphi(q)}{1+q}\right],$$

where $\varphi(q)$ denotes the term in braces in (17) and

$$\frac{d\varphi}{dq} = \frac{2\varphi(q)}{1+q} = \left(\frac{3q-1}{1+q}\right)^{2T-1}\left[\frac{6q+2}{(1-q)^2} + \frac{2(1+q)(3q-1)}{(1-q)^3} + \frac{8T}{(1-q)^2}\right] +$$
$$\left(\frac{3q-1}{1+q}\right)^{2T-2}\left[\frac{8T(1-q) + (3q-1)(1+q)}{(1-q)^2(1+q)^2}\right](8T - 6q - 2) + \frac{2}{1+q},$$

which is positive for $1/3 \leqslant q \leqslant 1 - \delta$. It follows that there is some value of q, say q_T, which depends on $T(T \geqslant 1)$ and satisfies $1/3 \leqslant q_T \leqslant 1 - \delta$, such that

$$\frac{\partial\bar{\theta}(2, q, T)}{\partial q}\begin{Bmatrix}<\\=\\>\end{Bmatrix}0 \text{ for } q\begin{Bmatrix}<\\=\\>\end{Bmatrix}q_T.$$

We can, moreover, say something about the relation between q_T and T. To do so, let T take, for the moment, all positive real values (not merely integers) in the interval $1 \leqslant T \leqslant 1/C$. Observe that $\partial\bar{\theta}(2, q, T)/\partial q = 0$ when $\varphi(2, q, T) = 0$, and that

$$\frac{\partial\varphi}{\partial T} = \frac{1}{(1-q)^2}\left\{8\left(\frac{3q-1}{1+q}\right)^{2T-1}(1-q) + 2[8T(1-q) + \right.$$

$$(3q-1)(1+q)]\left[\log\left(\frac{3q-1}{1+q}\right)\right]\left(\frac{3q-1}{1+q}\right)^{2T-1}\right\} +$$

$$2\left(\frac{3q-1}{1+q}\right)^{2T-1}\left\{4(1-q) + [8T(1-q) + (3q-1)(1+q)]\log\left[\frac{3q-1}{1+q}\right]\right\},$$

which is negative for $q \geqslant 1/3$. Since it is also true that $\partial\varphi/\partial q$ is positive for $1/3 \leqslant q \leqslant 1 - \delta$ we have that as T increases the value of q for which $\varphi(2, q, T)$ vanishes, i.e. the value q_T, increases.

Let us summarize, extending the results to the case of any n. We have studied the expected distance left to go when Q is the equal-interaction matrix and the decentralized convergent process (5) is operated for $T \geqslant 1$ iterations while h is kept arbitrarily close to its permissible maximum. The expected distance left to go bears the following relation to the strength, q, of the interaction between members of the team: as q rises above $-1/(n-1)$ the expected distance left to go goes *down* but starts to rise at q_T, a value of q lying between zero and one; as q approaches one the expected distance left to go increases without limit. The value q_T is an increasing function of T.

What happens in the interval $0 \leqslant q \leqslant q_T$ might quite possibly be surprising. One might intuitively feel that as $|q|$ increases the value of complete information must rise: since, roughly speaking, the impact of each member's action on the desirability of others' actions rises, the importance of knowing u_is other than one's own rises and the expected distance by which the decentralized payoff $W[a(T, \mu, 0, \mu]$ falls short of the full-information payoff $W[\hat{a}(\mu)]$ ought to rise. This is in fact the case at $T = 0$, for then the expected distance left to go is

$$E\hat{W} - EW[\hat{a}(\mu)] = \frac{1}{4}\sum_{i=1}^{n}\bar{q}_{ii} = [n + qn(n-2)]/4[1 - (n-1)q^2 + (n-2)q],$$

which increases without limit as q approaches one. (The case $T = 0$ corresponds to a degenerate kind of decentralization in which no iterations are performed but only the best constant action (namely $a_0 = 0$) remains perpetually in force.) But in fact it is easily seen that for $T \geqslant 1$ the expected 'distance travelled', i.e. $W[a(T, \mu, 0), \mu]$, also increases without limit as q approaches one; it depends on the steepness of the slopes $\partial W[a(t, \mu, 0), \mu]/\partial a_i$ at the iterations $t \leqslant T$. For the interval $-1/(n-1) < q < q_T$, increasing q increases the expected distance travelled by more than it increases $E\hat{W}$; for the interval $q_T < q < 1$ the reverse is true.

Translation of the above results about expected distance left to go into results about the performance of the process (5) as compared to a centralized process are not quite so straightforward as might be expected. Suppose that the information-handling equipment used to operate the centralized process is such that the process attains the optimal action $\hat{a}(\mu)$ in $\bar{C}$ time units, $\bar{C} < 1$. Let Arrangement A be used in the centralized process, so that the interim action — in force until $\hat{a}(\mu)$ has been computed and its respective components made known to the appropriate members — is the best constant interim action, namely $a_0 = 0$. Then, if the cost of the given equipment is ignored, the centralized process is preferred to the decentralized process if $E[(1-\bar{c})\hat{W}] > E\{(1-CT)W[a(T, \mu, 0), \mu]\}$. Now the translation of the previous result, which involves the derivative of $E\{\hat{W} - W[a(T, \mu, 0), \mu]\}$ with respect to q, is as follows: As q rises in the interval $-1/(n-1) < q < q_T$, the superiority of the centralized process, i.e. the difference $E(1-\bar{C})\hat{W} - E\{(1-CT)W[a(T, \mu, 0), \mu]\}$, rises if $\bar{C} > CT$; otherwise it may fall. In the interval $q_T < q < 1$ the superiority of the centralized process falls if $\bar{C} > CT$; otherwise it may rise.

If the cost of the information-handling equipment is to be taken into account, then the relation of the centralization-decentralization comparison to the original result about expected distance left to go is even more remote — though it is less so if cost can simply be subtracted from the 'gross' payoffs $(1-CT)W[a(T, \mu, 0), \mu]$ and $(1-\bar{C})W$ to obtain the relevant 'net' payoffs.[1]

In any case, the example has shown the extreme caution with which one has to view intuitively appealing statements such as 'the stronger are interactions ('externalities'), the stronger the case for centralization'.

Similar caution is warranted in viewing another appealing statement which can again be tested with respect to the process (5) under Arrangement A. This is the statement that if we drop the part of Assumption 2 which states $E\mu_i\mu_j = 0$, $i \neq j$, then the stronger is the correlation between any two environment components the less the advantage of centralization or full information, since (roughly speaking) the more member i's own environment component tells him about

[1] As discussed in IV.8 below.

member j's the less the penalty due to not knowing j's component. To test this conjecture in the present context we assume that the μ_is have constant variance-covariance matrix with ones on the diagonal and all off-diagonal elements equal to σ, where $-1/(n-1)<\sigma<1$, to ensure positive definiteness.

For the case $n = 2$, with the same identical-interaction matrix Q as before, we find that the expected distance left to go for fixed h is

$$E\hat{W} - EW[a(T, \mu, 0), \mu] = \frac{1}{4}E\mu'H_T\mu$$

$$= \frac{(1+\sigma)[1 - 2h(1+q)]^{2T}}{1+q} + \frac{(1-\sigma)[1 - 2h(1-q)]^{2T}}{1-q}.$$

Proceeding as before, we set $h = \dfrac{1}{1+q}$ and obtain

$$\frac{1+\sigma}{1+q} + \frac{(1-\sigma)[(3q-1)/(1+q)]^{2T}}{1-q}.$$

The derivative of this expression with respect to σ is constant and for $T \geqslant 1$ is

$$\left.\begin{array}{r}>\\=\\<\end{array}\right\} 0 \text{ for } q \text{ satisfying} \begin{cases} -1<q<q_T^* \\ q = q_T \\ q_T<q<1. \end{cases}$$

The number q_T^* increases with T, $T \geqslant 1$. For $T = 0$, on the other hand, the expected distance left to go decreases as σ increases for all q in the interval $-1<q<1$. So again the intuitive conjecture is correct if no iterations are carried out and one has instead the degenerate decentralization of a perpetually unchanged action; it is not correct when one or more iterations are performed.

IV. 2. *Arrangement B: Constant Interim Action, Constant Initial Value, Best Current Terminal Iteration*

Suppose next that the organization uses a less routine arrangement: following each new environment it carries out the adjustment process (starting from a constant initial value) for a number of iterations that is some function of μ, maintaining a constant interim action $\tilde{a}$ in the meantime. Of particular interest is the function of μ that yields the *best current terminal iteration* for that μ, that is, since we can continue to ignore discounting the iteration T that maximizes $W(a, \mu)CT + W[\tilde{a}(T, \mu, a_0), \mu](1 - CT)$. This iteration depends, in general, on $\tilde{a}$ and a_0 as well as μ.

The argument leading to the theorem of the previous section is again relevant here. We have that if $\Delta^2 W_t < 0$ on an interval contained in the interval $0 \leqslant T \leqslant 1/C$, then there is a T that uniquely maximizes $W(\tilde{a}, \mu)CT + W[a(T, \mu, a_0), \mu](1 - CT)$ on that interval. This means that for any decision process (2) (with strict concavity) there is, in particular, for each μ a unique best current terminal iteration among all the iterations that occur prior to overshooting. For the quadratic case there is a unique best current terminal iteration on the entire interval $0 < T < 1/C$.

A natural interpretation [1] of each of these unique best current terminal iterations is as follows: it is that iteration within the appropriate interval at which the *marginal cost* of an additional iteration first exceeds the *marginal gain* of an additional iteration; or, if no such iteration exists in the interval, it is the latest iteration in the interval. The marginal cost of an additional iteration, when t have already been performed, is $C[\{Wa(t, \mu, a_0), \mu] - W(\tilde{a}, \mu)\}$, i.e. the payoff foregone by prolonging the interim payoff $W(\tilde{a}, \mu)$ for the time it takes to perform one more iteration. The marginal gain from an additional iteration is $\{W[a(t+1, \mu, a_0), \mu] - W[a(t, \mu, a_0), \mu]\}$ $(1 - CT)$, the increase in the total payoff enjoyed after the terminal iteration due to postponing the terminal iteration one more time. The condition that the marginal gain exactly equals the marginal cost (a condition not in general met for any integer) is seen to be equivalent to the condition that the first difference of $W(\tilde{a}, \mu) + W[a(t, \mu, a_0), \mu]$ with respect to t be exactly zero.

To apply the marginal-gain = marginal-cost rule in deciding when to stop iterating, the organization must approximate the marginal gain at each iteration t by the preceding marginal gain, since it cannot, at iteration t, know the term $W[a(t+1, \mu, a_0), \mu]$ without performing the next iteration. More serious is the fact that to compute the values of $W[a(t, \mu, a_0), \mu]$ and $W(a, \mu)$ requires all of the components μ_i of μ. If the process is of the form (4), it is difficult to see how the best current terminal iteration can be selected without depriving the process of decentralization, presumably its main virtue.

If the best current terminal iteration is used (and a constant initial value and interim action) the performance of the process is measured by

$$\pi_3(C) \equiv E \max_{0 < T < 1/C} \{W(\tilde{a}, \mu)CT + W[a(T, \mu, a_0), \mu](1 - CT)\}.$$

[1] An analogous interpretation of the best terminal iteration is given by Marglin (1963).

We observe that $d\pi_3/dC$ is certainly negative, as long as $EW(a, \mu)$ $<EW[a(T, \mu, a_0), \mu]$ for the best current T, but that it differs from $\partial \pi_1(T, C)/\partial C$ and from $d\pi_2/dC$.

IV. 3. *Arrangement C: Constant Terminal Iteration, Constant Initial Value, Interim Action Equal to Preceding Action*

In the last two arrangements considered, the organization, following a new environment μ, has to change its action *twice*: once from the previous action to the constant interim action and again from the interim action to the action obtained at the termination of the adjustment process, which is initiated in response to μ. We now consider an arrangement which requires only one change of action and may therefore be useful to organizations whose changes of action must be kept infrequent. The arrangement is also worth studying because it may be a very desirable one once we drop the assumption that successive environments are independently distributed. In this arrangement, the preceding action is continued, after the new environment μ is observed, until the new action has been generated; the new action is generated by operating the decision process until iteration T (T a constant), starting always at the same initial value a_0. (If T is the largest integer not exceeding $1/C$, then there is one action in force throughout each period, namely an action computed in the preceding period.) [1]

The expected total payoff between successive environments again measures performance and is

$$\pi_4(C, T \equiv \underset{\mu^*, \mu}{E} \{W[a(T, \mu^*, a_0), \mu]CT + W[a(T, \mu, a_0), \mu](1 - CT)\},$$

where the expectation is taken over all pairs μ^*, μ. We observe immediately that *for any adjustment process $\pi_4(C, T)$ never exceeds $\pi_1(C, T)$ — the payoff under Arrangement A — when Arrangement A uses the best constant interim action $\tilde{a}$ and the same initial value as Arrangement C.* For the current environment μ is independent of the preceding environment μ and the action $a(T, \mu^*, a_0)$ is, for a fixed adjustment process, a random variable distributed independently of μ. Therefore to use the preceding action as the interim action that follows μ is, in effect, to use a *randomized* interim action following each new environment μ.

But consider the general question of choosing an action (out of

[1] 'Period' means here the interval between successive environments.

some set of actions) so as to maximize the expected value of a function of the action and an unknown state of nature. It is well known that if the probability distribution of the possible states of nature is known, and if there exists an action in the set for which the expected value of the function is not less than for any other action in the set, then the expected value of the function cannot be further increased by randomizing over the set of actions. Hence for fixed T and a_0 the expected payoff $\pi_1(C, T)$ cannot be improved by substituting for the best constant interim action $\tilde{a}$ a randomized action — in particular, the randomized action obtained from the preceding period.

If the interim action is the preceding action, and if a fixed T and a_0 are used, it is *not* true for all adjustment processes, or even for all the processes (2) (with W strictly concave in a), that reducing C increases the expected total payoff between successive environments. For it cannot be ruled out that for the chosen T and a_0

$$\underset{\mu^*, \mu}{E}\ W[a(T, \mu^*, a_0), \mu] > EW[a(T, \mu, a_0), \mu], \tag{18}$$

i.e. that a T has been picked which yields actions that are, on the average, worse for the environment that initiated the decision process than for environments drawn at random. If (18) holds, then $\partial\pi_4(C, T)/\partial C > 0$ for $0 \leqslant C \leqslant 1$. If (18) is false for a given process, however, then $\partial\pi_4(C, T)/\partial C < 0$, and this is true even if the payoff path $W[a(t, \mu, a_0), \mu]$ fluctuates as t increases (i.e. decreases at some iterations and increases at others). For the quadratic gradient-method case, (18) is false.

Finally, we observe that by the argument above

$$\pi_5(C) \leqslant \pi_2(C) \text{ for all } C, \quad 0 < C < 1,$$

where $\pi_5(C) = \max_{0 \leqslant T \leqslant 1/C} \pi_4(C, T)$. If (18) is assumed false for every T, $0 \leqslant T \leqslant 1/C$, then $d\pi_5/dC < 0$. In any case $\pi_5(C)$ has a very different shape, in general, than the other functions π_i, $i = 1, \ldots, 4$.

IV. 4. *Arrangement D: Constant Terminal Iteration, Interim Action Equal to Preceding Action, Initial Value Equal to Preceding Action*

We briefly consider this arrangement, chiefly because of a distinctive property: discounting can no longer be ignored in measuring the performance of a process. In addition there may be an organizational advantage in the fact that each participant's interim action serves also as his initial tentative action in the adjustment process.

Let μ^j denote the jth of a sequence of successive environments. For a fixed terminal iteration T the total payoff in the interval between the environment μ^j and the next environment is

$$\pi^j(C, T) = W(a^{j-1}, \mu^j)CT + W(a^j, \mu^j)(1 - CT),$$

where a^j denotes the action generated by the decision process in response to the environment μ^j and $a^j = a(T, \mu^j, a^{j-1})$. Thus the total payoff between two successive environments is recursively defined. For a given initial environment μ^1, a stochastic process (easily seen to be Markov) generates the sequence of observed total payoffs. The performance of the process under Arrangement D is measured by

$$\pi_6(C, T) \equiv E \sum_{j=1}^{\infty} \rho^j \pi^j(C, T),$$

where ρ is the discount factor.

An analogous statement to that made in the previous section, about the superiority of a best constant interim action, applies here. An interim action a^{j-1} is taken and the interim payoff $W(a^{j-1}, \mu^j)CT$ depends on μ^j, which is unknown when the organization commits itself to the interim action a^{j-1}, although its probability distribution is known. The interim action a^{j-1} is a randomized action although its distribution is far more complicated than the distribution of the randomized interim action considered above. It follows that if $\tilde{a}$ is the best constant interim action, then $\pi^j(C, T)$ is not greater than

$$\bar{\pi}^j(C, T) \equiv W(\tilde{a}, \mu^j)CT + W[a(T, \mu^j, a^{j-1}), \mu^j](1 - CT);$$

that

$$\pi_6(C, T) \leqslant \pi_7(C, T) \equiv E \sum_{j=1}^{\infty} \rho^j \bar{\pi}^j(C, T);$$

and also that

$$\pi_8(C) \equiv \max_{0 \leqslant T \leqslant 1/C} \pi_6(C, T) \leqslant \pi_9(C) \equiv \max_{0 \leqslant T \leqslant 1/C} \pi_7(C, T).$$

IV. 5. *Arrangement E: Constant Terminal Iteration, Best Current Local Interim Action, Constant Initial Value*

An interesting arrangement, but one that is less routine with respect to interim action than any of the preceding ones, is as follows. After each new environment μ, each participant i takes an interim action which is a function $\bar{\alpha}_i$ of μ_i, the component of the environment that he observes, but not of any other μ_j, $j \neq i$. Thus the interim actions

338

are decentralized (or 'local'), preserving the distinctive virtue of such processes as (5), while yet making some use of the organization's knowledge of the new environment. The chosen functions $\bar{\alpha}_i$ are to yield a higher expected interim payoff than any other functions $\alpha_i(\mu_i)$. If the initial value is kept constant we have

$$\pi_{10}(C, T) \equiv EW\{[\bar{\alpha}_1(\mu_1), \ldots, \bar{\alpha}_n(\mu_n)], \mu\}CT + EW[a(T, \mu, a_0), \mu](1 - CT),$$

where

$$EW\{[\bar{\alpha}_1(\mu_1), \ldots, \bar{\alpha}_n(\mu_n)], \mu\} = \max_{\alpha_1, \ldots, \alpha_n} EW\{[\alpha_1(\mu_1), \ldots, \alpha_n(\mu_n)], \mu\}.$$

It has been shown by R. Radner (1962) that for the quadratic case, under the assumption of zero correlation between the components of μ,

$$\bar{\alpha}_i(\mu_i) = \mu_i/2q_{ii}, \qquad i = 1, \ldots, n.$$

For the quadratic case, then, we have, under Assumption 2

$$\pi_{10}(C, T) = \tfrac{1}{4}\Big(\sum_{i=1}^{n} 1/q_{ii}\Big)CT + \frac{1}{4}\sum_{i=1}^{n}(q_{ii} - H_{T_{ii}})(1 - CT).$$

We observe that $\pi_{10}(C, T) \geqslant \pi_1(C, T)$ and that $\partial\pi_{10}/\partial C$ is again negative as long as the expected payoff for the interim action is less than expected payoff for the action generated by the adjustment process at iteration T.

IV. 6. *Arrangement F: Constant Terminal Iteration, Best Constant Interim Action, Locally Best Current Initial Value*

In this arrangement, and in others for which the initial value is chosen in the same manner, the situation may be drastically changed. The initial value is now a *variable* initial value; after each change of environment each member i chooses his initial action afresh as a function of the new μ_i. This means that if a process is defined by a function f in the first-order difference-equation system (1), then using Arrangement F formally requires an addition to the process. The additional step, which precedes the process defined by f, is the formation of the initial actions, each of which has then to be sent to every member who needs it in order to compute his component of $a(1)$. If the process defined by f is temporally homogeneous — as are the price mechanisms that have been proposed — then the augmented process loses temporal homogeneity, unless one formally preserves it by adding some artificial 'dummy' actions not effectively entering the payoff function. Unless one does this the operations which each member performs on his current information to obtain his next tentative action are no longer the same prior to every iteration: the operations performed prior to the first iteration are different from the operations after the tth and prior to the $(t+1)$st, $t \geqslant 1$. This is not the case when a_0 is a constant, as in the previous arrangements.

The sacrifice of temporal homogeneity, or its artificial preservation through dummy variables, would deprive the process of the 'decentralized' label given in our definition; it may also be undesirable from the point of view of routineness or for the study of processes most resembling price mechanisms. If one is willing to make the sacrifice, however, then Arrangement F offers a striking possibility: it may become possible to achieve the optimum action $\hat{a}(\mu)$ after a *finite* and perhaps quite small number of iterations while still preserving the main property of decentralization — avoiding the direct transmission of the μ_i. This is the case for the quadratic payoff function and the process (5), at least for certain matrices Q. If it is not possible to achieve optimality at a finite iteration in this fashion, it is at least possible (except for very special distributions of μ) to achieve a higher expected value of W at each T than is permitted by a fixed initial value.

Arrangement F requires that we find functions $a_0^{iT}(\mu_i)$ which maximize $EW\{a[T, \mu, a_0^T(\mu)], \mu\}$, where $a_0^T(\mu)$ is the vector $[a_0^{1T}(\mu_1), \ldots, a_0^{nT}(\mu_n)]$. The superscript T indicates that the optimal values for generating the best initial actions generally depend on the terminal iteration T. When $W\{a[T, \mu, a_0^T(\mu)], \mu\}$, viewed as a function of $a_0^T(\mu)$, has convenient properties (principally strict concavity) a theorem of R. Radner [1] can be used to determine the required functions $a^{iT}(\mu)$.

In the quadratic case, we see from (12) that the problem may be put: find the vector of functions $a_{0T}^i(\mu)$ maximizing

$$EG_T = E\{\lambda'_T[a_0^T(\mu)] - [a_0^T(\mu)]'S_T[a_0^T(\mu)]\},$$

where S_T is the symmetric positive definite matrix $(I - 2hQ)^T Q$ $(I - 2hQ)^T$ and λ_T is the vector $SQ^{-1}\mu$. Thus G_T has exactly the same form as the function $\mu'[\tilde{a}(\mu)] - [\tilde{a}(\mu)]Q'[\tilde{a}(\mu)]$, the maximization of whose expected value with respect to the functions $\tilde{a}(\mu)$, using the theorem of Radner, yields the best local interim actions of Arrangement E. Applying the theorem here, one obtains, under Assumption

[1] The 'person-by-person optimality' theorem (Radner, 1962).

2 (zero correlation)[1] that the optimal functions $\hat{a}_0^{iT}(\mu_i)$ are

$$\hat{a}_0^{iT}(\mu_i) = \frac{\mu_i[i\text{th diagonal element of } (I - 2hQ)^T Q (I - 2hQ)^T Q^{-1}]}{2[i\text{th diagonal element of } (I - 2hQ)^T Q (I - 2hQ)^T]}$$

$$\equiv \alpha_0^{iT} \mu_i.$$

Using the functions $\hat{a}_0^{iT}(\mu_i)$, the team travels, in T iterations, a greater expected distance toward the optimal payoff $\hat{W}$ than is true for any other rules for determining fresh initial values.

We next ask the following question: Suppose we vary h. For what matrices Q can we find an h such that

$$EW\{a[1, \mu, \hat{a}_0^{1\prime}\mu], \mu\} = E\hat{W}(\mu), \tag{19}$$

so that optimality is achieved in a single iteration?[2] Since for each μ there is a unique maximizing action $\hat{a}(\mu)$, this condition is met for all distributions satisfying Assumption 2 if and only if $a[1, \mu, \hat{a}_0^1(\mu)] = \hat{a}(\mu)$ for each μ, i.e. if and only if for every μ

$$\frac{1}{2}[I - (I - 2hQ)]Q^{-1}\mu + (I - 2hQ)A\mu = \frac{1}{2}Q^{-1}$$

or

$$[(I - 2hQ)(A - \frac{1}{2}Q^{-1})]\mu = 0, \tag{20}$$

where A is the diagonal matrix with ith diagonal element equal to $\hat{\alpha}^{1i}$. This in turn implies that the matrix in brackets equals zero.[3]

Now consider again the equal-interaction matrix Q with ones on the diagonal and qs off the diagonal. After some calculation one finds that (20) is solved (for any n) by $h = 1/2(1 - q)$, for which $\hat{a}_0^{1i} = (1 - q)/2[1 - (n - 1)q^2 + (n - 2)q]$. In a formal sense the augmented process fulfils both conditions of our decentralization definition (which we restricted, however, to temporally homogeneous processes) and yet for the h just found optimality is achieved after a single iteration (subsequent iterations would merely repeat the same tentative actions). Note that the convergence property has been sacrificed, since for $q > 1/3$, $h = 1/[2(1 - q)]$ violates the convergence requirement (14). For this h, in other words, there is no longer convergence to the maximizing action for *any* fixed initial value and any μ, which,

[1] For the case of non-zero correlation among the μ_i, adaptation of Radner's procedure is also straightforward.

[2] The vector $(\hat{a}_0^{1T}, \ldots, \hat{a}_0^{nT})$ is denoted $\hat{a}_0^T$.

[3] For specially chosen distributions — e.g. those assigning zero probability to the set of μ's not on the hyperplane defined by (20) — a weaker condition on Q insures an h satisfying (19).

as we saw, is a useful property for some arrangements when a best terminal iteration is to be chosen. But since the initial value is now to be chosen afresh for each μ the sacrifice is of no consequence.

Just as in IV. 1, the identical-interaction matrix — a weak case from the point of view of the advantages of process (5) over a centralized process — provides here the most easily obtained illustration of a general point. The point is that optimal local choice of initial value following each environment may considerably improve the performance of a decentralized process. In the case of a gradient-method process, combining such choice of initial value with choice of h (or more generally choice of a vector $(h_1, \ldots, h_n)$, where h_i describes the ith member's adjustment at each iteration) provides still further improvement, sometimes permitting optimality at a finite T. The condition (20) for optimality at $T = 1$ in the quadratic case is satisfied when the interactions display sufficient 'similarity' so that $(I - 2hQ)$ $(A - 1/2Q^{-1}) = 0$ for some h. It seems worthwhile to explore whether or not this is a special case of some more general proposition according to which greater 'similarity' of interactions (a property of the payoff function) implies better performance of decentralized processes when one is free to adjust their initial values.

Needless to say for Arrangement F the increment in the performance of a process as C decreases — the increment in

$$\pi_{11}(C, T) = EW(\tilde{a}, \mu)CT + EW\{a[T, \mu, \hat{a}_0^T(\mu)], \mu\}(1 - CT)$$

as C decreases — is different than for other arrangements (it is greater, in particular, than for Arrangements A and B).

IV. 7. *Other Possible Arrangements*

We have considered arrangements in which the interim action is a constant (arbitrary or best), equals the preceding action, or is the best current local interim action; in which the terminal iteration is a constant (arbitrary or best), or is the best current terminal iteration; in which the initial value is a constant (arbitrary or best), equals the preceding action, or is composed of the best functions of the current local environment. We have by no means examined, even for the quadratic case, all possible combinations of these categories. And other categories, as well as expanded definitions of 'arrangement', can be studied. If one expands the definition of arrangement too much, however, one risks leaving the manageable study of a restricted class of processes with each of which any of the possible arrangements can be used ; one risks enlarging the inquiry toward the very general problem sketched at the start.[1]

Each arrangement considered, and others, may be of serious interest to the organization contemplating a proposed adjustment process. For though some arrangements are better than others with respect to the appropriate function π_j, each has a generally advantageous property : routineness, preserving complete decentralization (as Arrangement B does not), permitting the interim action to become also the initial value and so on. The exact measurement of these advantages for each arrangement (e.g. the 'costs' of changing actions once or twice), and the balancing of these advantages against the appropriate π_j, would take us into still less explored areas in the study of organizations. Short of such measurement, the comparison of two proposed processes will have to be made for several different arrangements. For any arrangement considered, moreover, a 'technology-free' statement of comparison can be made, in which the missing knowledge of the communication and computation technology is precise and perhaps obtainable. We shall briefly illustrate.

IV. 8. *Technology-free Comparison of a Decentralized and a Centralized Adjustment Process*

Suppose a team with a quadratic payoff function contemplates the process (5) but also contemplates the centralized alternative which we briefly considered in IV. 1. If one wished one could formally put the centralized alternative as a temporally homogeneous first-order adjustment process $a(t) = f[a(t-1), \mu]$, in which a central member has an action vector that does not effectively enter the payoff function and other members have action vectors some of whose components do not. The process reaches equilibrium after a small number of iterations, when an optimal action has been attained. In the case of two members (members 1 and 2) plus a central member (member 3) the process might be put, for example, as follows :

$$a_1 = (a'_1, a''_1), \qquad a_2 = (a'_2, a''_2),$$

$$a_3 = (a'_3, a''_3, a'''_3, a''''_3),$$

$$W(a_1, a_2, a_3, \mu) = \mu_1 a'_1 + \mu_2 a'_2 - 2q_{12}a'_1 a'_2 - q_{11}a'^2_1 - q_{22}a'^2_2$$

---

[1] The risk is run, for example, if one adds to the elements defining an arrangement a 'terminal operation', to follow the terminal iteration, in which each member uses *all* the information he has acquired through the process thus far in order to choose that new action which is best given that information.

$$a_1(t) = f^1[a_1(t-1), a_2(t-1), a_3(t-1), \mu_1]$$

$$= \begin{cases} (\mu_1, \mu_1) \text{ if } a'_3(t-1) \neq \mu_1 \\ [a''_3(t-1), \mu_1] \text{ if } a'_3(t-1) = \mu_1 \end{cases}$$

$$a_2(t) = f^2[a_1(t-1), a_2(t-1), a_3(t-1), \mu_2]$$

$$= \begin{cases} (\mu_2, \mu_2) \text{ if } a'''_3(t-1) \neq \mu_2 \\ [a''''_3(t-1), \mu_2] \text{ if } a'''_3(t-1) = \mu_2 \end{cases}$$

$$a_3(t) = f^2[a_1(t-1), a_2(t-1), a_3(t-1)]$$

$$= \begin{cases} a_3(t-1) \text{ if } a'_1(t-1) \neq a''_1(t-1) \\ \{a'_1(t-1), \hat{a}_1[a'_1(t-1), a'_2(t-1)], a'_2(t-1), \\ \hat{a}_2[a'_1(t-1), a'_2(t-1)] \} \} \text{ if } a'_1(t-1) = a''_1(t-1). \end{cases}$$

The process starts with any fixed initial action $(a_{0_1}, a_{0_2}, a_{0_3})$, for which $a'_{0_1} \neq a''_{0_1}, a'_{0_2} \neq a''_{0_2}, (a'_{0_3}, a'''_{0_3}) \epsilon M$. Members 1 and 2 merely repeat their environment components twice at iteration 1 while member 3 simply 'marks time', Member 3, observing the others' repeated actions, knows it is time to compute the optimal actions and does so, at iteration 2. Members 1 and 2 then observe, respectively, that member 3's first and third action components are now equal to μ_1 and to μ_2 (initially they are not, since they then lie outside M, the set of possible μs). This is the signal that member 3's first and third components are the required optimal values. At iteration 4 equilibrium has been reached; from then on members 1 and 2 repeat the optimal effective actions (as first components of their action vectors), while member 3 also repeats his action.

Note that the process satisfies condition (ii) of our decentralization definition; if we did not also require condition (i) it would be a decentralized process.

Now let $\bar{C}(0 < \bar{C} < 1)$ be the time required to attain the iteration at which the optimal actions are in the possession of the appropriate members. If the organization uses such a centralized process it has no effective choice with respect to terminal iteration or initial value, but it does confront choices with respect to interim action, namely *all the choices it confronts if it uses a decentralized process*. Thus suppose the organization plans to use, for both of the contemplated processes, the best current local interim action. For the decentralized process it also plans to use the best constant initial value and the best constant terminal iteration. It must then compare $\pi_{10}(C)$ with

$$\bar{\pi}(C) = \frac{1}{4} \left(\sum_{i=1}^{n} 1/q_{ii} \right) \bar{C} + \frac{1}{4} \sum_{i=1}^{n} \bar{q}_{ii}(1 - \bar{C}), \text{ where } (\bar{q}_{ii}) = Q^{-1}.$$

Assume now that if the costs of achieving the completion times C and $\bar{C}$ are measured in the proper units and denoted $\varphi(C)$, $\varphi(\bar{C})$, then $\bar{\pi}(\bar{C}) - \bar{\varphi}(\bar{C})$, $\pi_{10}(C) - \varphi(C)$ give the organization's expected total 'net' payoff between successive environments for the two processes; the quantity $W(a, \mu)$ may now be called 'gross' payoff. This is the additivity assumption frequently made in decision problems in which the cost of acquiring information has to be taken into account; without it few such problems would be manageable. The assumption states that the organization ranks alternative choices of adjustment process and information-handling equipment according to expected discounted total net payoff; the additivity assumption is therefore a restriction on the organization's preferences among gambles whose outcomes are gross payoff-completion–time-equipment cost combinations.

The organization can proceed to find *conditions on the functions* φ and $\bar{\varphi}$ under which the decentralized process yields a higher neat net payoff than the centralized process. *The statement of these conditions is the required technology-free comparison.* The communication and computation expert can then (in principle) be consulted to determine whether or not the conditions are met. Different arrangements imply different technology-free comparisons.

Some general remarks are now in order concerning the tacit assumption in much current discussion that decentralization (in the sense of retention by individuals of their observations of the environment) is not a virtue but a *necessity*.

However complex the environmental information, there ought to be some amount of time and money by which it can be gathered in a central place. If necessary, the 'device' which performs the transmission may be the temporary physical displacement of each specialized observer from his normal location to the central place. Perhaps a more questionable, but still plausible assertion is that alternative transmission times can be purchased at alternative costs.

Consider the decentralized price mechanisms currently proposed. In several of these schemes each individual's specialized information about the environment is explicitly assumed to be a vector (or matrix) of functions (e.g. the functions $g_{ij}(x_i)$ which give the amount that participant i, in charge of activity i, requires of commodity j when he operates his activity at level x_i). The vector may be an enormously long one and each function in it may take many parameters to identify. But the messages which *are* transmitted in these schemes are also vectors (price vectors, demand vectors) and are generally transmitted many times during the operation of the process (whereas in a centralized scheme the environment vectors would have to be gathered only once in each operation). The difficulties of transmitting the messages which are transmitted as compared to those which are not should be measurable in a precise fashion for a sufficiently well-specified communication technology.

We can briefly illustrate a simple (and extremely clumsy) technology.[1] Suppose all messages transmitted from participant i to participant j in all repetitions of the process belong to a set P_{ij} of p_{ij}-dimensional real vectors (this has been the case in the processes we have considered). Now let a *round-off* rule be specified: each co-ordinate of a message that the process requires to be transmitted is rounded off so as to achieve always a number composed of D_{ij} decimal digits. Let the transmission line from i to j carry ten distinct signals corresponding to the ten symbols of the decimal system. A message from i to j then requires $p_{ij}D_{ij}$ successive signals. The capacity of the transmission line is the number of signals it can transmit per time unit and this determines the time required to send a message. Capacity is continuously variable. If appropriate assumptions are also made about the computing technology, the assumption of our previous discussion (in the present section and in preceding ones) is satisfied; by suitable choice of capacities the time required for each participant — and hence for the organization — to complete an iteration in the decision process $a(t) = f[a(t-1), \mu]$ can be made equal to a specified number C.[2]

The costs of achieving alternative transmission capacities, and corresponding information about computation costs, are the missing pieces in a technology-free comparison of centralized and decentralized processes, if the clumsy but simple technology just described is assumed to obtain. In the absence of such cost information it is by

[1] I am grateful to C. B. McGuire for useful suggestions on matters of technology.

[2] The transmission technology described is very inefficient. Some messages from i to j will in fact occur more frequently than others (the frequency distribution depends, for a given process, on the distribution of μ). Codings can be used that take advantage of this fact so as to require shorter sequences of signals for the more frequently sent messages. The result is that much lower transmission capacities (than in the technology described) suffice to achieve a given *average* iteration-completion time. For this more efficient technology, all our previous discussion would have to be restated so that the number C becomes a random variable whose expected value is chosen. The possibility of transmission inaccuracy (noise) is a further complication.

We note also that if the technology described above is used, the validity of our previous discussion rests on a tacit assumption: that there exist round-off numbers D_{ij} such that all the properties of adjustment processes that we have found are preserved when the messages specified by the original processes are rounded off to D_{ij} decimal digits for each pair of participants ij.

no means clear that the decentralized schemes that have been proposed dominate the centralized alternatives even for the simple technology just described.

V. THE CASE OF SERIALLY DEPENDENT ENVIRONMENTS

If the probability distribution of the environment at a given time depends on the preceding environments — if the environment is generated by a (non-degenerate) stochastic process — then the performance of a decision process is much more difficult to measure. Moreover, the same range of choices of interim action, terminal action, and initial value is now open to the organization as in the case of independent environments.

For certain choices, however, it may be possible to draw some conclusions about the performance of a given decision process for a given payoff function from very incomplete knowledge of the environment's stochastic process. We shall give a very simple illustration.

Suppose the payoff function W has the form (3) and some adjustment process $a(t) = f[a(t-1), \mu]$ is used such that $\Delta W[a(t), \mu, a_0] > 0$ for all μ, a_0, t. Suppose that the environmental stochastic process, generating successive environments μ^1, μ^2, ... has the following property — the martingale property:

$$E[\mu^j/(\mu^{j-1}, \mu^{j-2}, \ldots, \mu^1)] = \mu^{j-1}.$$

Let a fixed terminal iteration T be used. We shall show that it is always *worse — in the sense of yielding a lower expected sum of discounted total payoffs π^j — to use a constant interim action $\tilde{a}$ and to let the initial value also be $\tilde{a}$ than to use the preceding action as the interim action while again using $\tilde{a}$ as the initial value.*

Proof: Let π^j denote the total (undiscounted) payoff in the interval following μ^j, the jth environment, when a constant interim action $\tilde{a}$ is used, and let $\bar{\pi}^j$ denote the total (undiscounted) payoff when the interim action equals the preceding action. The term of π^j giving the part of the total payoff experienced after the iteration T is identical with the corresponding term of $\bar{\pi}^j$. It suffices to investigate the interim payoff under the two arrangements. We have, for the interim payoff when the interim action equals the preceding action,

$$\underset{\mu^j/\mu^{j-1}\mu, \ldots, \mu^1}{E} \{(\mu^j)'a(T, \mu^{j-1}, \tilde{a}) + S[a(T, \mu^{j-1}, \tilde{a})]\}.$$

347

By the martingale assumption this equals

$$(\mu^{j-1})'a(T, \mu^{j-1}, \tilde{a}) + S[a(T, \mu^{j-1}, \tilde{a})],$$

which is precisely the value of $W(a, \mu^{j-1})$ obtained when the process has been operated for T iterations starting with the initial value $\tilde{a}$, and is therefore strictly greater than $(\mu^j)'\tilde{a} + S(\tilde{a})$ — the initial value of $W(a, \mu^{j-1})$ in the same process. Hence for any j and any $(\mu^1, \ldots, \mu^{j-1})$,

$$E(\pi^j/\mu^{j-1}, \ldots, \mu^1) < E(\bar{\pi}^j/\mu^{j-1}, \ldots, \mu^1),$$

which implies the proposition stated.

VI. CONCLUDING REMARKS

We shall cut short here our survey of the issues that have to be faced in comparing adjustment processes.

We have argued that studying a general problem of optimal design of teams is unlikely to be fruitful for the comparison of specific adjustment processes such as price mechanisms. A more restricted framework is needed. One such framework is provided by the assumption that computation has to cease before a new environment and that between environments only two actions (the interim action and the freshly computed one) are in force. Comparisons among the members of a restricted class of processes, each of which can be used in a number of arrangements, are then possible.[1] For a fixed process arrangements may differ radically with respect to performance for a fixed iteration-completion time, with respect to change in performance as iteration-completion time is varied, and with respect to the

---

[1] Among the specific comparison problems not discussed above which can be studied within the framework is the comparison of the Dantzig–Wolfe process for solving ('decomposing') linear programming problems (Dantzig and Wolfe, 1961) and the 'non-decomposed' standard simplex process. Consider a team which wants to achieve a good feasible solution to a linear programming problem following each new environment (a new environment defines a new problem). Make Assumptions 1 and 2 and suppose that the team adopts Arrangement A, with an always feasible interim action and initial programme. Then the condition for the superiority of the decomposed process over the non-decomposed process could be put as a simple technology-free statement if for the tth basis obtained (at iteration t) in the decomposed process payoff is not lower than at the tth basis in the non-decomposed process. The missing technological information would then have to do with the cost of achieving alternative iteration times in the two processes. If the condition were satisfied and the decomposed process completed each iteration more quickly (for a fixed cost) than the non-decomposed process, the decomposed process would be superior. Unfortunately the condition is not in general satisfied (in fact the reverse of the condition is sometimes true), and no other condition implying a simple comparison has been found.

support that one can give to intuitive statements about the advantage of decentralization and its relation to 'externalities' or 'interactions'. For arrangements in which the best terminal iteration (constant or current) is to be chosen the classic property of convergence to payoff-maximizing actions was seen to be a useful property if it implies positive first difference and negative second difference of the payoff for iterations in a relevant interval. The usefulness of other classic properties of recently developed decentralized price mechanisms — temporal homogeneity, informational 'privacy', and so on — depends in a complex way on payoff function, arrangement, environmental probability distribution, and information technology. Our discussion suggests that it is simply not possible to defend these properties in isolation.[1]

REFERENCES

Almon, C. (1962), 'Central Planning with Complete Information at the Center', in Dantzig, G. B., *Linear Programming and Extensions*, Princeton, N.J.: Princeton Univ. Press.

Arrow, K. J., and Hurwicz, L. (1962), 'Decentralization and Computation in Resource Allocation', in *Studies in Mathematical Economics and Econometrics*, ed. Phouts, R. W., University of North Carolina Press.

Barone, E. (1935), 'The Ministry of Production in the Collectivist State', *Collectivist Economic Planning*, ed. Hayek, F. A., London: Routledge.

Dantzig, G. B., and Wolfe, P. (1961), 'The Decomposition Algorithm for Linear Programs', *Econometrica*.

Hayek, F. (1945), 'The Use of Knowledge in Society', *Amer. Econ. Rev.*

Hurwicz, L. (1960), 'Optimality and Efficiency in Resource Allocation Processes', in *Mathematical Methods in the Social Sciences*, eds. Arrow, Karlin, and Suppes, Stanford, Calif.: Stanford Univ. Press.

[1] An alternative approach to that taken here would be to consider all processes that exhibit certain classic properties and that are 'satisfactory', in some sense, with respect to a class of payoff functions — they maximize such functions at equilibrium, for example. One might then attempt to show that no satisfactory process outside the class is 'informationally more efficient' than any process in the class, where the term in quotation marks is defined in the spirit of the definitions given by Hurwicz (1960): one process is informationally more efficient than another, for example, if it requires of each member the perception of fewer distinct signals (as one passes over the set of possible initiating environments). Such a definition, however, not only provides just a partial ordering of processes but is tied to a restricted information technology (one in which increasing the number of distinct signals perceived is costly, for example, rather than one in which increasing the number of distinct members to whom messages have to be sent is costly). Such a definition, to be workable, may also ignore the costs of computation, concentrating entirely on the costs of transmission. Nevertheless the approach seems well worth pursuing, perhaps in parallel with the one considered here.

Group Decisions and Market Mechanisms

Lange, O. (1938), 'On the Economic Theory of Socialism', in Lange, O., and Taylor, F. M., *On the Economic Theory of Socialism*, University of Minnesota Press,

Malinvaud, E. (1961), *On Decentralization in National Planning*, Technical Report No. 15, Center for Research in Management Science, University of California, Berkeley.

Marglin, S. (1963), *Approaches to Dynamic Investment Planning*, North-Holland Publishing Co.

— (1964), *Decentralization with a Modicum of Increasing Returns*, Santa Monica, California : The RAND Corporation.

Marschak, J., and Radner, R., *The Economic Theory of Teams*, Monograph, Cowles Foundation for Research in Economics, forthcoming.

Marschak, T. (1959), 'Centralization and Decentralization in Economic Organizations', *Econometrica*.

Radner, R. (1962), 'The Evaluation of Information in Organizations', *Proceedings of the Fourth Berkeley Symposium on Mathematical Statistics and Probability*, Berkeley, Calif. : University of California Press.

Uzawa, H. (1958), 'Iterative Methods for Concave Programming', in Arrow, Hurwicz, and Uzawa, *Studies in Linear and Nonlinear Programming*, Stanford, Calif. : Stanford Univ. Press.

Whinston, A. (1962), 'Price Guides in Decentralized Organization', Cowles Foundation Discussion Paper No. 141 (June) (mimeographed).

DISCUSSION OF THE PAPER BY
PROFESSOR MARSCHAK

Dr. Ullrich : The paper presented by Professor Marschak is very interesting not only from the point of view of economics but also from the point of view of mathematics.

The optimal design for choosing actions by different members of a team in a special case of decentralized price mechanism is given when different members of the team face only a part of the environment. The optimum for the team corresponds to the maximum of a given payoff function.

Professor Marschak considers different kinds of arrangements, i.e. different procedures for determining the interim action, the initial action for the adjustment process, and the terminal iteration of this adjustment process.

The paper contains many new results which are all proved mathematically.

I would like to ask the following two questions in connection with the paper :

(1) In the mathematical arguments in Section IV it is assumed that corresponding observations of the environment made by different members are uncorrelated or independent. I think that such an assumption is very limiting because the different observations are observations on the same things, i.e. parts of the same team's environment.

(2) The second question concerns the fact that Professor Marschak assumes in his considerations exact knowledge of the previous actions taken by other members of the team. I think that all information about these actions is communicated along channels which are in all cases noisy.

Professor Menges : Even if I am not too happy about such a long paper with so many symbols and formulae, I appreciate Professor Marschak's paper as an outstanding contribution to something that might be called 'design of optimal social organization'.

The theory of such a design seems to me of inestimable social and political importance because it enables us to compare centralized and decentralized social structures (including their combinations or mixtures) in *economic terms*, allowing thus at least for some abstraction of ideological controversies and 'philosophical backgrounds'.

The development of such a theory has, of course, to struggle with some major (and also some minor) difficulties. A few of these, which I want to discuss, are the following :

(1) Assumptions about environment.
(2) Process of decision-making.
(3) Uncertainty concerning the payoff function.
(4) Properties of the adjustment process.
(5) Quality of the adjustment process.
(6) Improvement of arrangements.
(7) Suitability of the assumptions inherent in the arrangements.

(1) *Assumptions about environment.* The environment μ is a discrete stochastic process ; the changes of the environment come to pass at discrete successive time points. The cardinal assumption made by Professor Marschak about the changes of the environment is that the stochastic process, its distribution, and the time points at which the changes happen are precisely known. This, of course, is a drastic assumption. I shall not go deeper into the implications of this assumption, but only ask Professor Marschak : What modifications in your model would take place if you remove these assumptions, especially if you allow for the changes to occur unexpectedly?

(2) *Process of decision-making.* The process of decision-making follows in Professor Marschak's model certain specified rules the whole of which is called a scheme. Such a scheme presupposes for its concrete operation a certain data-processing capacity. If we have two schemes, S_1 and S_2,

for which the costs of data-processing are the same whereas the speed s of data-processing is different,

$$s(S_1) < s(S_2),$$

then S_2 should be selected.

We recognize a certain stability problem. High speed of decision-finding is intended for the sake of quick adjustment to states having changes. But, as I tried to show in my own paper, there are several other factors limiting the stability interval.

(3) *Uncertainty concerning the payoff function.* There are several remarks to be made here.

(*a*) By definition, an action a_1 is better than another action a_2 if, when μ is known,

$$W(a_1, \mu) > W(a_2, \mu)$$

or, when only the distribution of μ is known

$$E(W(a_1, \mu)) > E(W(a_2, \mu)).$$

But there is another type of uncertainty concerning the payoff function likely to occur, viz. (irregular) changes of the external prices.

(*b*) The coincidence of a and μ is not considered as a momentary event, but as a lasting co-operation :

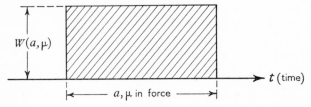

If $a = a(t)$ and $\mu = \mu(t)$, i.e. if a and μ are changing continuously in time, the payoff function would be given by

$$\int W(a, \mu)dt,$$

or, in the case of (continuous) discounting by using the discount factor ρ, by

$$\text{payoff} = \int_{0}^{t_1} \rho^t W(a(t), \mu(t))dt.$$

Professor Marschak considered the discrete case ; the corresponding formula should then be written, I think, as

$$\text{payoff} = \sum_{s=1}^{\infty} \rho^s \left(\sum_{r=1}^{k_s} C_{sr} W(a^{sr}, \mu^{sr}) \right).$$

This payoff is a fixed value provided the sequence μ^{sr} is known. If only the distribution of this sequence is known we again have to determine the payoff function.

(c) In Professor Marschak's model actions in operation have no influence, e.g. investments are excluded from consideration. This is another drastic simplification. Of course, his model would become too complicated if he were to make modifications in this respect.

(4) *Properties of the adjustment process.* The adjustment process in successive steps, with $t = 1, 2, \ldots$ denoting the numbers of the steps which consist of an exchange of information between the members of the team, accompanied by an information-processing process.

The tth step of the ith member leads to a tentative action $a_i(t, \mu, a_0)$, where μ is the present state, and a_0 is the vector of the actions originally proposed by the team members on the basis of the known aspect μ_i of the new state μ without knowing the actions of the other members. The adjustment process is of the recursive form

$$a(t) = f(a(t-1), \mu, t).$$

Thus, the adjustment process consists of four components :

(a) the initial values $a(0) = a_0$,
(b) the number T of iteration steps $t = 1, 2, \ldots, T$,
(c) the interim action $\tilde{a}$ which is in force as long as information processing lasts,
(d) the function f.

The first three components are called arrangements. In the terminology proposed in my paper the arrangements are predecisions. The problem is admirably treated by Professor Marschak. A disadvantage (probably unavoidable) of his treatment is that it leads to the requirement of numerous decisions outside any routine. Furthermore, it is questionable how far objective rules can be given for the settlement of the arrangements in concrete, actual problems.

On the other hand, there are some nice properties of the adjustment process in Professor Marschak's paper, viz. the following :

(i) $W(a(t, \mu, a_0), \mu)$ is monotonously increasing in time.

(ii) If there is, for a given μ, a definite maximum of $W(a, \mu)$ the process can become stationary only at this maximum.

(iii) The adjustment process is defined by difference equations (built after the gradient method) :

$$a_i(t) - a_i(t-1) = h \frac{\partial W(a(t-1), \mu)}{\partial a_i},$$

where h is a constant. One could say that it is this parameter by which the component f of the adjustment process is uniquely determined.

(iv) I am much in favour of Professor Marschak's concept of decentralization. An adjustment process is called decentralized if the members consult (at every step) only some of the previously proposed decisions of the other members, and if they must not take care of the knowledge about the environment possessed by the rest of the members.

(5) *The quality of the adjustment process* depends, first of all, on the payoff it yields. The total payoff, provided the adjustment process is applied on μ, is given by

$$TCW(a, \mu) + (1 - TC)W(a(T, \mu, a_0), \mu).$$

C is the (constant) duration of an iteration. State μ lasts one time unit. The following figure gives a graphical representation of this formula.

I think I am not quite in agreement with Professor Marschak when he considers the function f to be time-independent in order to equalize all computational steps. It seems to me that the process need not be time-

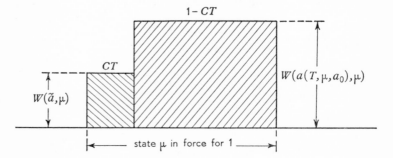

homogeneous in order to reach a constancy of C. I admit that the time-homogeneous process has the advantage of a higher degree of routine. Perhaps this was the leading idea.

(6) *Improvement of arrangements.* Instead of one and the same interim action a (depending or not on $\mu(t)$ and/or $a(t-1)$) during the whole information-processing time CT, the tentative actions $a(t, \mu, a_0)$ in force could be chosen immediately when they are available, I think. The argument at IV. 7 suggests that this could be an improvement with respect to the arrangements like A to F; in graphical representation we have :

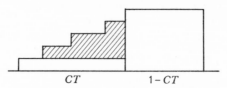

This method would then only be excluded — e.g. by consideration of the 'cost' of changing actions several times — which admittedly leads into

Record of Discussion

'still less explored areas in the study of organizations', as Professor Marschak puts it.

(7) *Suitability of the assumptions inherent in the arrangements.* I want to limit myself to a few points only.

Concerning Arrangement B, I see two problems : Every iteration causes costs, let us say amounting to C. Thus in the expression to be maximized TC should be subtracted :

$$CTW(a, \mu) + (1 - CT)W(a(T, \mu, a_0), \mu) - Tc.$$

If the optimal information-processing time TC is smaller than the time required for the determination of the optimum, the approach is useless.

Concerning Arrangement D it seems to be insufficient to consider only one environment together with the corresponding decision-finding, because the latter depends on the actions of the previous period and so on, and so on. Somewhere there must be an initial a_0, and one a has to be fixed arbitrarily. We are dealing with a Markov process ; to judge it we have to sum up all discounted payoffs. Because of the randomization of the interim action

$$a^t = a^{t-1}$$

it can, in the sense of Arrangement C, never be better than a constant interim action a.

Concerning Arrangement E, there must have been some calculation work before the interim action is found and put into force. The time required for this calculation is not taken into account. And even more : it not only requires the finding of the interim action some time, there is also a need for an *interim action* during that time.

Concerning Arrangement F : Every member of the team must have carried out some calculation work in order to get the initial action. Professor Marschak himself says : 'Arrangement F requires an addition to the process'. The difference lies in whether the members have, from the beginning, dealt with the actions a_0 of their colleagues, or if for once they deal with the environment at the very first step only. There is no doubt that the latter brings some inhomogeneity into the process, at least in its start.

Professor Marschak : I was concerned in this paper with what seemed to me the simplest interesting framework — hence also a very restricted framework — in which certain comparisons of adjustment processes are possible. The discussants' comments deal quite suggestively with elaborations of this simplest framework.

Dr. Ullrich's suggestions — dropping the no-correlation assumption for environment components and introducing noise into transmission of tentative actions — are reasonable next steps. The no-correlation assumption is in fact briefly dropped in the result given at the end of IV.1.

355

To answer Professor Menges's major question : removal of the assumption that the stochastic process is known would so generalize the problem that I would not know how to deal with it. Professor Menges's comments on specific arrangements are useful. It is correct that the recursive definition of payoff in Arrangement D requires an initial action in an initial period to be specified. It is equally correct that arrangements E and F require some time- and cost-free work. I am puzzled about the remark in connection with Arrangement B, however, since the issue of the cost of reducing iteration-completion times is discussed in the paper, most specifically in IV.7.

My thanks to both discussants.

PART IV

UNCERTAINTY AND NATIONAL PLANNING

Chapter 15

RISK AND UNCERTAINTY IN THE MANAGEMENT OF SOVIET FIRMS

BY

IVAN M. SIROYEZHIN

I

In a socialistic order many factors which to a typical private enterprise are major sources of risk and uncertainty are of minor importance. However, this does not mean that risk and uncertainty are absolutely non-existent under socialistic manufacturing conditions. They exist, and they are factors which have to be taken into account in the process of management and decision-making. But under the socialistic socio-economic conditions, the nature of risk and uncertainty is different from that of a capitalist manufacturing economy.

At the present stage of socialistic development, the policy of decentralizing gives the manager of a firm a broader range in which he can choose his decisions. This broadening of the range of possible decisions, as well as the appearance of a greater number of alternatives available to management, imply that risk and uncertainty become important elements in decision-making.

II

Naturally, under socialistic manufacturing conditions, the formal models of risk and uncertainty are similar to those used in the international literature on scientific management. Analysing the decision-making process by scientific methods, Soviet managers are compelled to solve the same problems as their opposite numbers in a capitalistic economy. They have to formulate the behavioural strategies for their enterprises, assess probabilities and determine output levels. They do this at present, but without the formal tools of management science.

Usually the manager approaches his decision problem with more or less authentic information about the probabilities of the different

359

states of nature. He will then try to meet a series of specific indices or conditions, which reflect the overall targets of the socialist society.

III

The first, and main problem, is to determine the choices, or strategies which are available. When this is settled, the actual choice will, for Soviet management, be determined by the economic indices, representing the overall target. This leads to problems quite different from those familiar to private enterprises. For a Soviet manufacturer who has to decide on automation there is no need to take into account the possibility that different producers of automated equipment may supply the same machines at different prices.

The manufacturer also knows that 100 per cent demand is guaranteed for the product put on the market by his automated factory. Thus, one would think that in the decisions matrix there should be one single column, with the lines representing different machine combinations.

IV

However, under conditions in which the Soviet firms seek to solve problems of automation, different states of nature can occur. These must be analysed, and it is necessary to work with a decision matrix having more than one column. There may, for instance, be uncertainty about delivery times, or the time it will take to put different machines into operation.

V

Western economists, studying risk and uncertainty, take it for granted that the main mechanism generating different states of nature is the free play of market forces. This source of uncertainty is of little practical importance to Soviet enterprises. Even the consumer-goods industry has a guaranteed demand, and a more or less guaranteed supply of raw materials. If necessary, they can dump their production to the wholesale commercial outlets. If the enterprise is directly connected with retail shops, the socialistic enterprise is virtually protected against any unforeseen event. Hence, the main source of risk and uncertainty is the instability of criteria or targets and temporary conflicts between the interests of a single enterprise and the society as a whole.

In other words, under the socialistic system the main mechanism creating risk, and hence complicating the decision-making, is a situation similar to that of a co-operative game.

VI

If an enterprise in a socialistic economy makes consistent losses, it is no longer a producer but a consumer of National Product. This does not lead to the destruction of the enterprise (bankruptcy), but it places severe limits on the independence of management. The state will abruptly change the financial regime of the enterprise — to the so-called card-index No. 2 state.

This limited independence was disregarded for a long time in the economic research of the Soviet scientists. But the existence of this card-index No. 2 dates back to the 1920s, and it is now recognized in practice and to some extent in theory.

VII

According to this, risk and uncertainty in the decision-making of Soviet firms are not caused by uncertainty over prices as in private enterprises, but by imperfect knowledge of basic forces behind a price mechanism. Thus, a decision which is optimal under present prices and targets may turn out to be a non-optimal when we consider its overall economic effects.

The following situation may illustrate the point. The tools of economic planning, developed under the centralized system, may not be adequate in the real economic situation, and may lead to low quality of the equipment installed in a plant. This is the fault of an R. & D. institution, which in outward appearance seems profitable. The actual inefficiency of this institution does not show up in the activity of this unit itself. It leads to the situation when the plant using the equipment pays at its own expense for the mistakes of the R. & D. unit.

Hence there is (if I may say so) a redistribution of the economic fault. The possibilities of such faults are connected with the conflicts characteristic of our industrial state, and is the main source of risk and uncertainty in the Soviet economy.

VIII

If we consider the case of plant automation, it seems that there should be three sets of columns in the decision matrix.

361

The first of these sets reflects uncertainties over targets, and fluctuations due to inadequate economic methods, used in planning at higher levels.

The second set relates to supply times for equipment. This is an important source of uncertainty.

The third set is connected with the very quality of the project, and hence with the efficiency and ultimate result of the automation.

IX

It is evident that the conditions of centralized planning lead to relatively small fluctuations in economic activity, and hence little risk and uncertainty.

But such small fluctuations in economic activity do occur, and may often lead to great economic losses. These losses are due to incorrect analysis of risk and uncertainty, or even the refusal of admitting the existence of risk and uncertainty in decision-making. So delayed delivery of equipment supplies, with all its frustrations, low-quality products and other shortcomings occur, and are openly criticized in the Soviet press.

In the decision-making practice of the Soviet firms these fluctuations do not cancel out. Because the system has neither a market mechanism nor competition, it is not capable of solving the problem by automatic action. Thus, the main causes of economic losses connected with decision-making in Soviet firms are :

(i) The refusal by current theory to recognize the existence of risk and uncertainty. This means that the available techniques are not used to forecast and clarify the potential losses, which may result from risk and uncertainty ;

(ii) The lack of an effective price system to transmit information for purposes of planning and decision-making.

X

If one succeeds in developing the desired price system one will obtain economic tools and indirect economic information, which will improve the activity of separate economic units and settle the conflicts of interest between units of the economy in the favour of society.

This will eliminate some specific forms of risk and uncertainty of the decision-making in some enterprises. Only the sources of risk and uncertainty which spring from technological conditions will remain.

For example, under any conditions, construction of residential buildings in new regions will involve decisions with uncertainty. It is very difficult to forecast the population and the characteristics of its family structure for a period of thirty to forty years.

It is possible that a correct price system, while reducing the risk and uncertainty in economic decisions, may create new social factors, which in their turn will increase the risk and uncertainty. This should, however, not prevent us from using the correct system of management, or from recognizing the existence of the problems.

XI

Some forms of risk and uncertainty are due to the unpredictability of human behaviour.

An example may illustrate the character of this element, which obviously must be considered.

In 1950–9 the municipal transport fares were completely revised in some large cities of the U.S.S.R. In some regions the reaction of the population to the changes was estimated incorrectly or simply disregarded, although this element should be taken into account in the decision-making process. As a result, the passenger-streams changed so radically that municipal transport, as well as the economy as a whole, suffered serious losses.

The aim of scientific management in socialist firms is to develop a theory for making economic decisions — a theory which is suitable for the socio-economic framework of the socialist community. The fact is that only under the conditions of an absolutely and ideally centralized system, can risk and uncertainty be ignored as factors inherent in the decision-making process.

Some of the elements which bring risk and uncertainty into economic and technological decisions are of a nature common to any kind of industrial and socio-economic structure. At the same time each industry has its specific social factors, giving rise to risk and uncertainty in decision-making. The aggregate consideration of both common and specific factors makes it possible to develop a socialistic decision theory, a part of which is related to decision-making under risk and under uncertainty. This theory may improve the national economic mechanism in the U.S.S.R., and eliminate a number of undesirable phenomena.

DISCUSSION OF THE PAPER BY
PROFESSOR SIROYEZHIN

Professor Hester : Professor Siroyezhin has prepared a very interesting discussion of the presence of risk in Soviet firms and also briefly compared types of risk facing firms in private-enterprise and socialist economies. I note parenthetically that to interpret private enterprise as completely characterizing economic activity in the West is very misleading — a straw man. Western governments interact with private firms there in many complex relationships ; however, for the most part on this occasion I agree to discuss this straw man. Let me briefly summarize my understanding of his paper and then comment on some of his comparisons.

He argues that risks and uncertainties face firms in the Soviet Union, but they are of a very different nature from those facing private-enterprise firms. These risks have become more pronounced recently because independent managers have been allowed a broader range of choice. How do these risks differ between private-enterprise and Soviet firms ? Private-enterprise firms must (i) take risks because of unpredictable actions by rival firms, (ii) run the risk of experiencing bankruptcy, and (iii) run the risk of being unable to dispose of all their production due to unpredictable changes in consumer demand.

Soviet firms on the other hand face none of these risks ; there are no rival firms, they are guaranteed freedom from destruction by bankruptcy, and the output of a firm is always absorbed by the economy. Private-enterprise firms on the other hand do not endure the following risks which plague Soviet firms : (i) unpredictability of financing due to changes in the plan goals and planning-errors, (ii) unpredictability of the delivery time of goods and equipment, and (iii) unpredictability of the quality of goods acquired from other firms.

Both groups of firms are subject to unpredictability of supply and 'technology' owing to such independent stochastic variables as the weather, mechanical breakdowns, population growth rate, technical change, etc. These last variables are viewed as being independent of socio-economic structures.

Professor Siroyezhin recognizes that risks afflicting Soviet firms 'may and do result in great economic loss' and attributes these losses to (i) planners' theoretical rejection of the existence of risk and uncertainty, (ii) planners' failure in practice to consider possible losses and to study the distribution of possible losses, and (iii) improperly constructed plans. He believes that better planning techniques including the implementation of modern statistical decision theory can reduce losses to tolerable levels, attributable to unavoidable supply and technological factors.

A most interesting theme in his paper is his characterization of the Soviet firm and society as players in a game in which the two players may have strategies which do not lead to a joint maximum. It would be most useful and interesting to see a rigorous mathematical characterization of the argument.

I agree with Professor Siroyezhin that Soviet and private-enterprise firms are subject to some different risks. This is hardly surprising for penalties and rewards are administered by very different authorities, the plan administrators and the market respectively. But one should be cautious not to let superficial institutional differences obscure some basic similarities in risk exposure. To be sure the frequency and severity of risk-induced 'inconveniences' differ between the economic systems. Some examples of what I mean follow :

(1) Unpredictable delivery lags occur of course in Western economies as in the Soviet Union. However, the Western market mechanism has responded by establishing bonuses for early delivery and penalties for post-deadline deliveries. By these devices Western firms have reduced but not eliminated unpredictability of delivery schedules.

(2) Free-enterprise bankruptcy and 'card No. 2' status for Soviet firms are quite analogous. Managers of firms in either system may fail to achieve viable performances and are penalized by being removed from control of their establishments. In neither system is destruction of physical plant or inventories a necessary counterpart of this financial re-organization. Consequently, bankruptcy-type risks are common to management in both systems, not solely a problem for Western entre-preneurs. Both systems properly recognize the possibility and desirability of occasional reorganization of firm decision-making structures.

(3) Similarly, the inability of private-enterprise firms always to dispose of their production at profitable prices has its counterpart in the Soviet firm, although the argument is more subtle. Is it socially desirable for Soviet firms always to sell their total output without delay ? It is con-ceivable that an economy would benefit if a firm's output were not distri-buted but stockpiled or, more likely, that a plant should occasionally close and shift its employees to other socially significant jobs. The fact that a firm can dispose of all its output at fixed prices should not be interpreted to mean that it is always wise for the firm or the economy to have firms inflexibly behaving in this manner.

(4) Professor Siroyezhin notes that changes in plans owing to revised policy objectives are a cause of risk in the Soviet firm. This has a Western counterpart in discretionary fiscal and monetary policy. For example, restrictive monetary policy or reduced government expenditures will cause Western firms to alter their production and investment plans. Western firms are vulnerable to these policy changes as are their Soviet counter-parts.

In conclusion, it seems to me that both advocates of private enterprise and socialism could well agree on the importance of the following research questions. How do different penalties, whether they be bankruptcy, card

No. 2 status, loss of market share, or criticism from the planning board affect the willingness of managers or entrepreneurs to take risks ? What new programming techniques can be developed for ameliorating the presence of uncertainty at the firm level ? Can stochastic variables such as weather, population growth, etc. be controlled ? Can forecasting techniques for the remaining uncontrolled variables be perfected ?

Dr. Winsten: Professor Siroyezhin has brought out well the many similarities in the types of risk in the two broad types of economies. But there were some points on which I had some doubts. He discusses, for example, the possibility of taking equipment from a variety of suppliers. Now these suppliers may be developing and improving their equipment at different rates and they may not know what the other suppliers are doing. Each supplier then faces risk. This is particularly true in the case (often found) where the same needs are fulfilled by different technological ends. In the case of the need for power, for example, nuclear power has often been predicted as the most economic source of electricity for the future. But coal power stations have steadily improved, and the nuclear power stations have been shown to have been a risky venture, which still have to justify themselves. Similar points could be made about the sudden improvement in the cost of gas since the large-scale tapping of natural gas. Again in manufacturing, there may be sudden improvements in techniques of a rival form of manufacturing ; die-casting instead of machining, for example. In all these cases, the providers of one sort of equipment cannot predict what technical advances there will be in another sector, and they therefore face risks.

The same can be true even without rivals. Not all developments are predictable in a particular sector. One may therefore predict the life of equipment wrongly if better equipment comes along unexpectedly soon.

To take now the case of consumption goods. Professor Siroyezhin points out that demand is predictable because the goods can be 'dumped on the wholesale commercial boards'. The word 'dumped' seems very appropriate, for this method merely transfers the risk of a change in demand from the manufacturer to an intermediary. This dumping merely transfers the risk.

We have been hearing in the last day or two of the Czech government's aim to increase the range of choice of consumer goods. Similar aims are apparent in other countries. If consumers choose, they may choose not to buy so much of a particular good, and the manufacturer (or some intermediary) may take the risk. Market research will be helpful here, but it will not predict infallibly.

The author raises just such a point when he discusses the change in fare structure of the municipal bus services in Rusisa in the 1950s. There some market research would be needed into the effect of fares on demand for services. Unfortunately, market research on the demand for public transport has been a much-neglected field everywhere, and I doubt if the best predictions available would have been right. Incidentally, I notice that the author assumes that municipal transport services should pay their way. All over the world such services are in difficulties, especially when car-ownership grows. Such services often need subsidies for the maximum usefulness for the community. When they go bankrupt the state or municipality do not allow the equipment to go unused. They step in and keep the service running.

Professor Siroyezhin touches on the interesting question of the design of new communities, and the difficulty of predicting population or transport technology twenty years hence. The time lags are long here. Professor Siroyezhin comes from a department of cybernetics. Cybernetics suggests flexibility and adaptability to changing conditions. The towns should be designed with just such flexibility in mind, so that they can be adapted to changes in household structure and other needs when they happen.

Dr. Walter : I shall limit my discussion to certain points that can be useful for further research. For example, it seems to me that the author treats risk and uncertainty as something which possesses only negative influences on the decision process. He is further concerned with the difference between the influence of socio-economic factors and technological ones, but he limits the influence of the former to a very narrow interval. It seems that in the concluding sections he assigns to these factors a more important role than at the beginning.

As far as the problem of guaranteed demand in Section III is concerned I think the problem is treated in a simplified form. I could imagine a broader formulation of the decision process of a firm. I think the problem of guaranteed demand in socialist retail enterprises must be studied by means of the tools of market analysis. There are many examples where the underestimation of these problems has led to great losses in our retail organizations. I think also that the situation described in Section VI overestimates the administrative tools ; these can be very expensive and not so efficient as intended.

There is a possibility of starting with a model in which not only the negative role of risky situations can be treated but also a positive one. There exists also a possibility of combining centralization and decentralization models.

Dr. Pelikán : First I would like to restate some ideas of Professor Siroyezhin's paper just to verify whether I have understood it well. I suppose that every national economy has to face the uncertainty, which comes, roughly speaking, from two kinds of sources.

The first kind is that which is common to every type of national economy and cannot be avoided. This is the uncertainty of external political, economic, or natural events (as, for example, changes in the international situation, earthquakes, etc.) and the progress of science, which changes the technological conditions of production.

367

The second kind concerns the uncertainty due to shortcomings of the internal communication on which the co-operation of production and consumption units depends. This can be different in different types of national economies. For instance, we can compare the results which can be obtained by the price mechanism or by some system of central management and planning or by some combination of both.

If I am right in this interpretation I cannot agree with Professor Siroyezhin that we could look at prices of the free market as a source of uncertainty comparable, say, with the secrecy of commercial or investment activity if we want, at the same time, to look at plan indices of the planned economy as sources of information which diminishes uncertainty. I think that the function of prices for decision-making of production units is comparable with the function of plan indices and in principle we can look at both as sources of information. We could, of course, study their respective advantages or shortcomings with regard to this function, as, for example, the amount and the quality of conveyed information, the coding and reliability of its understanding, the predictability of its changes, etc. We can find many differences between the system of prices and the system of plan indices but from the point of view of decision-making we must look at them as comparable concepts.

Then I would not agree that the uncertainty connected with the sale of production is diminished by the fact that the enterprise dumps its production on to some wholesale commercial base. Saying this we should either suppose that in the end people must buy this production whether they like it or not, or we should limit our studies to the decision-making of the 'pure' production units, where the problem of social utility of their production is not involved. The first supposition is, of course, not admissible as a permanent feature of a socialist economy. Even if some forms of administratively planned systems have shown tendencies to make people buy things not for the quality but for the lack of other choice, even then many products can remain unsold. The second supposition would make the whole study of little interest because we would limit ourselves to the problems of decision-making comparable with those of foremen in some large factory. The foremen may really face only a small amount of uncertainty in their decision-making; only this look is too partial and we could not find out whether the whole factory were flourishing or going bankrupt. Generally speaking, uncertainty cannot be diminished otherwise than by receiving information. In this example it means that the uncertainty connected with the social utility of the production can be decreased only by some better system of verifying the consumers' real needs (and this is, of course, not only a question of quantity) and not by transferring administratively the uncertainty from the producer to some wholesale unit.

Professor Rosett : I should like to go back to a question that was raised earlier because I think that a discussion of it will be illuminating here. In the United States, when an individual is received into bankruptcy, two things often happen at once. The purpose of the bankruptcy proceeding is to assure an equitable distribution of his property among his creditors, but this transfer of property should be of no interest to us. The second thing that may happen is that in selling some of his property some of it may be revalued by the market. Let me give a concrete example. Suppose I borrow money from a bank in order to build a factory. I intend to repay the loan from the profits of operating the factory. The factory proves to be less profitable than I thought and I cannot repay the loan. I resort to bankruptcy and my factory is sold. Since it was not very profitable it will be sold at a low price; a price at which it can be operated profitably. Because of my unpleasant experience others will be discouraged from building a similar factory. I have made a mistake and the price system has penalized me. Our way of expressing this penalty is to say that the price system has reduced the value of my factory.

Now it seems to me that whether an economy is governed by a price system or by a central plan, it is possible for a decision-maker to commit an error of the sort I committed when I built that factory. Just as I did, a planner might decide to build a factory that turns out to be less valuable to society than he thought it would be. Under either system there must be some incentive for individuals not to make such mistakes.

I do not mean to suggest that risk has the same effect in both systems. It may be, for instance, that risks are more readily taken in a centrally planned economy than they would be by an individual because of the operation of the insurance principle. Or perhaps they are less readily taken because the rewards for success are not great enough. I do want to try to make it clear that the risks of a market economy do not flow from the price system, but from the fact that decision-makers are uncertain of the social value of their acts and that this source of risk is common to both market and planned economies.

Professor Borch : Several speakers have talked about 'wrong decisions'. I think it is important to stress that when we bring in uncertainty it is not always possible to classify decisions as right or wrong. Whether we shall take a chance or not depends on our personal 'attitude to risk'. The decision cannot be right or wrong in any absolute sense.

If a boat goes out from Bergen to fish in the North Sea, it may happen that it comes back with a small catch. We then say that the skipper and the crew had 'bad luck', not that they made the 'wrong decision'.

Professor Rosett : I must, of course, agree that a decision made under uncertainty cannot be called an error simply because the result is bad. But there are such things as errors. Some people make more good decisions than others. We do want to have a way of encouraging the making of good decisions.

Dr. Madej: I should like to discuss some methods of safeguarding against effects of risk and uncertainty in economic planning and illustrate how such methods have been applied in Polish national planning.

The activities of different economic institutions (different sectors of the economy) are generally interdependent in the sense that in order to reach given targets in one sector it is necessary that other sectors reach theirs. In practice, a plan (or a set of plans) specifies only single values of the relevant variables, and it is then desirable or necessary to provide some sort of buffer between different activities in order to absorb the effect of random deviations from the planned figures.

There are two principal methods of such safeguarding against uncertainty, both of which make use of what may be termed reserves, but which are quite different in nature. The first, and simplest, concept of reserve refers to a *stock* of something (e.g. physical goods or foreign currency) which may be drawn upon to offset unexpected variations in a plan variable. These may be termed *real reserves*, and aim in the first place at safeguarding against negative deviations from planned figures.

The second concept of reserve refers not to a stock but to a *flow* variable in the sense that at the time of planning it is not specified how the flow is going to be used ; this will be determined later as deviations from planned figures occur. They therefore represent a margin allowing decisions to be postponed, and may be termed *potential reserves*. Reserves in investment planning are the typical potential reserves. They can absorb both positive and negative deviations from planned figures.

In the Polish investment plan for the years 1966–70 a central investment reserve has been set up which remains at the disposal of the Government and also some reserves at ministerial and Voivodeship levels. These reserves amount to 5 per cent of the investment expenditure in the first three years and to 10 per cent in the last two years of the plan. The growing uncertainty with the extension of the time horizon has thus been taken into account. The reserves will be used in the course of executing the plan by making decisions on new investments, changing previous decisions, and so on. It is hard to say, however, whether the magnitude of these reserves will correspond closely to actual uncertainty. They have been determined on the basis of practice from a few past years by estimation of discrepancies between investment plans and their actual execution, allowing a margin for improvements in planning methods.

In the case of real reserves resources are temporarily withdrawn from circulation and put aside. The optimal amount of such reserves may be ascertained on the minimal loss principle, where the total loss is the loss from maintaining the reserve minus the expected reduction in loss as an effect of mobilizing the reserve. An interesting example of the application of this method in Polish planning is the calculation of an optimal amount of livestock feed reserves. This calculation is based upon estimates of the probability distribution for yearly crop yields. Crops are converted into meat value and expected deviations below the mean compared with the costs of maintaining the reserve.

Record of Discussion

Professor Siroyezhin : First of all I would like to thank the discussants for the attention given to my paper. Let me react to some points of the discussion in the order in which they have been brought out.

From my point of view the main difference in the nature of risk and uncertainty (R. & U.) in the two types of economies can be visualized quite easily. If we consider all the sources of R. & U. phenomena we will find that in a private-enterprise system they all stem from the same main origin : the price mechanism of competitive markets, which all individual firms are facing. This price mechanism acts spontaneously in the private-enterprise system. This is not the case in a socialist system. Here the price system is regulated consciously and is not acting as a source of R. & U. for a particular firm. So we can conclude that the generators of R. & U. are working quite differently. And this is not by accident because the spontaneous working of the price mechanism in a private-enterprise system is a reflection of a deeper process going on. For a firm in a socialist economy the factors generating R. & U. are the following :

(*a*) The degree of error in setting prices for products and services when they are administratively prescribed. By 'error' I mean the deviation of prices from the level at which they would work as a good tool for indirectly regulating the firm's activity in the benefit of society and at the same time providing a profitable result for the particular firm ;

(*b*) The uncertain character of criteria due to the fact that there are many criteria to be taken into account and that there are difficulties in comparing and evaluating these criteria and aggregating them in a single-valued functional. For this reason I speak about the usefulness of co-operative models for the treatment of R. & U. situations in managerial practice ;

(*c*) The comparatively high level of administrative regulation of industrial processes with rather extended parallelism of several acting administrative systems. With the recent development of new methods of industrial management in our country this factor will decrease in importance.

I would like to stress that from the very beginning I have put aside all the technological reasons for R. & U. as I am sure that there are no great differences in this respect among different socio-economic systems. The central point for me is R. & U. factors for Soviet firms that rest in the social and economic conditions for their activity.

With respect to some of the specific points made by Professor Hester, I would like to say that it would be more to the point to say that the problems of delivery lags and quality levels have not been investigated in the practice of our firms, than that these phenomena are unpredictable. I am sure they can be predicted. The situation is that because the existence of R. & U. in this connection has so far been rejected in theory, no appropriate tools for dealing with their economic analysis have been developed. Nevertheless, such tools must be produced in the near future.

Professor Hester said that it would be useful to develop mathematical specifications of R. & U. situations under conditions of socialist production. I would like to assure him that my colleagues and I will try to do our best. But I felt it was not worth while to make any mathematical constructions for the very initial representation of the issue. I think that it is first of all necessary to understand better the processes going on in R. & U. situations within the framework of a socialist economy, and then to elaborate some hypothesis of the nature of the stochastic processes that would give us a chance to use the apparatus of modern mathematics to study the problem.

As to the bankruptcy issue which has been raised by Professor Hester and others I would say that card No. 2 status is a parallel to that in a socialist society. So I will not say that there is no parallel in this respect in the two systems. I am sure that both have to react on ineffective work at some point. Still I think that the relations between ineffectiveness on the one hand and bankruptcy or card No. 2 status on the other are quite different in the two systems. Card No. 2 status is a set of particular measures undertaken by local divisions of our State Bureau towards an enterprise which is considered to work badly. Theoretically it occurs when an enterprise starts to consume national income instead of producing it.

It so happened that my remark on a guaranteed demand for a firm's products caused the most extended discussion by all the participants. Clearly, it was not a very well-expressed point and I will try to offer an explanation. Under socialist production conditions we have to consider two different types of consumers. One type is represented by enterprises and institutions. The supplier to these consumers is determined by plan, so that demand is guaranteed in this area of industrial activity. I am not saying that such pairs (producer–consumer) are predetermined once for a whole planning interval (e.g. a year). Changes may occur but they are discussed beforehand and for that reason not unexpected.

The other type of consumers are individuals (families). Here the situation is somewhat more complicated. At present a yearly plan for firms involved in the production of consumer goods is settled on the basis of contracts with the retail-shop system. This system is assumed to represent the interests of the individual consumer. If it fails and a contract between some particular trade institution (for example, a city retail administration) and a particular producer (for example, a shoe factory) has to be changed during the planning period, then all the expenses connected with changeovers in production processes are charged to the retail system. The latter therefore assumes a real risk while the producer's demand is again guaranteed. The R. & U. facing the retail system and the service I consider elements of technology inherent in any economic system. So, firstly, I am excluding such R. & U. situations from consideration in my paper and, secondly, I do not make a serious distinction between the nature of R. & U. situations for the retail system in a planned economy and in a private enterprise economy when it is confronted with individual choice behaviour.

What could be viewed as different in this confrontation are the perspectives for future development. As far as I know there are no attempts even to imagine socialization of consumption under the private-enterprise system. But this is a goal of our economy. At present about 30 per cent of population needs are satisfied from social funds free of charge, and this part is to increase permanently. With a decrease in the volume of goods sold for money I see a new form of R. & U. arising. The analysis of consumer preferences based on elasticity, prices, and budget research will lose its significance. We shall have to find some new tools for guiding action in situations involving R. & U. about people's demand. There are two ways out. One is to accept large expenses for society to produce all imaginable goods and services with a high probability of satisfying every need. Fortunately, this is not necessary. In our view a consumer is a product of his particular socio-economic environment as well as the conditions under which he has to live and the goods and services he consumes. So we feel that an appropriately established educational system can produce a consumer who will agree to consume what he should consume from society's point of view. This does not mean that he must eat no more and no less than five rolls a day. But the part of food consumption which is covered by wheat production can be regulated rather strongly without any form of sacrifice on the part of consumers. Thus it will be enough to plan only a modest amount of 'insurance' inventories to meet unexpected short-term disturbances in the normal process of satisfying needs. Techniques for calculating such inventories and an educational system to realize a regulation of demand are waiting to be elaborated. Actually, we have already made some efforts and obtained some results about educational work as a tool for regulating demand, although the major part of consumption is satisfied by trading. So we have every reason to expect success in regulating demand when prices and trade will be out of use. Of course, we have a long way to go before we reach that era.

Next, I have to make some short remarks in connection with the discussion by Drs. Winsten, Walter, and Pelikán. To begin with, I would like to say that we have made an attempt to predict changes in demand, for transportation-service tariffs are changed. It proved to be realistic and some practical measures were implemented on that basis. The work was done with the advice of Academician L. V. Kantorovich in 1959–1960.

I fully agree with Dr. Walter that R. & U. situations have not only negative but positive aspects as well. I further agree with Dr. Walter that the use of administrative and economic tools have to be carefully balanced against each other. Only I would prefer not to make a distinction between tools of management working administratively and economically, but to distinguish those working automatically and those working at the discretion of a central authority. But the difference here may only be one of terminology.

I think that the interpretation of the difference in R. & U. situations in a private-enterprise system and a planned economy given by Dr. Pelikán is quite possible. Evidently, R. & U. generators have in both cases certain information systems built into them. But there are still some properties to be listed for each generator of R. & U., and so I cannot give up the idea that generators are different.

Chapter 16

SOME PROBLEMS OF RISK IN A
SOCIALIST ECONOMY

BY

LADISLAV UNČOVSKÝ

R I S K in the broader sense of the word exists when there is uncertainty
about the consequences of a decision. Risk in a narrower sense is
used when some of these consequences may be unfavourable. The
standard for measuring risk must be chosen according to the respective
sphere of life, or type of consequences. In economics, the risk is
usually measured in terms of costs or losses.

The decision theory calls situations where the states of the world
and their probabilities are known *situations of risk*. We shall call
situations where only the states are known *situations of uncertainty*.
Situations where not even the states are known will be called
situations of ignorance. If not differently stated, we shall use the
term of risk in the broader sense, given above.

The subject of this paper is risk in economic life. The risks we
shall study may be classified as :

(i) *Common risks*, connected with decisions about, say, plant
capacity, size of inventory, or maintenance of machinery.
(ii) *Risk of development*, connected with decisions such as :
expanding capacity, introducing new techniques, putting new
products on the market, etc.
(iii) *Risk of loss*, caused by natural disasters, etc.

As to its causes, risk may be classified as :

(i) Risk due to uncertainty about the future,
(ii) Risk caused by uncertainty about the decisions made by
partners,
(iii) Risk due to lack of information.

In economic life the risk caused by partners is above all connected
with the consumer's activity. It also includes the producer's activity,
which in the capitalistic system appears in the form of competition.

375

The third cause of risk also requires further explanations. It seems that the cause of any sort of risk may be attributed to a lack of information. But if this is the case, it is a question of risk, caused through deciding on the basis of insufficient or inaccurate data.

The theory of economics has concerned itself mainly with the risk of development. The mathematical methods of operations research on the other hand, have been developed to deal with common risks. The theory of insurance deals with problems concerning risk of loss.

The fact that the theory of economics in practice deals only with the risk of development, is not accidental. This risk is the most important one in economic life. The risk of loss, though important, can be distinguished from other risks, in theory as well as in practice. Common risk became only recently the object of scientific research, with the development of management science.

The various types of risk in economics are closely related to functions of ownership and control. The risk of loss is connected mainly with the function of ownership. Common risk relates mainly to the function of management, and the function of investment bears mainly upon the risk of development.

The problem of the risk-taker has been of interest to economists for a long time. At the beginning of capitalism this problem was simple. The capitalist was, as a rule, simultaneously the owner, manager, and entrepreneur. Naturally there could be no other risk-taker in these conditions. During the monopolistic period of capitalism the functions of ownership and control very often separated. In big companies control becomes the task of paid experts. The function of management was also transferred to company agencies and managers. These agencies have to make decisions under risk, but it is the owner who finally bears the risk.

Assuming risk with a possibility of loss must naturally be compensated by adequate profits, or at least, prospects of profits. Many economists, from Say right up to Keynes, dealt with the problem of assuming risk. The neo-classical school developed the theory of risk and rentability in detail. It is, however, not the object of this paper to deal with this theory or the criticism of it.

In economic theory, and in practice, little attention has been paid to the problem of risk in socialist countries. There are several reasons for this. The main reason may possibly be found in the fact that the role of planning, as a factor limiting uncertainty and risk, has been overrated. The assumption prevailed that it should be possible to eliminate all risks except those caused by weather and natural disasters. It was also assumed that the elimination of capitalistic markets would completely eliminate risks due to the activity of partners. The possibility of reducing risks due to lack of information has also been overrated.

In a socialist economy all means of production are owned by the state. The firms (corporations) control a part of the assets in an operative way. In a centralized economic system this does not mean that the function of control is transferred to the firms. The central administrative authorities actually perform the function of management. Decisions which should be taken by firms are, as a rule, taken by the central authorities. Thus the state becomes the final risk-bearer, and there is no incentive to assume risk at the level of the firm.

It is necessary, to appreciate the role of risk in socialist economy, to distinguish between the centralized and decentralized model of socialist economy.

The basic feature of the centralized model is that all decisions concerning important economic problems are taken at the centre. The only exceptions are consumption and employment.

The independence of enterprises is limited by conditions laid down in centralized decisions. Only decisions concerning measures to secure fulfilment of the plan are left to firms. Consequently it is the central authority which bears the risk, as it is the one competent to make the decisions. On the other hand, a centrally controlled economy makes possible a considerable concentration of brains and knowledge at headquarters, and it is therefore able to face eventual losses successfully.

The disadvantage of centralized management consists above all in the loss of initiative and incentives. Incentives, as far as they are available, are designed to secure fulfilment of the plan. The lack of incentives causes an aversion to risk. Moreover, there is no reward which could compensate the taking of risk. The centralized model does not create such conditions.

Centralized management and the concentration of power has led to a neglect of the role which risk plays in a socialist economy. It is possible to hide consequences of risk by using the great concentration of resources controlled by the state. In the first place it is possible to transfer resources from other sectors to cover the risk. On the other hand, there are central resources earmarked as reserves.

In a centralized socialist economy there is no competition. As there are no free markets, and as producers act in accordance with the central plan, there is no place for competition. The sovereignty of the consumer is limited, and it is difficult to estimate how a contingent refusal of the consumer will affect the economic results for the producer.

The black market, which in practice eliminates some risk, has its disadvantages. In theory the market is a place where the various factors of production are being evaluated. By eliminating the market, one makes risk evaluation very difficult.

The absence of competition does not mean that in a socialist economy risk caused by the partner's activity has disappeared. This type of risk is a result of the planning methodology itself. Planning is basically deterministic. It assumes that all factors influencing the plan are known and unambiguously determined. This is the basis of directive planning. The actual output often differs considerably from what the plan anticipated. This has an unfavourable effect on co-operative relations, and can lead to direct retaliation by partners.

When analysing risk caused by the partner's activity in a socialist economy, one takes for granted that there is no problem of harmony or disharmony between the partners. These partners cannot be direct competitors, but there are many situations of conflict in the relationship between subordinate and superior authorities, between supplier and customer, etc., also in a socialist economy.

An important source of this type of risk appears in the export trade. It is obvious that the more open the particular economy, the more acute is this problem. Foreign partners who are not subject to a central control are an important source of risk. International relations also lead to increased risk, due to uncertainty about the future. It is difficult to forecast the development and activity of foreign partners not under centralized control.

The firms face common risk in a centralized socialist economy. This is due above all to the uncertainty about fulfilment of the planned targets. For the firms the risk is minimal, provided the admissible alternative, prescribed in the plan, is realized. The different partial decisions of the firms must aim at the realization of the headquarters' central decision, which had been incorporated in the plan. Minimizing of the risk to the firm consists of maximal adjustment to the planned targets. In such a manner it is possible to define a decision criterion. It is a criterion of minimizing risk through maximal adaption.

The problem of choosing the decision criterion for the central authority raises a number of questions. On the one hand it seems advantageous to use optimistic criteria in view of the possibilities that a centralized economy has of meeting a sudden crisis. There are, on the other hand, a number of reasons which dictate a pessimistic criterion.

Mathematical methods play an important part in solving problems of risk in a centralized model. As the risk problem is of macroeconomic nature, it is necessary to investigate, in the first place, the part which risk plays in macroeconomic theory. In econometric models based on stochastic relations it is fairly simple to include also the factor of risk. In deterministic models based either on input–output analysis or on linear programming, the question is more complicated. The problem can be solved with the help of existing techniques, based on stochastic programming.

It seems that the simplest solution is to estimate the relevant parameters, and make some allowance for risk. This process supposes that the risk is given in the form of 'risk coefficients' or 'safety levels'. Using these coefficients, we can adjust the original values of the parameters. One disadvantage of this method is the difficulty of giving a quantitatively expressed risk rate, and to use it consistently. The rate of risk should be established uniformly, as an exogenous parameter, for the entire economy.

The use of more challenging models of stochastic programming, meeting targets with an approved probability (Katacka, Charnes, and Cooper), are based on the assumption of a uniform acceptable risk rate.

Another approach is parametric programming, where the risk coefficient, or the safety level, appears as a parameter. This approach had been put forward by the Hungarians, Kornai and Lipták. The main advantage of this method is that the risk appears as an endogenous parameter.

Improvement of decision theory is the main method which can reduce risk in the centralized model. When making decisions it is dangerous to accept a risky alternative, which can lead to losses above the given reserves, or in the potential of the economy. It is also dangerous to select the overcautious alternative, for — as a rule — this will be a poor solution. Consequently the possibility of accepting an adequate, but risky alternative, depends on the amount of reserves available, on the amount of information, and the quality of the decision model.

Uncertainty and National Planning

In the near future it will be hardly possible to solve all these problems connected with centralized decision-making. This gives us an argument in favour of a decentralized model of the socialist economy.

In a decentralized socialist economy firms have considerable independence and they compete among themselves. The law of value is used, and the market mechanism is being asserted. The customer's sovereignty finds stronger assertion. The central planning authority will only fix the basic rules, which result only in the broadest instructions concerning the activities of a single firm. The firm itself plans its own activity in detail.

The increased independence results in a transfer of a corresponding part of the risk to the firm. Provided the problem of incentives can be solved, it will be possible for the firm directly interested in the results to widen the range of its own decisions. This means also a better chance of co-ordinating risk and rentability.

If responsibility for some basic decisions is left with the central authorities, these have also to carry the risk involved. It is obvious that the consequences of unfortunate decisions may appear only after a long time. This will make it difficult to find the responsible party. As an instance we might think of a plant using unsuitable equipment, which had been assigned to the firm by a superior authority. One possible solution in such a case could be a guarantee, given by the superior authority. This liability carried by superior authorities should be waived in situations where the initiative of the decisions belonged exclusively to the firm. This is coherent with the question of carrying risk, which, as a matter of fact, is interrelated with ownership.

Because risk in a decentralized model is carried by firms, it will be necessary to set aside reserves in these firms. Provided the market relations work in a satisfactory manner, these reserves may, to a greater extent, be in the form of money. This could lead to an increased use of insurance to deal with problems of risk.

The transfer of decision-making authority and risk to the firms leads to new demands for information. The firms need information as a basis for their decisions. The central information arrives in the form of instructions concerning only a narrow range of problems. The central authorities acquire some importance as information centres, helping the enterprises to take right decisions. Gathering information by the enterprises themselves also plays an important role. Thus market research asserts itself in a socialist economy, in the market as a whole as well as on the level of the firm.

With the decentralized system, the risk in firms consists not only of *common risk*, but also *development risk*. This means increased demands put on the competence of the management, and it increases the importance of theory and models of mathematical nature. The mathematical methods in the firm are basically similar to the methods used in the centralized model. The problem then consists of harmonizing the macro- and microeconomic decisions. But these questions lead to many unsolved problems, in the theory of risk in a socialist economy, and in general economic theory.

———

DISCUSSION OF THE PAPER BY DR. UNČOVSKÝ

Professor Borch : Dr. Unčovský discusses practically the same problems as Professor Siroyezhin, and we should really have discussed the two papers together.

In most economic theories it is assumed that a firm, or a factory, can be described by a *production function* of the form :

$$y = f(x_1, \ldots, x_n).$$

This relation says that if we use the amounts $x_1, \ldots, x_n$ as inputs (factors of production), we obtain an output y.

One of the perennial problems of economic theory is to maximize an expression of the form

$$P = p_0 y - \sum_{i=1}^{n} p_i x_i.$$

In a capitalist economy it is natural to take $p_0, p_1, \ldots, p_n$ as market prices. The problem is then to determine the input vector which will maximize the profits of the firm.

In a socialist economy we can take $p_0, p_1, \ldots, p_n$ as weights, which determine the 'social importance' of the various goods. The problem is then to determine the input vector, which will optimize the plant's contribution to the National Product.

It seems, therefore, that this simple classical problem has some importance, regardless of the economic system in which the plant operates. Let us now introduce uncertainty as a step towards a more realistic theory.

A businessman in a market economy will then immediately think of uncertainty about prices, and he may be delighted to see a more general model where $p_0, p_1, \ldots, p_n$ are stochastic variables.

A government official in a centrally planned economy may have prices

381

under complete control, and he may not be very interested in the more general model. If, however, export and import enter into his problem, some prices will be beyond the control of our planner, and he may take some interest in the model which delighted our businessman.

It is quite natural that Dr. Unčovský should give more attention to this problem than Professor Siroyezhin does. Foreign trade, and hence uncertainty about prices, must be far more important to a small country like Czechoslovakia than to the U.S.S.R.

Prices do not, however, constitute the only uncertain element in economic life. Any engineer, farmer, or fisherman can tell us that the connection between input and output must be of stochastic nature. He will accept the classical production function only as a mathematical expectation, i.e.

$$E\{y\} = f(x_1, \ldots, x_n).$$

This means that we can work with the classical production function if we are interested only in the average long-term output of a production process. If the short-term fluctuations are of importance, we must construct a stochastic model — for instance of the type discussed by Dr. Thore in his paper.

If output or prices are stochastic variables,

$$P = p_0 y - \sum_{i=1}^{n} p_i x_i$$

is also a stochastic variable. The problem of maximizing P is then meaningless. The real problem in the general model is to determine the values of the decision variables (some or all inputs, and possibly some prices), which will give the optimal stochastic variable — i.e. the optimal probability distribution for P.

Such problems occur, and should be important under any economic system.

Dr. Unčovský : Professor Borch points out some very important aspects of the problem under discussion. I should only like to emphasize again my opinion that perhaps the most important tool for solving problems of risk in an economy, especially in a socialist economy, is stochastic programming.

In this connection I should like to refer to the paper by Mr. Lipták from Budapest, which was to be presented at this Conference, where the apparatus of parametric programming is used for solving some problems of risk.

Chapter 17

THE POWER ELEMENT IN THE
CONTROL OF AN ECONOMY

BY

ANTON KLAS

In this paper we shall study an element for controlling the economy which so far has received little attention — the power element. We are fully aware of the danger points on our way.

At the outset we should like to stress that we do not intend to analyse the quantification possibilities of power in general. We shall study only the aspect of the problem which has economic interest. We take this approach because the concept of power is very broad, and includes many factors, which from our point of view are irrelevant.

Having narrowed the problem down, we can distinguish two basic groups of power elements in the control of an economy. The first group is related to the economic possibilities of the society, i.e. the degree to which the material needs of its members are being satisfied. The second group is related to the process of decision-making and the choice of targets — in view of the economic possibilities of the society.

The first group is given by the long-term historical development of the country. The second group contains elements of a more elastic nature, and will as a rule refer to shorter periods.

In this paper we shall be concerned only with the quantification possibilities of power, elements in the first group although, in practice, elements in both groups are interrelated.

As long as there is a shortage of goods capable of satisfying human needs there will be tendencies and attempts to change the existing distribution.

Such changes may concern the distribution of the basic production of material wealth itself, for instance a change in ownership of means and production. In such cases the power element may appear in its purest form, i.e. violent expropriation. Changes can also appear in more moderate forms, affecting only the distribution of income to various groups of the society.

Both these types of change reflect the different material incentives of people. The forces capable of bringing about such changes are obviously due to economic causes.

If these forces were given a free run they would cause various forms of violence in the distribution process. This would destroy the stability of the economic system, and finally lead to its complete disintegration. Every society, therefore, tends to control these forces.

Such controlled forces we shall call 'power', taking this as a definition of the term. This definition implies that power is not an element entering into the society from the outside. There is no chance of the society wiping out this power as long as goods are in short supply. The society is only capable of regulating this power, and of putting it under conscious control.

It is, therefore, not the intensity of the power, but the method of its control — as applied by the society — that establishes whether a control system should be called democratic or undemocratic.

Having given our definition of the power element, we turn to the problem of quantification.

Let us suppose we have a total of k needs: $S_1, S_2, \ldots, S_k$. The different social groups are $G_1, G_2, \ldots, G_r$. We shall call the number of members who are able to satisfy their jth need $n_{1j}, n_{2j}, \ldots, n_{rj}$. The following table illustrates the satisfaction rate of the various material needs:

TABLE 1

	S_1	S_2	S_3	S_4	S_5	.....	S_j	.....	S_k	
G_1	n_{11}	n_{12}	n_{13}	n_{14}	—	.....	—	.....	—	
G_2	n_{21}	n_{22}	n_{23}	n_{24}	n_{25}	.....	—	.....	—	
.	.	.	.	.	.		.		.	
.	.	.	.	.	.		.		.	
.	.	.	.	.	.		.		.	
G_i	n_{i1}	n_{i2}	n_{i3}	n_{i4}	n_{i5}	.....	n_{ij}	.....	—	
.	.	.	.	.	.		.		.	
.	.	.	.	.	.		.		.	
.	.	.	.	.	.		.		.	
G_r	n_{r1}	n_{r2}	n_{r3}	n_{r4}	n_{r5}	.....	n_{rj}	.....	n_{rk}	
	n_1	n_2	n_3	n_4	n_5	.....	n_j	.....	n_k	n

where $n_j = \sum_i n_{ji}$ and $n = \sum_j n_j$.

384

The table shows that the income of group G_1 allows its members to satisfy needs S_1 to S_4. The needs S_5 to S_k are not being satisfied. According to the table, the last group is able to satisfy all its needs.

If the target has been established in this manner, it is possible to express the satisfaction rate by the probability $p_{ij} = n_{ij}/n$. We shall write:

$$p_{ij} = p_j \cdot p_{i/j},$$

where $p_j = n_j/n$ and $p_{i/j} = n_{ij}/n_j$.

If all probabilities are equal, i.e. if all members of every group have the same chance of satisfying all their needs, we obtain the maximum rate of satisfaction of needs.

If this method of recording is used it is possible to take entropy H, defined as:

$$H = \sum p_{ij} \log p_{ij},$$

as an appropriate measure of the aggregate rate.

This quality will reach its maximum value, i.e.

$$H(S, G)_0 = H\left(\frac{1}{m}, \frac{1}{m}, \ldots, \frac{1}{m}\right) = \log m,$$

where $H(S, G)$ is the expression for the entropy of the total situation and $m = kr$ (k representing the number of needs and r the number of social groups), if all probabilities are equal.

By decomposing the aggregate entropy, we get

$$H(S, G)_0 = \log kr = \log k + \log r = H(S)_0 + H_S(G)_0, \qquad (1)$$

where $H(S)$ is the entropy corresponding to the probability distribution of needs (S), and $H_S(G)$ is the conditional entropy, corresponding to the probability distribution according to social groups (G).

The bigger the differences between the various probabilities, the lower will be the entropy value.

It is probably worth mentioning that the entropy, if used in this manner, is very similar to the concept of physical entropy. The lower its value — and this occurs always when the difference between the chances of satisfying the various needs increases — the bigger are the forces required to effect a certain task in connection with a change of the distribution pattern. The tension caused by these forces disappears when the entropy reaches its maximum value, i.e. when the probabilities of satisfying all needs are equal.

Supposing the volume of power is proportional to the tension caused by unsatisfied material needs, we may define power intensity

M as a quantity proportional to the difference between two entropy values, i.e.

$$M(S, G) = h[H(S, G)_0 - H(S, G)], \tag{2}$$

where h is a proportionality factor, $H(S, G)_0$ the maximum entropy, and $H(S, G)$ the actual entropy.

The relation (2) states that the volume of the power, M, required for control, increases the more the given satisfaction diverts from its maximum. It also illustrates that it is possible to liquidate this need for use of power only through an increase in the material wealth of the society.

Rewriting formula (2) we get:

$$M(S, G) = hRH(S, G)_0, \tag{3}$$

where R is 'redundancy' defined as $1 - H(S, G)/H(S, G)_0$.

Relation (3) shows that the power required for control depends only on the redundancy, provided the value of $H(S, G)_0$ is given.

There is nothing to stop us from regarding production as information, and the various needs and groups as the code alphabet. Hence the quantity R measures the informational content. This means that production is not able to satisfy all needs of the members of the various groups. It then follows that the power required is proportional to a lack of information expressed by the quantity R. This also can be derived from formula (1).

As the entropy is used to measure information I, we may well rewrite relation (1) as

$$M(S, G)_0 = h[I(S, G)_0 - I(S, G)].$$

Taking $h = 1$, we get:

$$I(S, G)_0 = I(S, G) + M(S, G). \tag{4}$$

This shows that the power element represents subsidiary information. Thus, it supplies the given economic system with the information, which for reasons of limited production cannot be supplied by a material incentive system.

In our study we have so far taken $H(S)_0 = \log k$ and $H_S(G)_0 = \log r$. To obtain a reduction in the number of needs, let us choose as a maximum value the entropy corresponding to the social group having the highest income. This entropy we shall call $H(S)_x$. Similarly we replace $H_S(G)_0$ by $H_S(G)_x$, representing the entropy corresponding to the relative number of members in the various social groups.

It is then possible to divide total power, on the one hand into components resulting from the differences between satisfaction rates within social groups, and on the other hand into components resulting from the differences between groups.

$$M(S, G) = h[H(S)_x - H(S)] + h[H_S(G)_x - H_S(G)]. \tag{5}$$

Writing respectively $M(S)$ and $M_S(G)$ for the two differences, we can rewrite relation (5) as :

$$M(S, G) = M(S) + M_S(G). \tag{6}$$

From this relation it follows that the value of $M(S)$ will decrease to zero only if $H(S) = H(S)_x$.

Similarly $H_S(G)$ must be equal to $H_S(G)_x$ if $M_S(G)$ is to be zero. This is the case of absolute income levelling, where

$$H_S(G) = \sum_j p_j H_S(G)_x = H_S(G)_x \sum_j p_j = H_S(G)_x.$$

These considerations show that it is quite impossible to liquidate the power element by levelling incomes. Such a levelling might lower the value of $M_S(G)$, but, as it at the same time reduces the number of satisfied needs, the value of the second element $M(S)$ automatically increases.

If on the other hand we try to increase the number of needs which can be satisfied with given limited sources, we will also increase the differences in income in various groups. This will result in a decrease in $M(S)$ and an increase in $M_S(G)$.

As an illustration we give, in Table 2, the relationship between various levelling rates, measured by the Gini concentration coefficient

TABLE 2

K_G	$M(S)$	$M_S(G)$	$M(S, G)$
0·389	0·6699	1·5000	2·1699
0·375	0·7949	1·3750	2·1699
0·347	0·9669	1·2030	2·1699
0·306	1·1699	1·0000	2·1699
0·250	1·3959	0·7740	2·1699
0·181	1·6389	0·5310	2·1699
0·097	1·8979	0·2720	2·1699
0·000	2·1699	0·0000	2·1699

Note : The value K_G decreases if the levelling increases. $K_G = 0$, if all incomes are equal.

K_G, and the values $M(S)$ and $M_S(G)$, provided the volume of the material resources stays constant.

If for the sake of simplicity we neglect the probability distribution of satisfied needs and instead classify needs as satisfied or not satisfied, we may rewrite the expression for $M(S)$ as follows:

$$M(S) = h[\log k_0 - \log k] = h \log \frac{k_0}{k},$$

where k_0 is the number of all needs, and k represents the number of satisfied needs. The dependence of the quantity $M(S)$ upon the percentage rate of satisfied needs is represented by the following diagram.

FIG. 1

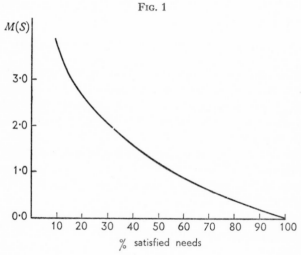

As already might be seen from Fig. 1, the groups with the lowest income rate are the main source of tension, i.e. they are the groups having the lowest percentage of satisfied needs. A still better illustration of this is given by Table 3.

It can be seen that a 10 per cent increase in the satisfaction rate in group 1 results in a 30·1 per cent decrease of power required. The same increase of the satisfaction rate in group 9 reduces the power only by 4·2 per cent.

The only source of tension left when $M_S(G) = 0$, is the demand for satisfaction of a higher number of needs. All tensions are then due to the requirements of the total mass of consumers, against the co-ordinating organ. The power element of the co-ordinator's activity will affect the whole mass of consumers with equal intensity, because

TABLE 3

Group	Percentage of satisfied needs	Decrease of power in per cent, provided the satisfaction rate of needs in the respective groups is increased by 10%
1	10	30·1
2	20	18·1
3	30	12·0
4	40	9·6
5	50	8·4
6	60	7·2
7	70	5·4
8	80	4·8
9	90	4·2

in these conditions all groups are in the same position. From the point of view of the application of power there will be no differentiation. Everybody is subject to the same effect of power pressure and this causes a narrowing of the area of non-power criteria in decision-making.

FIG. 2

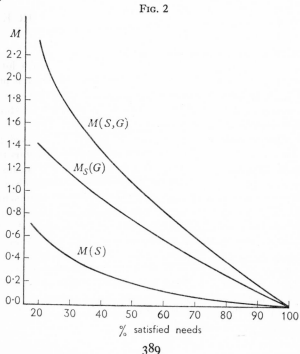

% satisfied needs

To illustrate this point, we use Fig. 2, showing how the quantities $M(S, G)$, $M(S)$, and $M_S(G)$ depend on the percentage of satisfied needs at a constant size of the various groups.

In conclusion we want, even if only briefly, to mention the second group of power elements.

It is clear that to reach an established target more power will be required the smaller the material resources are.

A similar effect can be noticed at the level of decision-making. If the decision taken is wrong — irrespective whether this is due to subjective or objective reasons — it will lead to a reduction of the material resources used to reach the assigned target. If sufficient reserves are not available, the fulfilment of the planned target will require a power-control system. Since the probability that all decisions will be right is very small, the development will always tend toward the more probable. One may, therefore, speak about a real force, which tends to push the society away from the direction leading to the planned target. This force will be greater the more specific the target.

———

DISCUSSION OF THE PAPER BY PROFESSOR KLAS

(The paper was summarized by Professor Klas)

Professor Borch : Economists and sociologists have written a lot about power and the possibility of measuring power. This literature is not very conclusive, and much of it is rather confusing. It seems, however, that if we analyse the problem in the framework of game theory, it should be possible to come to grips with the concept of power.

To illustrate the point, we can consider the game discussed by Dr. Selten and Dr. Schuster. On intuitive reasons it seems obvious that the 'big player' has more power than the other players. This means that a complete description of a game must give us a distribution of power among the players. The natural measure of power is then the payoff which the player can expect to obtain, i.e. the measure of power must be given by the allocations, which are contained in our 'solution' of the game.

If we want to impose an allocation which is not in the solution, we will have to use some 'power' against the players, and it is this power concept which Professor Klas tries to define and measure. The amount of power which must be used can be taken as equal to the *tension* created in the group of players, and it appears that it really is social tension which Professor Klas wants to measure.

Record of Discussion

Professor Klas assumes that the Government wants to enforce a certain distribution of income. His problem is then to determine the amount of power which has to be used — or equivalently, the amount of social tension which will be created — if this decision shall be enforced. The analysis could be carried out with reference to the 'original game', for instance the income distribution resulting from the free play of market forces. Professor Klas's point of reference is, however, the egalitarian society, where the available income is distributed to 'everybody according to his needs'.

Professor Klas introduces kr numbers n_{ij} $(i=1, 2, \ldots, r), (j=1, 2, \ldots, k)$, defined so that $n_{ij}=1$, if need j of person i (or social group i) is satisfied, and $n_{ij}=0$ if this need of person i is not satisfied.

He then introduces

$$p_{ij} = \frac{n_{ij}}{\sum_{ij} n_{ij}}.$$

Since the ps sum to 1, they can formally be treated as probabilities, and one can define the entropy of the system as

$$H = -\Sigma\, p_{i_j} \log p_{ij}.$$

The entropy takes its maximum value H_0 if all ps are equal, i.e. if $p_{ij}=1/kr$.

As a measure of tension Mr. Klas takes

$$M = H_0 - H.$$

As a measure of tension this measure makes some sense. If we require tension to be zero when everybody has the same proportion of his needs satisfied, and lay down some other conditions which a measure should meet, we can prove that entropy is the only possible measure.

I have two objections of special nature to the argument of Professor Klas,

(i) He does not seem to gain anything by abandoning the classical tools of marginal analysis. The natural starting-point for an economist should be to define tension as zero — or at its minimum — when marginal utility of purchasing power is the same for all persons,

(ii) Professor Klas ignores existing economic forces, or what I called the 'original game' earlier. If the Government wants to enforce an income distribution against these forces, it seems natural to assume that this will create more tension than a passive policy, just giving these forces a free run.

My general objection is that I do not think measures of this kind are very useful. The situation which Professor Klas wants to analyse, is described by a $k \times r$ matrix and he tries to represent this situation by a single scalar number M. This is really the familiar 'index problem', which economists have struggled with for generations. By now it should be well known that no index is best in any absolute sense. We can only hope to find the index which is best for some particular purpose. We must then ask what use Professor Klas proposes to make of his measure. Is there any simple relationship between M and, say, the number of officials which must be engaged to ensure that a particular income distribution is enforced ?

Dr. Selten : I cannot see that the power concept proposed by Professor Klas measures what it intends to measure. The power which must be exerted by a government to enforce a certain distribution of need-satisfaction seems to be very different from the amount of information measured by Professor Klas. I think that this power is more related to the cost of enforcing the distribution of need-satisfaction ; it is related to the cost of the police force, to the cost of the administrative apparatus, etc. I cannot see why the amount of information measured by Professor Klas should be proportional to the sum of such costs or to any other intuitively meaningful measure of power in the given situation. Nevertheless I think that the paper by Professor Klas is very interesting because even if he does not measure power, his measure may describe something which is interesting from other points of view.

Professor Bühlmann : I have great doubts as to the concept of power introduced in Professor Klas's paper. The measure of power is smaller the more equally the needs of each social class are likely to be fulfilled. I think that different classes may have differences in needs according to their function in the economic process. This should in any case be taken into account.

Professor Klas : May I in the first place express my sincere thanks to all who commented on my paper.

Since the question of whether we will in fact measure what we intend to with the given way of quantification has been raised in the discussion, I would like to give a more detailed explanation of my approach.

If we want to control a certain economic system we have to supply it, above all, with an adequate quantity of information. This can be supplied to the system through various channels, for instance by using material incentives or through a power-administrative channel.

But at the same time it is of the utmost importance to realize that the volume of information we intend to supply to a system during a certain period also depends on the capacity of the communication channel used. Thus, if the material resources are limited it is impossible to supply, by means of material incentives, more than a limited quantity of information.

Let me give you an analogy. If we want to transmit a certain amount of information by means of light signals, using a flashlight for this purpose, we evidently require a sufficiently strong source of energy. This source may be a battery, and with a weak battery we shall not be able to transmit the whole volume of information, but only a certain part of it. For the rest we shall have to use other methods such as acoustic signals.

Conditions are similar in an economy. If we have only limited resources it is impossible to supply the economic system with all information through the channel of material incentives and therefore a part of the information has to be supplied through the power channel.

When it comes to carrying out given tasks and meeting targets laid down by the society we must consider not only the capacity of the channel but also the uncertainty connected with its use. If this type of uncertainty contains H_1 bits and if the material incentives channel is capable of handling only a smaller amount of information, then an auxiliary channel, e.g. a power-administrative channel, has to be appended if the system is to remain stable. This is analogous to the problems arising with fixed prices, which, because of lack of variety, are not able to guarantee the required assortment. And should this be the case, we know that the lacking information has to be supplied to the economic system through a power-administrative channel.

If the total volume of material incentives is given, only a limited number of possible material incentives can be employed, i.e. a limited number of ways in which the available amounts of resources can be expended. The greater the number of these possibilities, the more complex the situation we shall be able to control.

There is therefore a good analogy in the system-control concept of cybernetics. This fact brought me to the conviction that the entropy will be a good measure for expressing the quantity of information which we are able to supply to an economic system using the channel of material incentives.

Accepting the hypothesis that information which cannot be transmitted to the system through the channel of material incentives has to be supplied to it through the power-administrative channel, we may establish its volume by the difference between two entropy levels $H_0 > H_1$, where H_0 is the total entropy and H_1 the entropy of usable means for material incentives.

Nevertheless it has to be realized that in no way do I want to identify the amount of information exceeding the capacity of the material-incentives channel directly with the power volume. All I assert is that the power is proportional to this quantity. Thus, if the tasks of society are too big, there is always the menace of an increase in the power-administrative element in the control of the economy. And it is well known that such a type of economic control is far from ideal.

The fact that any decision concerning the expenditure of labour might be realized either through material incentives or by the use of administrative measures is the reason why I am of the opinion that there are two different channels essentially transmitting the same type of information but using different ways of coding.

The weak point of the quantification attempt is, for the time being, the fact that it is very difficult to obtain data for empirical verification of the theory.

There are certain data, however, helping to verify at least *some* of the consequences of our considerations.

For example, it is known that the relation between labour output rate and the wage rate is, in all wage systems, mostly of a logarithmic form. This is also proved by psychological research, where, according to the well-known Weber Law, people will not react to absolute but to relative increases in stimuli.

It is also known that the distribution of recipients with respect to income follows roughly a logarithmic function. These facts evidently are not accidental.

Professor Borch objects to my neglect of existing economic forces. This problem is clearly connected with the centralized and decentralized ways of control. But I am of the opinion that even with a completely decentralized type of control, where economic forces assert themselves freely (as for instance in the case of operation of a market mechanism), power forces come into existence. We may find their manifestation in the fight which political parties put up to see certain programmes through. I have tried to express this by dividing the entropy into two components (elements).

Regarding the rest of the comments I should like to express my gratitude for them as they are of great value to me and will certainly be taken into consideration in my further work.

Chapter 18

MODERN THEORIES OF ECONOMIC FORECASTING AND SHORT-TERM FLUCTUATION[1]

BY

ARKADIY A. GRETCHIKHIN

I

SOVIET economists pay great attention to the theoretical work by Western economists on short-term fluctuations and to their attempts to forecast long-term economic development.

The development of state-monopolistic capitalism has led to a sharpening of the contradictions within the capitalist economy, and this forces the bourgeois society to intense theoretical investigations in the search for more effective ways and methods of regulating the capitalist economy. Beginning with Keynes, the study of these problems has led to a theory of cycles and crises, and to the development of programmes for anti-cycle policies in general, and anti-crisis policies in particular.

The Keynesian teaching has directly influenced the development of econometrics as well as certain sections of economic statistics, especially national accounting. The most significant elements in the development are the great attention paid to 'effective demand', and the quantitative relations established between the more important entries in the national accounts. Under the influence of the Keynesian teaching, recent developments in the bourgeois theory of economics have mainly consisted of developing mathematical models for transitory changes (the theory of business cycles) and lasting changes (the theory of economic growth).

II

Econometric research on capitalist production was introduced into

[1] An earlier version of this paper was withdrawn by the author before it could be discussed at the Conference. The present, revised version, was submitted to the editor of the Proceedings after the Conference. — K. B.

bourgeois economics as far back as the 1920s by the American economist Mitchel. He claimed that most economic time series contained
the following four components :

   (i) A secular trend,
   (ii) Cyclic fluctuations,
   (iii) Seasonal fluctuations,
   (iv) Irregular fluctuations, which can be included neither in cyclic
       nor in seasonal fluctuations.

The last group of fluctuations may be caused by events such as
strikes, wars, uprisings, and natural calamities.

The analysis of 'dynamic time series' is based, as a rule, on the
secular trend, and all fluctuations are measured as deviations from
this trend. The usual methods for determining the secular trend are
either drawing a curve based on subjective judgement, or some
statistical procedure as moving average, or least squares.

III

The theory of time series by Mitchel and his followers rests on a
very doubtful scientific foundation.

The most disputable element is the division into trends and cyclic
fluctuations. In a capitalist economy, close and inherent ties exist
between the general parameters of development for a certain period
(e.g. the average rate of growth) and the frequency and strength of
cyclic crises. The methods suggested for separating trends and
cyclic fluctuations are also doubtful, since they to a great extent
depend on the subjective judgement by the persons who make the
calculations. For instance, when a secular trend is apparent, subjec-
tivity enters when it comes to choosing the type of curve representing the trend. Thus it follows that most calculations by Western
economists, trying to reveal trends and cyclic fluctuations, have a
dubious character. One cannot, however, deny that some of these
calculations, particularly those relating to specific industries, have a
certain value, and that they may indicate the direction of technical-
economic changes.

IV

The time series analysis, widely accepted by Western economists,
was used to build the first simple models of cycles in the so-called
barometer form. It is well known that the forecast based on economic

barometers proved unsuccessful. The failure of the Harvard business barometer during the crisis of 1929–33 can be mentioned as an example.

The failure of these economic barometers had a double effect on Western economists working on the problems of capitalist production. Some of them, including Mitchel, Burns, and Kuznets, concentrated their attention on economic-statistical research of a more descriptive nature. Others tried to build more complex models of capitalist production, in order to forecast economic development and determine future cyclic fluctuations. One of the first attempts was Tinbergen's work on the theory of economic cycles. Although his models for the U.S.A., Britain, and Holland have not been used in practice, they have promoted research by other Western economists in the same direction.

V

In some capitalist countries mathematical models have been used to forecast economic development, and they have been included in the general system of economic regulation and programming used by the state. It is, therefore, necessary to discuss some of the main features of these models.

The models give in a mathematical form the global relations within a capitalist economy, without any differentiation. The most important elements in the national accounts, such as income, investments, savings, profits, dividends, and interest, are connected by equations, without any serious attempt made at class, socio-economic, or inter-industry division. For example, in the Klein–Goldberger model an important variable, such as capital investment, is determined through complex equations by all unearned income (including depreciation, but excluding taxes).

All these models depend on the subjective estimates made by the authors. This may be unavoidable, since experience shows that mathematical calculations alone are insufficient for economic forecasting. We see that the application of these models leads to continuous corrections, taking account of changes in the economy, revision of statistical data, etc.

VI

Another trend in mathematical economics was started by Leontief, who used the experience from the inter-industry balance sheets, prepared by the U.S.S.R. in 1923–4. Leontief established linear equations, which connect final demand with activities in different sectors, and presented the results in the form of a chess-board table of input and output. In this table, based on cost of production, the first quadrant indicates inter-industry flows of intermediate products.

The input–output table for any past period has great economic significance. It makes it possible to analyse the cost and composition of the National Product, and to determine the most important inter-industry relations in the economy. It should be noted, however, that due to incorrect assumptions, inter-industry tables prepared in capitalist countries have serious theoretical and practical short-comings. The most important among these are the following:

(i) There is no distinction between productive and non-productive sectors.

(ii) Class and social character of the national income distribution are not taken into consideration.

(iii) There is no division of output into means of production and consumer goods.

(iv) Certain aspects of the table depend on the existing classification of industries.

At present there is a growing tendency to unite the input–output model and the production model. As an example we can mention Leontief's attempt to develop his static model into a dynamic input–output model.

VII

The next step in the development of forecasting models was the attempt to determine the optimum for the national economy, using the linear-programming technique, suggested for the first time by Kantorovich in 1939. After the Second World War, linear programming has been used in a number of capitalist countries, particularly in the U.S.A. Most of these applications have been oriented towards specific problems, such as optimal transportation plans, optimal utilization of capacity or manpower within individual enterprises.

Successful use of linear programming in such fields has induced some economists to use the method also to determine the optimum for the national economy. Thus Koopman and Frisch suggest that we should build a system of linear inequalities and equations, representing the scarcity of certain resources in the society. We should then choose a criterion (usually national income) and determine, by means of linear-programming technique, the optimal allocation of resources, i.e. the allocation which maximizes the criterion. This is essentially the same problem as the one found within a firm.

VIII

The work on national optimum by Koopman, Frisch, and other Western economists, is undoubtedly of great interest. It contains a number of rational elements, for example, use of mathematical techniques for optimization and precise formulation of the problems. At the same time it should be noted that a number of assumptions used in this work are questionable. This applies especially to the parallel drawn between the problems of a single capitalist firm, and the problem of the capitalist economy as a whole.

A number of other difficulties exist. The available statistics are usually far too unreliable to justify accurate calculations. The choice of a criterion presents special difficulties. Different indices may be used, and the solution which is optimal with respect to one of them, will not, of course, be the optimum with respect to other indices. *Therefore the problem of determining the optimum in a national economy should not be reduced to mathematical calculations alone.* The problem should be solved with the help of an economic theory which, at a given stage in the development of productive forces, lays down the basic elements of an optimum.

Parallel with these considerations one must also take into account the effect which the allocation of resources will have on economic development, and whether it is in conflict with long-term aims. Here the decision also rests with economic theory, and the theoretical analysis of economic processes.

IX

So far econometric models have not been very successful in making quantitative forecasts in a capitalist economy. The overwhelming majority of such forecasts have shown very great deviations from reality. This applies equally to control forecasts for past periods, and to forecasts for future periods. Thus the Klein–Goldberger model, used at the end of 1953 and in the middle of 1954 to forecast the U.S.A. economic development for the whole crisis year of 1954, overestimated the actual reduction of Gross National Product by 15 per cent and 19 per cent respectively. The model had forecast an increase in agricultural income of 800 million dollars, but it decreased by 200 million dollars. The model had forecast a reduction in depreciation by 2·2–2·6 billion dollars, while it increased by 1·1 billion dollars.

The Oxford model, used to make forecasts for the British economy for 1959, also gave very significant errors. Forecasts based on input–output models have also given large errors. The difference between actual and predicted changes in capital investment and employment were more than 30 per cent in the forecast made by the American economists Kornfeld, Evans, and Hoffenberg for 1950.

At present preference seems to be given to forecasts for capital investment and other important economic indices. The forecasts are based on annual statistical returns from firms in the private sector, accounting for about two-thirds of total industrial output. It must be admitted that such forecasts have proved rather accurate for years, during which no serious changes occurred in the economy.

X

What are the main causes of the failure of so many economic forecasts based on mathematical models of capitalist countries ?

First of all, it is the erroneous nature of the assumptions on which the mathematical models are based. The most important is probably the mechanical identification of spontaneous processes in capitalist economy with random stochastic processes. This is done by some Western economists when building forecasting models.

Another cause is the spontaneous character of the capitalist economy itself. Even modern mathematics cannot identify and deal accurately with all the ever-changing relations and interdependences which are characteristic of the fluctuating economy of capitalist countries. The spontaneous character of the capitalist economy makes it virtually impossible to make correct forecasts for exogenous variables, such as final demand in the input–output model.

The inaccuracy of the statistical data should also be mentioned. It is generally known that the statistical indices for any given year become stable only two or three years later. During this period they undergo very frequent revisions, often rather significant. A forecast based on these raw indices may prove to be inaccurate, if only because of later changes of the indices.

The lack of up-to-date statistics makes it necessary to use models based on relations observed to hold in earlier periods. The assumption is then that these relations are not subject to change. It is, for instance, usual to assume that the technical coefficients in the input–output model, and the coefficients in production models, remain constant over time. Since in practice these coefficients do change, forecasts based on such models deviate from reality, often to a considerable degree.

These are the main causes of the failure of economic forecasts derived from mathematical models. It should be stressed, however, that the above does not aim at lessening the significance of mathematical methods in the capitalist economy. These methods make it possible to identify and study relations within the national economy; relations which it would be impossible to handle by any other methods.

XI

Since the Second World War bourgeois economics have developed a series of theories of economic growth. On the practical plane, these theories have led to programmes aiming at securing a sufficiently high and stable rate of growth in capitalist production.

American economists — Domar, Duesenberry, Fellner, Hansen, and others — have studied the rate of economic growth, and have tried to develop concrete programmes, i.e. to find methods of state regulation which could increase the present unsatisfactory rates of growth in the American economy. This development in economic theory is the direct effect of the slow rates of growth in the American economy, and of the general slackness in the economic development of that country. The lack of growth has caused alarm among bourgeois economists, and made them look for new means of reviving the out-of-date system of capitalist production.

Many political leaders and economists in the U.S.A. have pointed to the need for higher rates of economic growth. In their papers, speeches, and monographs, one can find calls to raise the rates of economic growth (the Gross National Product) to 4·5 per cent and even to 6 per cent a year. In a number of papers published recently, attempts were made to define a 'required rate of growth': The report by Burns, Butler, and others under the title of 'Prospects for America', 'The Rockefeller Panel Report', and 'Long-Range Projections for Economic Growth. The American Economy in 1970', edited by Colmar, of the National Planning Association.

The authors of the first of these papers lay down the restriction that government share of Gross National Product shall not increase, and come to the conclusion that the most desirable rate of growth from 1957 to 1967 is 5 per cent a year.

In the work of the National Planning Association the necessity of providing so-called 'full' employment, (i.e. 3·5 per cent of the labour force unemployed) has been taken as the basic restriction in the calculation. Then the required rate of growth from 1957 to 1970 is calculated to be slightly lower — 4·2 per cent a year.

XII

As a result of such calculations, American economists have come to the conclusion that to reach the target rate of growth, a special policy for economic development was required. This policy should first of all include anti-crisis measures, but not be limited to this aspect alone. Apart from anti-crisis measures, the policy for economic development should include increased investments in the so-called 'human resources', i.e. increased expenditure on education, training, and retraining of workers and stimulation of scientific and technical research. Further the policy should include an increased role of the state in the development and conservation of natural resources, and certain measures to encourage private capital investments. The political aspect of this programme, especially the development of the 'human resources', undoubtedly contains much social demagogy apt to deceive the working masses.

It would, however, be wrong to see only social demagogy in such programmes. The requirement of 'full employment' is intended to save capitalism from its most acute social problem. Similarly the programme for increased public expenditure on socio-economic tasks is devised to help capitalism solve a still more difficult and politically important problem — to win the competition with socialism — a competitor which has all the advantages of a planned economy.

XIII

Economists of the neo-liberal school stress the need for creating favourable conditions for the growth of private capital, and at the same time call for maximum saving of state resources. On the other side, the followers of Keynes argue for increased government expenditure, including deficit financing. They stand decisively for increased public expenditure on tasks such as research and development of natural resources. A theoretical justification for increased expenditure of this kind is given in the works of outstanding economists (Hansen, A., 'Economic Issues of the 1960s'; Galbraith, J., 'The Affluent Society', and others).

The difference between the neo-liberal and the Keynesian approach to the problem of economic growth lies in the methods proposed to achieve increased capital investments which both recognize as the basis for economic growth. The increase in capital investment should, according to Keynes' followers, follow from expanded consumption, including various forms of public consumption. This school maintains that insufficient demand is the prime cause of low rates of investment. This point of view is being defended by Keyserling, Hansen, Rostow, and the majority of the Council of Economic Advisers.

Economists of the neo-liberal school joined by representatives of big business put forward measures aimed at increasing the profits of monopolies and thus making greater funds available for investment. W. Butler, vice-president of the Chase Manhattan Bank, wrote that he could not agree with arguments that investments were hindered by excess capacities, due to insufficient purchasing power. In his opinion, such arguments do not hold water. The problem over a number of past years, he says, was not insufficient purchasing power, but — on the contrary — that purchasing power tended to grow too fast, so that with stable prices for industrial goods, profits did not grow fast enough. This, in turn, slowed down capital investment and economic growth as a whole.

XIV

The economic programme, proposed by frank advocates of monopolies, demands higher profits and redistribution of national income in favour of monopolistic capital. They maintain that this will lead to the highest growth of the productive forces. These economists exaggerate when they speak of the reduction in the profits of monopolies over the last years. According to the official statistics, the profits of corporations, after taxes, was higher in 1964 than ten years ago — 4·3 per cent of GNP against 3·7 per cent in 1954. Since the focal point of this programme is the growth of monopolistic profits and reduced public consumption, it can lead only to further sharpening of the inherent contradictions of the capitalist economy.

XV

There is an impression that the Keynesian programme corresponds better to the real need for increased economic growth in the U.S.A. The shortcoming of this programme is that Keynes' followers defend the foundations of the capitalist economy. They see a possibility of increasing demand only in increased public expenditure, which includes enormous military budgets, and leads to inflation and to further economic difficulties. This is especially serious when military expenditure in the U.S.A. has reached an unprecedented level. Therefore it is clear that the Keynesian programme cannot solve the problem of economic growth for a long period of time.

At the same time it should be stressed that increased public expenditure on socio-economic needs, with simultaneous reduction of military expenditure, can lead to growth of both output and productivity, and also to an expansion of the home market. Whether this will happen depends on the strength of the forces of democracy when it comes to exercising influence on the economic policy of the Government.

PART V

SEQUENTIAL DECISION PROBLEMS

Chapter 19

SOME PROBLEMS OF ECONOMIC GROWTH
IN A PLANNED ECONOMY

BY

JAROMIR WALTER

I. INTRODUCTION

ALTHOUGH there exists a great deal of literature treating the problems of economic growth under different assumptions, little attention has so far been paid to the mutual influence of plans and target fulfilment. We can find the concept of a plan also in non-socialist countries, but we shall not discuss these.

Let us accept the hypothesis, which is probably not far from reality, that the plans in socialist countries are generally *directive* plans. The plans of industrial production, for instance, are directive, and in this way, they affect all the workers and employees of a given plant or enterprise. There exist also plans of a different nature, e.g. in the sphere of consumption, but we shall not be concerned with these in our study. The direction of activity of the workers need not however be the same as was originally aimed at. There can be different ways of studying the problems, some of them exceeding the frame of economics. We have selected some economic-growth models, including planned levels as factors of economic growth.

Having introduced a planned level of an event (of production, in most cases) as a factor, we must classify it as connected with uncertain results. It is well known that an unrealistically high plan acts in the opposite direction to that of a reasonable one. In different conditions the role of a plan as a stimulant is, of course, followed by different quantitative results. A well-constructed plan should reflect all relations existing in a given economic situation. If it ignores some relations, discrepancies arise which cannot be exactly foreseen. They are a type of noise event arising when a plan is not compatible with certain objective economic trends. The economy defends itself and disturbances of a random type arise.

It seems useful to study first the consequences of a type of growth, where the level of a planned event influences this event itself. In such models no elements of uncertainty of probabilistic type are contained. The uncertainty in some decisions made without models is mere lack of knowledge, and has no common elements with a probabilistic model. An investigation of such models is not only a starting-point for more complicated (or probabilistic) ones, but can show some tendencies which are not evident at first sight.

From these models we shall go on to study their modifications, including random disturbances. It is these that create uncertainty in the proper sense of this word. We treat uncertainty as resulting from some main factors, the unessential ones being the source of the mentioned disturbances. We shall ignore problems such as natural disasters (as factors of disturbances) and problems of peace and war.

II. SOME MODELS OF ECONOMIC GROWTH TREATING THE PLAN AS FACTOR

Suppose a directive plan is treated as a factor of growth of some economic event. In most cases we are interested in the production of some good, or in the production of some enterprise or plant.

Ignoring other factors (which we shall introduce in the model later), we can illustrate the link between 'reality' (corresponding to the fulfilment of a plan) and 'plan' as a sequence of impulses :

$$p_t, r_t, p_{t-1}, r_{t-1}, \ldots .$$

This is a sequence of the 'plan' for the period 't' followed by the 'reality' in the same period, this sequence being repeated for succeeding periods.

Such a model can be formulated as a system of difference equations

$$p_{t+1} = ar_t$$
$$r_t = cp_t,$$

the coefficients a, c representing some rate of growth (a being a rate in a project of a plan for the subsequent period, c being a coefficient of the 'fulfilment' of the last plan).

The real level of an event is, in this way, a result of a directive plan, which cannot be ignored during the construction of a new plan. We assume the disturbance term can be neglected at this stage.

The solution being found in a trivial form as

$$r_t = (a \cdot c)^t r_0 \tag{1}$$

does not contain the planned level of a studied event explicitly; the effect of the plan is 'hidden' partly in the projected growth rate a, and in the fulfilment of a past plan c. The question could be put whether the relation between a and c would influence the way in which some event would grow. It seems premature to answer this without introducing other growth factors.

To proceed more concretely let us pay some attention to production-growth models, output being determined by labour and investment funds (or perhaps machine-investment funds) used. There is no obstacle to enlarging such a model and including any number of factors of production. Naturally we need not limit ourselves to production problems, but we shall treat them as the best known and simplest ones.

Having introduced I_t as investment,[1] L_t as labour, and P_t as production (in period t), we can propose

Model (1)

$$P_t = \eta, \ L_t + \eta_2 I_t$$
$$I_{t+1} - I_t = k(P_t - P_{t-1})$$
$$L_t - L_{t-1} = v(P_t - P_{t-1}),$$

η_1, η_2, k, and v being some parameters to be determined later (possibly from statistical data) and the disturbance terms being neglected at this stage. The variables P_t and I_t are expressed in some constant prices (representing the volume of production or investment). The variable L_t can be represented by the number of employees and workers, but we may also express it by a wage bill, which should be measured in 'constant' wages representing a volume of labour of different quality. The analogy with the Cobb–Douglas production function and also with some growth models of the multiplier type is evident. The linearity in the production function can be deleted by writing

$$\lg \frac{P_{t+1}}{P_t} = \eta_1 \lg \frac{L_{t+1}}{L_t} + \eta_2 \frac{I_{t+1}}{I_t}$$

and

$$\lg P_t = p_t, \ \lg L_t = l_t, \ \lg I_t = \iota_t$$

and by changing the two other equations of Model (1) to logarithmic form, we get

---

[1] It is possible to think of this variable as capital stock, in a Cobb–Douglas model.

Sequential Decision Problems

Model (1a)

$$p_t - p_{t-1} = \eta_1(l_t - l_{t-1}) + \eta_2(i_t - i_{t-1})$$
$$i_t - i_{t-1} = k(p_t - p_{t-1})$$
$$l_t - l_{t-1} = v(p_t - p_{t-1}),$$

where the parameters η_1, η_2, k, v are, of course, different from the corresponding ones in Model (1).

Both these models are equivalent to the difference equation of the following form

$$P_t - P_{t-1}\left(1 - \frac{\eta_2 k}{1 - \eta_1 v}\right) + \frac{\eta_2 k}{1 - \eta_1 v}P_{t-2} = 0, \tag{2}$$

where p_t would be written instead of P_t in the case of Model (1a).

The equations of Model (1) or (1a) describe

(i) the relationship between production and the factors;

(ii) the evidence that investment is made from the lagged increment of production;

(iii) the hypothesis that the increments of labour and production in the same period are proportional.

The last hypothesis can be modified in different ways. Let us mention two of them, introducing

Model (2)

$$p_t - p_{t-1} = \eta_1(l_t - l_{t-1}) + \eta_2(i_t - i_{t-1})$$
$$i_t - i_{t-1} = k(p_{t-1} - p_{t-2})$$
$$l_t - l_{t-1} = v(p_t - p_{t-1}) - c(i_t - i_{t-1}),$$

and

Model (3)

$$p_t - p_{t-1} = \eta_1(l_t - l_{t-1}) + \eta_2(i_t - i_{t-1})$$
$$i_t - i_{t-1} = k(p_{t-1} - p_{t-2})$$
$$l_t - l_{t-1} = v(p_t - p_{t-1}) - c(i_{t-1} - i_{t-2})$$

The only modification concerns the last equation, which describes the (logarithmic) increment of labour as a proportional increment of production reduced by a proportional increment of investment (in the same period in Model (2) or in the preceding period in Model (3)). The corresponding difference equations can be written in the form

$$p_t - p_{t-1}\left(1 + \frac{k\eta_2 - c\eta_1}{1 - \eta_1 v}\right) + p_{t-2}\frac{k\eta_2 - \eta_1 c}{1 - \eta_1 v} = 0 \tag{3}$$

$$\text{and } \Delta p_t - \frac{\eta_2 k}{1 - \eta_1 v} \Delta p_{t-1} + \frac{\eta_1 c}{1 - \eta_1 v} \Delta p_{t-2} = 0 \qquad (4)$$

respectively.

All these models and the corresponding difference equations make it possible to study conditions of such a 'path' of growth that is free from irregularities (oscillations, for instance).

The solution of equation (2) can be written in the form

$$P_t = c_1 + c_2 K^t, \; K = \frac{\eta_2 \cdot k}{1 - \eta_1 v}$$

or, corresponding to the 'logarithmic' form of the production function

$$p_t = c_1 + c_2 K^t, \; K = \frac{\eta_2 \cdot k}{1 - \eta_1 v}.$$

If the parameter K is not greater than one (η_1, η_2, k, v being positive and not greater than 1), the second component will vanish as t approaches infinity.

For Model (2) the solution takes the form:

$$p_t = c_1 + K^t_1, \; K_1 = \frac{k\eta_2 - \eta_1 c}{1 - v\eta_1}$$

analogous to the preceding one. Model (3) opens broader possibilities. It is possible to solve the difference equation of third order (4) as a second order equation for the difference Δp_t. The solution can be written

$$\Delta p_t = c_1 \lambda_1^t + c_2 \lambda_2^t,$$

where $\lambda_{1, 2}$ are the roots of the characteristic equation

$$\lambda^2 - \frac{\eta_2 k}{1 - \eta_1 v} \lambda + \frac{\eta_1 c}{1 - \eta_1 v} = 0.$$

These roots take the form

$$\lambda_{12} = \frac{1}{2} \frac{\eta_2 k}{1 - \eta_1 v} \pm \sqrt{\frac{\eta^2_2 \cdot k^2}{4(1 - \eta_1 v)^2} - \frac{\eta_1 c}{1 - \eta_1 v}}.$$

The condition for them to be real, which is

$$\eta^2_2 k^2 > 4\eta_1 c(1 - \eta_1 v)$$

can act as a useful constraint.

Summarizing the treatment of the preceding models, we can say that, from a formal point of view, Model (1a) is not connected with the risk of oscillatory movement, Model (2) contains a possibility of some 'skipping' from negative to positive increments, and Model (3) contains a real possibility of oscillatory movements.

Let us now return to the problem of stability of the plan we are concerned with, citing the special case of a production plan.

We shall examine from this viewpoint, Models (1a), (2), and (3) and equations (2)–(4). We express the 'real' level of an event (as opposed to planned level) by the symbols $\bar{p}_t$, $\bar{l}_t$, $\bar{\imath}_t$ surmounted by a bar, and its relation to the plan by some combination of growth rates (as has been shown in equation (1)). The modified form of Model (1a) can be written as

$$\text{Model } (1^*a)$$

$$\alpha\alpha^*(\bar{p}_t - \bar{p}_{t-1}) = \eta_1\eta_1^*(\bar{l}_t - \bar{l}_{t-1}) + \eta_2\eta_2^*(\bar{\imath}_t - \bar{\imath}_{t-1})$$
$$\bar{\imath}_t - \bar{\imath}_{t-1} = kk^*(\bar{p}_{t-1}\bar{p}_{t-2})$$
$$\bar{l}_t - \bar{l}_{t-1} = vv^*(\bar{p}_t - \bar{p}_{t-1}),$$

where the parameters α, η_1, η_2, k, v are those of the plan and their counterparts with an asterisk are some corrections (which could be interpreted as a form of fulfilment of this plan).[1] The change of the parameters from one period to another is 'disaggregated' into a product of two rates of growth. The corresponding difference equation can be written

$$\bar{p}_t(1 - K_1) - \bar{p}_{t-1}(1 - K_1 + K_2) + K_1\bar{p}_{t-2} = 0,$$

with

$$K_1 = \frac{1}{\alpha\alpha^*}\eta_1\eta_1^*vv^*$$

$$K_2 = \frac{1}{\alpha\alpha^*}\eta_2\eta_2^*kk^*$$

and with the solution

$$\bar{p}_t = c_1 + c_2\left(\frac{K_2}{1 - K_1}\right)^t.$$

In the case

$$\frac{K_2}{1 - K_1} > 1$$

the solution will be a kind of explosive one.

[1] The parameter α is planned growth, and as such identical to a.

Proceeding to an analogous modification of Model (2), we get as a result the following equation

$$\bar{p}_t - \bar{p}_{t-1}\left(1 - \frac{K_2}{K_1} + \frac{K_3}{K_1}\right) - \frac{K_2 - K_3}{K_1} = 0,$$

where

$$K_1 = 1 - \frac{1}{\alpha\alpha^*}\eta_1\eta_1^*vv^*$$

$$K_2 = \frac{1}{\alpha\alpha^*}\eta_1\eta_2^*cc^*kk^*$$

$$K_3 = \frac{1}{\alpha\alpha^*}\eta_2\eta_2^*kk^*.$$

The solution has the form

$$\bar{p}_t = c_1 + c_2\left(\frac{K_2 - K_3}{K_1}\right)^t.$$

The conditions for different kinds of trends arising from the nature of the term

$$\frac{K_2 - K_3}{K_1} = \frac{KK^*(\eta_1\eta_1^*cc^* - \eta_2\eta_2^*)}{\alpha\alpha^* - \eta_1\eta_1^*vv^*}$$

are obvious. The nature of Models (1) and (2) is not much different. The analysis of the Model (3) would lead to an equation

$$\Delta p_t - \frac{\eta_2\eta_2^*kk^*}{\alpha\alpha^* - \eta_1\eta_1^*vv^*}\Delta p_{t-1} + \frac{\eta_1\eta_1^*cc^*}{\alpha\alpha^* - \eta_1\eta_1^*vv^*}3p_{t-2} = 0,$$

or in a simpler form

$$\Delta p_t - K_1\Delta p_{t-1} + K_2\Delta p_{t-2} = 0.$$

The condition for the trend not to acquire an oscillatory nature is

$$K_1^2 - 4K_2 \geqslant 0$$

or

$$(\eta_2\eta_*^2kk^*)^2 \geqslant 4\eta_1\eta_1^*cc^*(\alpha\alpha^* - \eta_1\eta_1^*vv^*).$$

One could object that we have not gained much, having developed the above-mentioned models without disturbance factors (random deviations). Although more detailed empirical investigations would be needed (not only of economic, but also of a sociological and psychological nature), it seems reasonable to show the final effect of decisions made about some planned growth rates on the proposed models.

III. SOME PROBLEMS RESULTING FROM DISTURBANCES

So far we have treated models without disturbances. There exist many possible ways of introducing these. The difference equations we have used to describe the behaviour of our system were the homogeneous ones. Let us assume the right-hand side of the said homogeneous equations may contain some term describing the disturbances (or deviations from average tendencies which were described by previous models).

This leads to stochastic difference equations of the form:

$$y_{x-1} - \rho y_x = \epsilon_x,$$

where ϵ_x is a random variable with mean $E(\epsilon_x) = 0$ and variance $E(\epsilon_x^2) = \sigma^2$. We thus get for Model ($1a$)

$$\Delta \bar{p}_t - \frac{\eta_2 \eta_2^* k k^*}{\alpha \alpha^* - v v^* \eta_1 \eta_1^*} \Delta \bar{p}_t = \epsilon_t$$

or

$$\Delta \bar{p}_t - \frac{K_2}{1 - K_1} \Delta \bar{p}_{t-1} = \epsilon_t,$$

and for Model (2)

$$\Delta \bar{p}_t - \frac{K_2 - K_3}{K_1} \Delta \bar{p}_{t-1} = \epsilon_t,$$

where the Ks are given above. The terms $\dfrac{K_2}{1 - K_1}$ or $\dfrac{K_2 - K_3}{K_1}$ can be identified with the term ρ of the previous general form. For the solution not to be an explosive one, the condition $|\rho| < 1$ must be fulfilled. The general solution is

$$\Delta \bar{p}_t = C \rho^t + Y_t,$$

where Y_t is a particular solution, which can be found in the form

$$Y = \epsilon_{t-1} + \rho \epsilon_{t-2} + \rho^3 \epsilon_{t-3} + \ldots$$

It is evident that a stationary solution must be a particular one, Y_t being a random variable with mean $EY_t = 0$ and variance $EY_t^2 = \dfrac{\sigma^2}{1 - \rho}$.

Though we do not know much about the long-term behaviour of time series of the 'plan fulfilment' (the plans are too frequently altered and thus an element of incomparability is introduced), the assumption $EY_t = 0$ implying the solution for $\Delta \bar{p}_t$ to be stationary does not seem real and reasonable.

It seems further that the concept of stationarity, finding its interpretation in the assumption that the event began in the infinite past and goes on in to the infinite future, does not fit with the case of changes caused by mutual interdependence of intended (planned) and real growth, the latter being of short-term character.

The approach through autoregressive schemes, studied from the viewpoint of stationariness by Yule and Slutsky, includes as essentials the conditions $E(\epsilon_t) = 0$, $E(\epsilon_t \epsilon_{t+1}) = 0$ for disturbances and the condition $(EY_t) = 0$ for a particular solution, which seems inappropriate for a growth model.

Another possibility of investigating disturbances may be achieved by varying parameters of 'plan fulfilment'. Instead of writing η^* for the corrective factors (which are a measure of plan fulfilment), let us express them in the form of deviations $(1 + \Delta \eta)$, including likewise the effects of random disturbances.

Models (1) or (2) seeming a little oversimplified for practical purposes, let us illustrate the above-mentioned possibility on Model (3). The roots of a characteristic equation being written

$$\frac{1}{2} \frac{\eta_2(1+\Delta\eta_2)k(1+\Delta k)}{1-\eta_1(1+\Delta\eta)v(1+\Delta v)} \left[1 \pm \right.$$

$$\left. \sqrt{1 - \frac{4\eta_1(1+\Delta\eta_1)c(1+\Delta c)\ [1-\eta_1(1+\Delta\eta_1)v(1+\Delta v)]}{\eta_2^2(1+\Delta\eta_2)^2k^2(1+\Delta k)^2}} \right],$$

further simplification is possible by neglecting the terms of higher order (i.e. the parameters are not greater than unity and an allowable approximation can be reached by neglecting their second differences), and writing

$$\frac{1}{2}\eta_2 k \left[1 + \Delta k + \Delta \eta_2 + \eta_1 v(1 + 2\Delta \eta_1 + 2v) \right] \left\{ 1 \pm \right.$$

$$\left[1 - 2\frac{\eta_1 c}{\eta_2^2 k^2} \left[1 + \Delta \eta_1 + \Delta c - 2\Delta \eta_2 - 2\Delta k - \right. \right.$$

$$\left. \left. \eta_1 v(1 + 2\eta_1 + \Delta v + \Delta c - 2\Delta \eta_2 - 2\Delta k) \right] \right] \right\}.$$

When some probability distributions of the parameters under investigation are available, lower and upper bounds will be estimated as a first approximation.

Assuming now for a moment the order of deviations to be much lower than the values of the parameters, it is possible to obtain a rough approximation of the roots in the form

$$\lambda_1 \sim \eta_2 k - \frac{\eta_1 c}{\eta_2 k}, \qquad \lambda_2 \sim \frac{\eta_1 c}{\eta_2 k}$$

In most cases these values will not rise above unity, and we shall obtain an equilibrium which, unfortunately, is not often encountered in practice.

More factors and more complicated schemes of linkage between the targets and real life have to be investigated.

IV. SOME POSSIBLE GENERALIZATIONS

The interdependence between 'plan' and 'reality' can be described also by a scheme

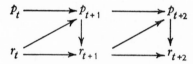

expressing the 'plan' as a result of preceding 'reality' and preceding 'plan' and the 'reality' as a result of the corresponding 'plan' and preceding 'reality'. The corresponding system of difference equations is then

$$p_{t+1} = ar_t + bp_t$$
$$r_t = cp_t + dr_{t-1}$$

and its second order difference-equation counterpart is

$$p_{t+1} - p_t/ac + d + b/ + dbp_{t-1} = 0.$$

The changes are of course connected with the changes of the factors of production (i.e. with planned and real investment, planned and real labour force in the simple case). Let us consider them in the following

Model (4)

$$\Delta p_{t+1} = a_1 \Delta p_t^* + a_2 \Delta p_t + a_3 \Delta i_t^* + a_4 \Delta i_t + a_5 \Delta l_{t-1}^* + a_6 \Delta l_{t+1}$$
$$\Delta p_t^* = b_1 \Delta p_t + b_2 p_{t-1}^* + b_3 \Delta i_{t-1} + b_4 \Delta i_{t-1} + b_5 \Delta l_{t-1}^* + b_6 \Delta l_t$$
$$\Delta i_{t+1} = c_1 \Delta p_t + c_2 \Delta p_t^* + c_3 \Delta i_t^* + c_4 \Delta i_t + c_5 \Delta l_t^* + c_6 \Delta l_t$$
$$\Delta i_t^* = d_1 \Delta p_{t-1} + d_2 p_{t-1}^* + d_3 \Delta i_{t-1}^* + d_4 \Delta i_{t-1} + d_5 \Delta l_{t-1}^* + d_6 \Delta l_{t-1}^*$$
$$\Delta l_{t+1} = l_1 \Delta p_{t+1} + l_2 \Delta p_t^* + l_3 \Delta i_t^* + l_4 \Delta i_t + l_5 \Delta l_t^* + l_6 \Delta l_t$$
$$\Delta l_t^* = f_1 \Delta p_t + f_2 \Delta p_t^* + f_3 \Delta i_t^* + f_4 \Delta i_{t-1} + f_5 \Delta l_{t-1}^* + f_6 \Delta l_t.$$

The factors introduced appear also in the form of 'plan' and 'reality' (the latter being shown by an asterisk). Investment depends on lagged production, labour force affects current production. Differences are introduced to exclude possible influence of the time-factor. The parameters are assumed to be constant. This assumption can be modified by introducing a common growth rate and when investigating the disturbance problems some corrective coefficients can be assigned to values expressing 'reality'.

It is cumbersome not only to solve the general system (even in the simplified case, where only two factors are given), but also to identify its parameters from statistical observations. A statistical analysis can provide us with estimates of parameters and the unsignificant ones can be deleted from our system. The investigation of this type can use some types of Klein–Goldberger models including the 'plan' as regressor.

Let us assume our model was simplified (the increments of labour force being neglected) and can be given in the following form:

$$\Delta p_{t+1} = a_1 \Delta p_t^* + a_2 \Delta p_t + \qquad a_4 \Delta i_t$$
$$\Delta p_t^* = b_1 \Delta p_t + b_2 \Delta p_{t-1}^* + b_3 \Delta_t^* i_{-1}$$
$$\Delta i_{t+1} = c_1 \Delta p_t$$
$$\Delta i_t^* = d_2 \Delta p_{t-1}^*,$$

the corresponding difference equation being

$$\Delta p_{t+1} - \Delta p_t(a_2 + a_1 b_1 + b_2 - b_3 d_2)$$
$$- \Delta p_{t-1}(a_4 c_1 - a_2 b_2 + a_2 d_2 b_3)$$
$$+ \Delta p_{t-2}(b_2 - b_3 d_2)a_4 c_1 \qquad = 0.$$

The parameters a_1, b_2, b_3, d_2 can be allowed to be affected by random disturbances. The investigation of the corresponding characteristic equation, including some error terms, makes it possible to analyse acceptable limits for the whole process.

The interdependence of 'plan' and 'reality', described as 'directive' planning, will probably take other forms when the plan has the character of a forecast. Nevertheless analogous forms of analysis can be used also in this field of investigation. Interesting problems will arise in studying possible contradictions of an 'elastic' price policy which should be introduced in connection with new methods of planning in our economy, and directive planning.

V. CONCLUDING REMARKS

The mutual relationship of targets and their attainment can be formulated with such tools as difference equations. A great deal of work must however be done to check the assumed forms of the relations and to determine the parameters. Although this can be done in various manners with equal or greater efficiency, it seems the interdependence of 'plan' and 'reality' and possible discrepancies arising therefrom should not be overlooked.

DISCUSSION OF THE PAPER BY DR. WALTER

Professor Marschak : Dr. Walter is concerned with the interaction between a planner on the one hand and the economy which he plans and to which he responds on the other, first in a deterministic setting and then in a stochastic one. He first considers a family of deterministic growth models without a planner ; the simplest one, restated in terms perhaps closer to those of recent growth models, is as follows :

$$P_t = F(L_t, K_t)$$
$$K_t - K_{t-1} = G(P_t)$$
$$L_t - L_{t-1} = H(P_t),$$

where P_t is production in a period t and K_t, L_t are capital stock and labour force at the end of period t. In Dr. Walter's case K_t in the first relation is replaced by current investment (i.e. by $K_t - K_{t-1}$), which gives the model a rather unfamiliar character : does all previously accumulated capital have no influence on current production ?

Dr. Walter considers in particular a Cobb–Douglas form of the first equation (with current investment replacing capital stock) and then, taking logarithms, gets a linear system of difference equations. The stability properties of such a system can be studied, that is conditions on the coefficients can be found implying oscillating growth on the one hand, or steady growth (explosive or convergent) on the other. Then, still in a deterministic framework, the planner is introduced. The very general form of the model is now

$$\text{plan}_{t+1} = f(\text{reality}_t)$$
$$\text{reality}_t = g(\text{plan}_t).$$

To introduce such an interdependence between plan and reality into the first model in a simple way, one assumes that current (planned) investment depends on previous realized production, that actual investment is a function of (but not equal to) planned investment, and that current

418

realized production depends on current labour force and current capital stock (including the additions to it which represent actual current investment). Giving relations a linear form, a stability analysis is again possible. Stochastic disturbances are then added to the family of models. One then has, ultimately, systems of stochastic difference equations and can then look, presumably, for conditions on the original coefficients which imply, under alternative assumptions about the distribution of the disturbances, convergence in probability to steady growth paths.

Dr. Walter's notion of the planner as a natural phenomenon whose behaviour is subject to study and to statistical estimation is an interesting one, especially for those who study certain planned economies as outsiders ; if appropriate data were ever available such students might fruitfully follow Dr. Walter's suggestion.

I wonder, however, whether a more realistic picture of the planner would not permit his behaviour to change over time, would not permit him to learn. Finally it should be remarked that from the point of view of the design of *appropriate* behaviour for planners, Dr. Walter's class of models is not relevant. The investigation of investment policies maximizing various sorts of objective functions defined on the stream of future production is relevant and is also under way.

Dr. Thore : The theme of Dr. Walter's paper can be seen, I think, as a natural continuation of the subjects we discussed earlier in connection with Professor Siroyezhin's paper. We discussed then the nature of uncertainty facing a planner, with special reference to the differences in this regard in market economies and centrally planned economies. Dr. Walter's paper invites us to take one step further, and to look at the step from planning to realization in an uncertain world, again with special reference to differences between market economies and centrally planned economies.

This step is the step from *ex ante* to *ex post*, to be taken in an uncertain world, and that is essentially what Dr. Walter's paper deals with. The paper sketches some variants of the simple multiplier–accelerator model and the author goes on to outline the modifications and extensions of this well-known analysis that seem to be called for when the difference between *ex ante* and *ex post* is allowed for and shown explicitly.

Dr. Walter's treatment refers to the case of a centrally planned economy, and then let me first, for the sake of reference, remind you of some features of the corresponding theoretical situation in the case of a market economy. Indeed, the idea of analysing dynamic processes of interaction between *ex ante* and *ex post* is not new, and the basic reference here is the classical work by Erik Lundberg (1938), the vice-president of our organization. Lundberg in his pioneering work, and building upon the theoretical tradition of the Swedish *ex ante–ex post* school, developed dynamic difference-equation-type models with a detailed discussion of the relationship between *ex ante* and *ex post*.

Let me illustrate in the diagram below by means of some simple catchwords the steps from *ex ante* to *ex post*, as it is developed by the Swedish economist relating to a market economy, and how it may have to be analysed for a controlled economy :

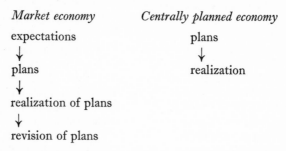

Market economy	Centrally planned economy
expectations	plans
↓	↓
plans	realization
↓	
realization of plans	
↓	
revision of plans	

I shall comment upon this diagram by way of posing two questions, which may be helpful for our discussion :

(1) How is the period closed ? That is, how are realizations reached ? In the case of the market economy, a common assumption is that the consumers carry through their plans, and that if production plans are not compatible with desired consumption, any surplus production is stocked and carried over to the next period, and deficit production covered by exhaustion of stocks. This assumption reflects the fact that the market economy is essentially consumer-oriented. How is the period closed in the case of a centrally planned economy ? This seems to me to be an important question, the answer to which I do not know. My interpretation of the situation would be, however, that it would be the producers, rather than the consumers, who would typically carry through their plans. The consumers would then have to absorb the differences between *ex ante* and *ex post*, rather than the producers. There is also the problem of what happens when different production plans are incompatible, and some of them have to give way. I may refer for instance to the situation mentioned in Dr. Walter's paper when targets have been set which are unrealistically high, and that the realization of production plans will have to fall short of the plan, and there will occur disorganization tendencies in the economy under the pressure of an *ex ante* which is unattainable *ex post*. An interesting problem then is which productive plans will be carried through, and which ones will break down.

(2) What implications from the events of the current period are drawn for the next period ? That is, how are the incompatibilities of different production plans being resolved for action in the next period ? In both types of economies this is a question of revision of plans. In the market economy such revisions of plans will, during the course of the period, be forced to take place by the market mechanism to result, at the end of the period, in compatibility. The new plans for the next period will be based upon these adjustments. In the case of the controlled economy, however,

there exists no automatic mechanism that will ensure eventual compatibility, and the new plans for the next period will not necessarily contain any adjustments intended to eliminate occurred incompatibilities. Such is the situation when, for instance, as Dr. Walter describes in the paper, the plans for the next period can be viewed as being extrapolated from realizations during the current period by the help of a constant multiplicative factor, regardless of the difficulties which may possibly have occurred in obtaining these realizations.

(3) A third problem, or rather subject for research, which I would like to formulate for the discussion, is the adaption of the *ex ante–ex post* scheme to multi-sector analysis. In an input–output system, for instance, there may occur discrepancies between planned technical coefficients, and the outcome of such coefficients *ex post*. Any such discrepancy in a given cell in an input–output table would then have consequences for the attainable levels of production in other productive sectors, so that any original discrepancy in any given cell would be propagated by means of dynamic processes of adjustment throughout the whole input–output table.

Dr. Walter : I am very grateful to both discussants for their comments. Concerning Professor Marschak's remark about the rigidity of behaviour of the planner I must say that the model was intended really to take account of such special conditions. There has been a tendency in the history of our planning to propose too-great growth rates and this has led to unreal plans. There exists also an opposite tendency, and they are both dangerous. The model is meant as a tool for studying the consequences of such behaviour.

The comment about possible maximization in setting up plans is a very important one. What I mean is that it is necessary to get some limits on growth rates which can be introduced into normative models, and that these growth rates can be obtained by studying the type of model proposed.

I agree with the remark by Professor Marschak that the model in its present form may be used as a tool for studying the behaviour of a planner. It is intended to adapt the model for some simulation processes describing the behaviour of a planner in certain situations.

The comments of Dr. Thore concern the problems of closing the period and the implication of the results for further periods. These viewpoints are contained implicitly in the variable representing the level of a newly constructed plan. Some improvements could be made by introducing the level of stock of production as a factor. The relation to other sectors of enterprises could be studied through an enlarged system of simultaneous equations. Such a model would be very complicated, but methods could be found for solving it.

I must close my answers by repeating my thanks to the discussants, whose comments are very helpful to further work in this direction.

Chapter 20

A DYNAMIC LEONTIEF MODEL WITH CHANCE-CONSTRAINTS

BY

STEN THORE

INTRODUCTION

MOST multi-sector growth models presented in the literature have been developed under the standard assumption of certainty. One then looks for optimal *deterministic* paths of growth of output and capital stock. The present paper explores the modifications of multi-sector growth theory which seem to be called for when uncertainty about the productivity of future capital is introduced explicitly into the model. We shall then be looking for optimal *stochastic strategies* for the accumulation of capital stock.

The text of the paper will speak for itself, but it may be worth while already at this introductory stage to point out that the formulation of stochastic planning will in fact involve a rather severe criticism of deterministic planning. The introduction of uncertainty into the model is not just a mathematical complication which makes the treatment technically more difficult without changing any essential feature of the results. As viewed inside the framework of stochastic planning, to fix a deterministic plan is to commit a mathematical error, yielding a *sub-optimal* position.

The essence of the stochastic planning which is going to be developed is that it is *flexible*, and contains built-in provisions for changing situations. Any modification of deterministic planning, introducing such elements of flexibility, will constitute a step towards a better use of the existing resources.

I. THE LEONTIEF MODEL

For reference, let us first take a look at the dynamic Leontief model under certainty.[1] Let a closed economy be divided into $i = 1, 2, \ldots, n$

[1] The present brief outline follows Dorfman, Samuelson, and Solow (1958) and Solow (1959).

productive sectors, the output of which are denoted x_i. The input requirements necessary to sustain the production of one unit of x_j, $j = 1, 2, \ldots, n$ are defined by the matrix of technical coefficients $[a_{ij}]$.

Let the amount of capital existing in sector i be S_i. The capital requirements necessary to sustain the production of one unit of x_j are defined by the matrix of capital coefficients $[b_{ij}]$.

The existing capital stock must at least suffice to sustain the volume of current production

$$S_i \geqslant \sum_{(j)} b_{ij} x_j. \tag{1.1}$$

Let final demand for the product of sector i be C_i. Total production in each sector must at least suffice to meet inter-industry demand, new capital formation, and final demand

$$x_i \geqslant \sum_{(j)} a_{ij} x_j + \varDelta S_i + C_i, \qquad i = 1, 2, \ldots, n. \tag{1.2}$$

All variables are supposed to be dated at time period t, $t = 1$, $2, \ldots, T$. The time index is suppressed when no misunderstanding can occur. New capital formation $\varDelta S$ is defined as $S(t+1) - S(t)$.

(1.2) can be written in matrix notation

$$x \geqslant ax + \varDelta S + C \tag{1.3}$$

or

$$x \geqslant A(\varDelta S + C), \tag{1.4}$$

introducing the matrix $A = (1 - a)^{-1}$ of total (direct + indirect) input requirements. Combining with (1.1) one gets

$$S \geqslant B(\varDelta S + C), \tag{1.5}$$

where $B = bA$ is the matrix of total (direct + indirect) capital requirements.

Optimal growth is now defined as a growth pattern which maximizes $K'S(T)$, where K is a vector of prescribed weights, subject to the intertemporal efficiency conditions (1.5)

$$B(S(1) - S(0) + C(1)) \leqslant S(0)$$
$$B(S(2) - S(1) + C(2)) \leqslant S(1)$$
$$\vdots$$
$$B(S(T) - S(T-1) + C(T)) \leqslant S(T-1). \tag{1.6}$$

One may also, if one so wishes, add the conditions

$$S(t) - S(t-1) \geqslant 0, \qquad t = 1, 2, \ldots, T. \qquad (1.7)$$

The solution will consist of an optimal stock pattern $S(t)$, $t = 1$, $2, \ldots, T$.

II. FORMULATION OF THE PROBLEM

The purpose of the present paper is to study the same multi-sector growth model as above, but under *uncertainty*. How is the analysis to be modified when we allow for the total capital coefficients b_{ij} to be *uncertain*?

Let $B_{ij}(t)$ be stochastic variables and define the matrices of mathematical expectations and of variances in the following way

$$EB(t) = [EB_{ij}(t)], \qquad i, j = 1, 2, \ldots, n \qquad (2.1)$$

$$\sigma^2 B(t) = [\sigma^2 B_{ij}(t)], \qquad i, j = 1, 2, \ldots, n. \qquad (2.2)$$

What can be said about the nature of the stochastic matrix process $B(t)$? It seems reasonable to assume that uncertainty increases with the distance from the present, in the sense that

$$\sigma^2 B(1) \leqslant \sigma^2 B(2) \leqslant \ldots \leqslant \sigma^2 B(T) \qquad (2.3)$$

denote deviations of the total capital coefficients from their mathematical expectations with caps. Our analysis will depend crucially upon the magnitude of the cross-moments of the type:

$$E[\hat{B}_{ij}(t)\hat{B}_{kl}(\tau)], \qquad \text{with } \tau < t, \qquad (2.4)$$

i.e. the dependence of single total capital coefficients in period t upon other single capital coefficients in earlier periods $\tau < t$.

A special instance of the cross-moments (2.4) is obtained for $k = i$ and $l = j$, and it seems then reasonable to assume rather strong positive autocorrelation

$$E[\hat{B}_{ij}(t)\hat{B}_{ij}(\tau)] \geqslant 0, \qquad \tau < t \qquad (2.5)$$

i.e. that if productivity declines in a period τ, then productivity relating to the same cell in the input–output table in a later period t must also be expected to be poor.

Another rather reasonable assumption would be that

$$E[\hat{B}_{ij}(t)\hat{B}_{kl}(\tau)] = 0, \qquad \tau < t, \text{ for all } j \neq l, \qquad (2.6)$$

i.e. that the capital requirement of process j in period t is stochastically independent of productivity in *other* sectors in earlier periods.[1]

The relations (2.3), (2.5), and (2.6) are mentioned only to shed light on the possible nature of the stochastic processes $B_{ij}(t)$, and will not necessarily be assumed to hold at all times.

Final demand $C(t)$, $t = 1, 2, \ldots, T$ is assumed to be exogenous and deterministic.

The task of planning is now more complicated than before, and in general a deterministic, rigid, capital stock pattern $S(t)$, $t = 1, 2, \ldots, T$ will no longer do, but a *stochastic stock strategy* $S(t)$ must be employed. We shall then assume that a growth pattern is optimal if it yields

$$\max E[K'S(T)]. \tag{2.7}$$

Now looking upon a typical intertemporal efficiency condition (1.6)

$$B(t)(S(t) - S(t-1) + C(t)) \leqslant S(t-1), \tag{2.8}$$

we see that we run into difficulties in interpreting this inequality. The inequality stipulates that total capital required to sustain planned capital formation and exogenous final demand during period t must not exceed total capital available during period t. Because of uncertainty about the B-matrix, however, the magnitude of these total capital requirements is not known. Given any planned capital formation, *they may happen to become so large that the inequality* (2.8) *cannot be upheld*.

The constraints (1.6) can therefore only be imposed in a *stochastic* sense, to hold a certain fraction α^t of all times, i.e.

$$\text{Prob } (B(t)(S(t) - S(t-1) + C(t)) \leqslant S(t-1)) \geqslant \alpha^t$$
$$t = 1, 2, \ldots, T. \tag{2.9}$$

Similarly, we shall write the constraints (1.7) in a stochastic form

$$\text{Prob } (S(t) - S(t-1) \geqslant 0) \geqslant \beta_t \quad t = 1, 2, \ldots, T. \tag{2.10}$$

Constraints of type (2.9) and (2.10) are called *chance-constraints*. The problem (2.7), (2.9), and (2.10) is one of *chance-constrained*

---

[1] Suppose that the stochastic variability in the B-coefficients were entirely due to variability in capital coefficients b, but that input–output coefficients a were deterministic. The total capital coefficient B_{ij} depends only upon $b_{1j}, b_{2j}, \ldots, b_{nj}$. Hence B_{ij} would reflect stochastic variability in all (direct) capital coefficients b relating to the productive process j only. The assumption (2.6) would then amount to assuming that (direct) capital coefficients b_{ij} are independent as between different processes

$$E[\hat{b}_{ij}(t)\hat{b}_{kl}(\tau)] = 0, \ \tau < t, \text{ for all } j \neq 1.$$

Sequential Decision Problems

programming (see Charnes, Cooper, and Symonds, 1959; Charnes and Cooper, 1962; Charnes and Cooper, 1963; Charnes and Thore, 1966).

In order to elucidate further the economic meaning of the chance-constraints, consider the interpretation of the violation of the deterministic constraints. Violation of (2.8) means that deficit stock capacity occurs during period t, so that the initial stock does not suffice to sustain the new stock formation and current demand during the period. How, then, is this deficit covered? Postponing the answer to this question for a moment, consider also the meaning of violation of (1.7). Violation of this condition means stock decumulation. Since it is assumed that all goods can be used interchangeably for consumption or for capital accumulation, there is no difficulty in interpreting stock decumulation as long as the initial stock is positive. But what if the initial stock is non-positive?

One answer to the two questions is to assume that there exists in the economy outside the model a reserve stock which is drawn upon when so required (imports, for instance). It is, however, not really necessary to go to any length in answering those questions at all. In any practical application the αs and the βs will be large, close to unity, and although the necessity of considering the risk of violation is the basis of the chance-constrained approach, actual violation will typically have so low a probability that we need not go into a discussion of the interpretation of this event at all. We can consider the chance-constraints as just a generalized mathematical formulation.

Some more words about the stochastic stock strategy $S(t)$ sought for. We shall look for the solution stock strategy within a certain class of functions, so-called *linear decision rules*:

$$S_i(t) = \gamma_i{}^t + \sum_{\tau=1}^{t-1} \{ \sum_{r,\,s} \Delta_{rs}(i,\ t,\ \tau)\hat{B}_{rs}(\tau) \}, \tag{2.11}$$

where $\gamma_i{}^t$ and Δ_{rs} are constants to be determined. This means that the stock decision in sector i during period 2 is made linearly dependent upon the observed outcomes of *all* B_{ij}s during period 1, the decision in sector i during period 3 is made linearly dependent upon the observed outcome of *all* B_{ij}s during periods 1 and 2, and so on and so forth (see Charnes, Cooper, and Symonds, 1959; Charnes and Cooper, 1962; Charnes and Cooper, 1963; and Charnes and Thore, 1966).

III. SOLUTION OF THE PROBLEM

The mathematical solution of the chance-constrained programming problem now formulated is essentially a routine affair and proceeds along the lines described, e.g. in Charnes, Cooper, and Symonds, 1959, Charnes and Cooper, 1962, and Charnes and Cooper, 1963. Some features of the solution will now be described.

Essentially, the solution is carried out by converting the chance-constraints into corresponding deterministic constraints, and then solving the corresponding deterministic programming problem thus obtained.

Explaining the idea somewhat more in detail, note first that insertion of the decision rule (2.11) into (2.7) gives the programme function

$$\max K' \gamma^T, \tag{3.1}$$

which is deterministic.

It is now, for the sake of the mathematical solution, necessary to introduce some weak regularity assumptions regarding the nature of the stochastic processes $B_{ij}(t)$, $t = 1, 2, \ldots, T$. Essentially, what will be needed is that the distribution functions of these processes (for all values of i and j) are symmetric around their mean in all dimensions and depend only on the moments of first and second order (see Charnes and Cooper, 1963, p. 26). For concreteness I shall assume that the distribution functions are multi-normal.

Then consider a typical chance-constraint in (2.9), say

$$\text{Prob } (x_i^t \leqslant 0) \geqslant \alpha_i^t, \tag{3.2}$$

where

$$x_i^t \equiv B_{i.}(t) \, (S(t) - S(t-1) + C(t)) - S_i(t-1). \tag{3.3}$$

Remembering that sums of normally distributed variables are also normal, it is clear that the $S_i(t)$s determined by the linear decision rule (2.11) are also normal, and hence that x_i^t is normal.

The chance-constraint (3.2) can then be treated in the following form:

$$\text{Prob } \left(\frac{x_i^t - Ex_i^t}{\sigma(x_i^t)} \leqslant \frac{-Ex_i^t}{\sigma(x_i^t)} \right) \geqslant \alpha_i^t \tag{3.4}$$

or, what is exactly the same,

$$F\left(\frac{-Ex_i^t}{\sigma(x_i^t)} \right) \geqslant \alpha_i^t, \tag{3.5}$$

where F is the univariate normal distribution. Assuming that all $\alpha_i^t \geqslant 1/2$, which will of course always be fulfilled in all practical applications (considering the nature of the problem), inversion of (3.5) gives the equivalent deterministic form

$$\frac{-Ex_i^t}{\sigma(x_i^t)} \geqslant F^{-1}(\alpha_i^t) \tag{3.6}$$

or

$$Ex_i^t + F^{-1}(\alpha_i^t) \cdot \sigma(x_i^t) \leqslant 0. \tag{3.7}$$

It only remains to compute Ex_i^t and $\sigma(x_i^t)$. Starting with Ex_i^t one gets

$$Ex_i^t = E\{B_{i\cdot}(t)S(t)\} - E\{B_{i\cdot}(t)S(t-1)\} +$$
$$EB_{i\cdot}(t) \cdot C(t) - ES_i(t-1). \tag{3.8}$$

Using the linear decision rule (2.11), we obtain

$$Ex_i^t = EB_{i\cdot}(t)(\gamma_t - \gamma^{t-1} + C(t)) - \gamma_i^{t-1}$$
$$+\text{terms linear in } \hat{B}. \tag{3.9}$$

The expression for $\sigma(x_i^t)$ is very complicated, and will not be required for the subsequent discussion.

The chance-constraints (2.10) can also be converted to corresponding deterministic constraints. Consider a typical chance-constraint in (2.10), say,

$$\text{Prob } (y_i^t \leqslant 0) \geqslant \beta_i^t, \tag{3.10}$$

where

$$y_i^t \equiv -S_i(t) + S_i(t-1). \tag{3.11}$$

It can be converted to the corresponding deterministic constraint

$$F\left(\frac{-Ey_i^t}{\sigma(y_i^t)}\right) \geqslant \beta_i^t \tag{3.12}$$

or

$$Ey_i^t + F^{-1}(\beta_i^t) \cdot \sigma(y_i^t) \leqslant 0. \tag{3.13}$$

The expressions for Ey_i^t and $\sigma(y_i^t)$ are given by

$$Ey_i^t = -\gamma_i^t + \gamma_i^{t-1} \tag{3.14}$$

and a rather complicated expression for $\sigma(y_i^t)$.

IV. A DEGENERATION THEOREM

Consider the chance-constrained programming problem (2.7), (2.9), and (2.10). Assume that *all* cross-moments (2.4) are zero (including $k = i$ and $1 = j$). Then the solution stock strategy (2.11) degenerates into a deterministic plan, i.e.

$$S_i(t) = \gamma_i^t, \ i = 1, 2, \ldots, n; \ t = 1, 2, \ldots, T. \tag{4.1}$$

This is the very special case when successive outcomes of the B_{ij}s are stochastically independent, both over time for a given i and j, and between different cells i, j. In particular, then, the successive outcomes for the (total) capital coefficient B_{ij} relating to a given cell i, j are supposed to be *purely random*, i.e. as obtained from random drawings over time.

Proof: (3.9) now collapses into

$$Ex_i^t = EB_i \,._{\cdot} (t) \,._{\cdot} (\gamma^t - \gamma^{t-1} + C(t)) - \gamma_i^{t-1}. \tag{4.2}$$

The variances are given by the expressions:

$$\sigma^2(x_i^t) = \sigma^2 \{B_i \cdot (t)(\gamma^t - \gamma^{t-1} + C(t)) \\ + \text{terms linear in } \Delta^{t\tau} \tag{4.3}$$

$$\sigma^2(y_i^t) = \text{a linear expression in } \Delta^{t\tau}. \tag{4.4}$$

Next, a rather beautiful mathematical artifice is in order, first employed in Charnes and Cooper, 1962. Note that the object function (3.1) does not contain the $\Delta^{t\tau}$s, and the $\Delta^{t\tau}$s can therefore be varied freely without affecting the object value attained. Hence, it can impose no new limitations on the solution of the problem to choose such values for the $\Delta^{t\tau}$s that the ranges of variability in the inequalities (3.5) and (3.12) become as large as possible. Varying the $\Delta^{t\tau}$s, the mathematical expectations (4.2) and (3.14) will not be affected, but the variances (4.3) and (4.4) will be affected. The mentioned ranges of variability are larger, the smaller are the variances (4.3) and (4.4). It is easy to see that the smallest values the variances (4.3) and (4.4) can possibly take (varying the $\Delta^{t\tau}$s) are obtained when all

$$\Delta^{t\tau} = 0, \qquad \tau < t, \ t = 1, 2, \ldots, T, \tag{4.5}$$

which gives (4.1). Q.E.D.

The constraints in this degenerate case take on rather simple forms. The first batch of constraints (2.9) collapses

Sequential Decision Problems

$$EB_{i\,.}(t)(S(t) - S(t-1) + C(t)) + F^{-1}(\alpha_i^t)$$

$$\left\{ \sigma^2(B_{i\,.}(t)) \begin{bmatrix} (S_1(t) - S_1(t-1) + C_1(t))^2 \\ (S_2(t) - S_2(t-1) + C_2(t))^2 \\ \vdots \\ (S_n(t) - S_n(t-1) + C_n(t))^2 \end{bmatrix} \right\}^{\frac{1}{2}}$$

$$\leqslant S_i(t-1); \quad i = 1, 2, \ldots, n; \quad t = 1, 2, \ldots, T, \qquad (4.6)$$

and the second batch of constraints (2.10) now simply read

$$S(t) - S(t-1) \geqslant 0. \qquad (4.7)$$

V. INDEPENDENT PROCESSES

From now on in the paper (2.6) will be assumed to hold. I shall show that it then follows that

$$\Delta_{j,\,kl}^{t\tau} = 0 \text{ for all } l \neq j, \ \tau < t, \ t = 1, 2, \ldots, T \qquad (5.1)$$

so that the linear decision rule (2.11) reduces to the simpler form

$$S_i(t) = \gamma_i^t + \sum_{\tau=1}^{t-1} [\Delta_i^{t\tau}], \quad [B_{.\,i}(\tau)]$$
$$i = 1, 2, \ldots, n; \quad t = 1, 2, \ldots, T. \qquad (5.2)$$

The vector $B_{.\,i}$ in this expression stands for the ith column in the matrix B.

In words, if the development of productivity in different processes is independent over time, so that (2.6) holds, then the optimal stochastic strategy for capital accumulation in sector i will depend only upon the development of productivity in the *same* sector i during earlier periods, and not upon the development of productivity in *other* sectors.

Proof: Note first that (3.9) now reduces to a simpler expression. The desired result then follows from the same artifice as in Section IV. Note that the object function (3.1) does not contain the $\Delta^{t\tau}$s, and the $\Delta^{t\tau}$s can therefore be varied freely without affecting the object value attained. It can impose no new limitations on the solution of the problem to choose such values for the $\Delta^{t\tau}$s that the ranges of variability in the inequalities (3.5) and (3.12) become as large as possible. Note further that the Δ-elements do not appear at all in Ex_i^t and Ey_i^t (as given by (3.13)). Hence, varying the Δ-elements appearing in (5.1), it is clear that the mentioned ranges of variability are larger, the smaller are the variances (4.3) and (4.4). It is easy to see that the smallest values the variances (4.3) and (4.4) can possibly take (varying the Δ-elements appearing in (5.1)) are obtained when (5.1) holds. Q.E.D.[1]

VI. THE FLEXIBILITY OF THE MODEL

The following result will now be proved: assuming independent processes, and assuming non-negative autocorrelation (2.5) for each B-coefficient, it follows that

$$\Delta_i^{t\tau} \leqslant 0, \qquad \tau < t, \, t = 2, 3, \ldots, T \tag{6.1}$$

$$\Delta_i^{t\tau} - \Delta_i^{t-1,\tau} \leqslant 0, \qquad \tau < t - 1, \quad t = 3, 4, \ldots, T. \tag{6.2}$$

The economic meaning of this result is as follows. Assume positive serial correlation as specified, so that any pattern of productivity has a tendency to remain over many periods. If then the performance of productivity in a sector during a certain period turns out to be poorer than expected (the mathematical expectation), the optimal plan calls for a *retardation* of the capital formation in this sector in subsequent periods; but if the productivity performance in a sector during a period becomes better than expected, the optimal plan calls for a *speeding-up* of the capital formation in this sector in subsequent periods.

The result (6.2) reinforces (6.1). It means that the optimal stock strategy for period t depends upon unexpected deviations (deviations from the mathematical expectation) of productivity during all earlier periods up to the experience during period $t - 1$, but that the influence on the current stock strategy for period t becomes gradually weaker the further back in time such an unexpected event took place.

In this manner the optimal stock strategy already at the initial moment when the strategy is designed makes provisions for deviations of the future development of productivity from its mathematical expectation. To describe this property of the optimal stock strategy

---

[1] The results in Sections IV and V can be viewed as special instances of the following more general theorem: Assume that $EB_{ij}(t)\dot{B}_{kl}(\tau) = 0$ for given and fixed $i, j, k,$ and l, and for all $\tau < t, t = 1, 2, \ldots, T$. Then $\Delta_{ij, kl}^{t\tau} = 0$ for all $\tau < t$, $t = 1, 2, \ldots, T$.

one can rightly use such terms as 'flexible', 'adaptable', 'versatile'.[1]

Note also that the optimal pattern of response to fluctuating productivity in each sector is very similar to the pattern that would follow if each sector were to maximize its *profits*. I hope to get the opportunity to clarify this matter in a subsequent paper.

The results (6.1) and (6.2) are obtained by employing the same reasoning as has now been used twice already. To repeat the argument, note that the object function (3.1) does not contain the $\Delta^{t\tau}$s, and that they can therefore be varied without affecting the object value attained. Hence, it can impose no new limitations on the solution of the problem to choose such values for the $\Delta^{t\tau}$s that the ranges of variability in the inequalities (3.5) and (3.12) become as large as possible. Let us then determine the $\Delta^{t\tau}$s in this manner. These ranges of variability are larger the larger are the expressions on the right-hand side of the inequality signs in (3.5) and (3.12). To make these expressions on the right-hand sides as large as possible, the expressions

$$E\{B_{ij}(t)[\Delta_j^{t,\,t-1}], \quad [\hat{B}_{.\,j}(t-1)]\} \tag{6.3}$$

and

$$E\left\{B_{ij}(t)\sum_{\tau=1}^{t-2}\left[\Delta_j^{t\tau} - \Delta_j^{t-1,\,\tau}\right], \quad \left[\hat{B}_{.\,j}(\tau)\right]\right\} \tag{6.4}$$

must certainly become non-positive. Paying regard to (2.5) it follows that

$$\Delta_j^{t,\,t-1} \leqslant 0, \qquad j = 1, 2, \ldots, n; \ t = 2, 3, \ldots, T \tag{6.5}$$

$$\Delta_j^{t\tau} - \Delta_j^{t-1,\,\tau} \leqslant 0, \qquad t-1, j = 1, 2, \ldots, n; \ t = 3, 4, \ldots, T. \tag{6.6}$$

The last equation has already been written down as (6.2). Successive combinations of (6.5) and (6.6) then yield (6.1). Q.E.D.

VII. CONCLUSION

In this paper we have studied a dynamic Leontief model of the type developed for instance in the well-known textbook (Dorfman, Samuelson, and Solow, 1958), but assumed that future productivity of capital, and hence future capital coefficients, are uncertain.

---

[1] By contrast, a deterministic plan is 'rigid'. More specifically, a deterministic plan is *sub-optimal*. As has been shown in Section IV, the deterministic plan corresponds to the case of serial independence. Thus the sub-optimal error involved in using a deterministic plan amounts to making the error of assuming serial independence.

Rather than look for a deterministic optimal stock path one has to determine an optimal stochastic stock strategy.

The uncertainty mentioned was formalized in the model by the introduction of so-called chance-constraints, i.e. constraints which are not imposed with certainty but only to hold at least a certain fraction of all times. Two such sets of chance-constraints were used : supply of goods must not fall short of demand too often ; and capital must not be decumulated too often. The problem thus took the form of an instance of chance-constrained programming, a programming technique which has been developed by A. Charnes, W. W. Cooper, and others.

The optimal stochastic strategy sought for is *flexible* as it contains built-in provisions for changing productivity.

The following results were derived :

(*a*) In the very special case when all (total) capital coefficients B_{ij} are stochastically independent and also each capital coefficient is purely random, i.e. can be viewed as obtained from independent drawings over time, the optimal stock strategy will degenerate into a deterministic plan.

But in all other cases when there is serial correlation in future productivity so that the solution stock strategy will be non-degenerate, the adoption of a deterministic stock path as the solution constitutes a mathematical error, and is sub-optimal.

(*b*) A rather reasonable assumption is that capital coefficients B_{ij} relating to a *given* process j are independent of capital coefficients B_{kl} relating to *another* process l, $l \neq j$. In this case the optimal stock strategy for a given sector will depend only upon the development of productivity during earlier periods in the *same* sector.

(*c*) Assuming positive serial correlation in each capital coefficient $B_{ij}(t)$, any increase of productivity in a sector above the mathematical expectation will call for an ensuing *stepping-up* of capital allocation to this sector, but any decrease of productivity in the sector (below mathematical expectation) will call for a subsequent *retardation* of the capital formation in the sector.

In this way the amount of capital formation planned for any future time period in a sector will depend upon the performance of productivity during earlier time periods, the influence of the immediately preceding time periods being the most important, and the influence of more distant periods of older date being weaker.

P
433

REFERENCES

Charnes, A., Cooper, W. W., and Symonds, G. H. (1959), 'Cost Horizons and Certainty Equivalents: an Approach to Stochastic Programming of Heating Oil', *Management Science*.

— — (1962), 'Chance Constraints and Normal Deviates', *J. Amer. Statist. Assoc.* (March).

— — (1963), 'Deterministic Equivalents for Optimizing and Satisficing under Chance-constraints', *Operations Research*.

— and Thore, S. (1966), 'Planning for Liquidity in Financial Institutions: the Chance-constrained Method', *J. Finance*.

Dorfman, R., Samuelson, P. A., and Solow, R. (1958), *Linear Programming and Economic Analysis*, New York: McGraw-Hill.

Solow, R. (1959), 'Competitive Valuation in a Dynamic Input-output System', *Econometrica*, 27.

DISCUSSION OF THE PAPER BY DR. THORE

Mr. Bessière: I consider Dr. Thore's paper to be really interesting, for I believe it is the first study where uncertainty is introduced into a dynamic multi-sector model. Being a first trial, this model is simplified. So my aim will be to discuss the main hypotheses of the paper and to suggest ways of dropping them by building more complex models. That is why, in the first part, I shall review these different hypotheses, and, in the second part, proceed to discuss them.

First, I want to summarize the various constraints on the production possibilities as follows:

(*a*) Current production should exceed total demand, where total demand is the sum of final demand, inter-industry demand, and increments of capital stocks (equation 1.2);

(*b*) Capital stocks must suffice to sustain current production, meaning that available capital stocks define a maximum of possible production (equation 1.1). By combining (*a*) and (*b*) it is possible to eliminate the production variables, so that (*a*) and (*b*) together imply

(*c*) Capital stocks must suffice to sustain final demand and capital increases (equation 1.5).

In addition, there may be constraints of the type

(*d*) Capital decumulation should not exceed certain limits (equation 1.7).

We now have to define the objective function of the model. Following the classical textbook by Dorfman, Samuelson, and Solow, this function

434

is written as a kind of utility function (which is to be maximized) and is assumed to be a function of final capital stock variables only. Of course, this will simplify the model, as the production variables no longer appear in (*c*) and (*d*). But it is a very strong hypothesis, which will be denoted and summarized as

H.I : *Utility is a function of final capital stocks.*

Then Dr. Thore proceeds to take uncertainty into account by using the 'chance-constrained programming' of Charnes and Cooper. As is well known, this method fixes some limits *p* to the probability of constraints being violated, thus defining so-called chance-constraints. We may refer to the *p*s as *guarantee levels*. Whenever chance-constrained programming is used two questions arise :

Question 1 : What is the meaning of the chance-constraints ?
Question 2 : How should the guarantee levels be chosen ?

Question 1 is briefly discussed in Dr. Thore's paper. New constraints being thus defined, a new objective function is generated using a linear decision rule. As it would be possible to use more complex decision rules, this hypothesis will be registered as

H.II : *Linearity of decision rules.*

Then the author proves his main results, involving two new hypotheses about the cross-moments of his probability distribution :

H.III : *Different sectors are independent.*
H.IV : *Autocorrelations are non-negative.*

H.III is involved in the proof given in Section V of the paper ; H.III and H.IV are both involved in the proof given in Section VI.

I shall now proceed to the discussion of these hypotheses and questions, using the notations (*a*), (*b*), (*c*), (*d*) for the constraints.

There is little to say of H.IV : this assumption seems to be true in general, and it would not be difficult to deal with the case when auto-correlations would be negative.

Again there is little to say about H.II : looking for non-linear decision rules would lead to most intricate computations, and give a spurious feeling of precision.

H.III needs a longer discussion.

This assumption means that the random variations of the productivity expansion rates in different sectors are supposed to be independent. In fact, an important part of the productivity expansion in any sector *S* is, let us say, 'inherited' from the productivity expansions realized in those other sectors which produce either materials or equipment used in sector *S*. For example, if there is some increase in the productivity of turbine production, this will induce lower costs when building new electric power plants, and then a better productivity in the electricity-generating sector. A very detailed study, recently made in *Electricité de France*, has shown that over a twelve-year period between 15 and 20 per cent of productivity increases in this firm were 'inherited' from other sectors.

I think this interdependence of productivities in different sectors is very important in that it reflects the global expansion of the economy. That is why I should wish Dr. Thore's model to be modified first in that direction. I would suggest taking the correlation coefficients as (i) constant in time, and (ii) *proportional to the coefficients of the matrix B*, which characterizes the global interdependence among sectors. This assumption, I believe, would not be too unrealistic, and perhaps would be convenient enough for computation.

Let us look at H.I (utility is a function of final capital stocks). Of course, this gives a simpler model as it is possible to drop production variables. But is it really a simplification ? If the dimensions of the model are reduced, its structure becomes more intricate. Moreover, a reduction of dimensions may be an advantage only if the model is to be solved numerically. But when the model is just a theoretical one, whose purpose is to provide general propositions, its dimensions are of no importance : it is clarity and structural simplicity which matter.

Furthermore, in the case of theoretical models, results obtained from the model itself are very often of no greater importance than the results which can be derived from the analysis of properties of dual variables (or, in non-linear programming, of Kuhn–Tucker multipliers ; hereafter, we shall say 'dual variables' for both). I, and many other people too, have often tried this method, and we have never been disappointed.

But for such an analysis to be possible and fruitful, the meaning both of the constraints and of the objective function must be simple and clear. And this is not the case in the present model, neither for the combined constraints (*c*), nor, owing to H.I, for the utility function.

On the contrary, if production variables were *not* eliminated and if constraints (*a*) and (*b*) were distinguished, their meaning would be clear, and it is easy to see that dual variables associated with (*a*) could be interpreted as marginal costs (or marginal utilities) of the different goods. As for dual variables associated with (*b*), they might be interpreted as marginal rents accruing to the equipment which runs at full capacity. If this latter interpretation is not evident to the reader, I may refer him to a paper I published in 1959 in *Revue Française de Recherche Opérationelle*.

Now, if these economic interpretations of dual variables are to be valid, the objective function must actually have the meaning of cost or utility. This may not be too difficult when dealing with a firm, but it raises enormous problems when we want to build a global multi-sector model. But I think that the D.S.S. assumption (H.I) does no more than touch upon these difficulties, without solving them at all. It would be better to introduce explicitly a weighted sum of personal utilities, as did Frisch in several

models, or to find an ingenious formulation such as the one employed by
Mr. Baudier in his paper.

Anyway, I think that for such a complex problem useful results cannot
be derived from a simple model. I believe that the last of simple *and*
fruitful models will have been Keynes's.

I will now discuss questions 1 and 2, which both concern the Charnes–
Cooper method. For this discussion to be clear, I will consider constraints
(*a*) and (*b*) separately.

Dr. Thore does not take into account uncertainty about final demand.
But if we consider constraints (*a*) we can see that this would be possible
without making the model more complex. Indeed, the probability of one
of constraints (*a*) being violated is by definition equal to the probability
that the difference 'production minus demand' shall be negative. This
difference is no more stochastic when both terms are, than when just one
of them is. Thus it would be a useful change in the model, and a very
simple one, to take into account the uncertainty of final demand.

Now, what happens when some constraint (*a*) is violated ? Of course,
we may reduce demand, either in an authoritative way or, more likely, by
increasing prices. This can be translated into the terms of the model by
saying that *the dual variable associated with a chance-constraint* (a) *is a
function of the guarantee level* p. This is a very important remark which
will be useful later.

Dr. Thore suggests another possibility : If production is insufficient to
meet demand it is possible to import. But what he does not say is that
this will be costly for the economy, particularly if we take into account the
monetary consequences of a trade deficit. Apart from this, I think the
best way to represent foreign trade in the model is to introduce a new
sector where there is no capital involved so that there is no constraint of
type (*b*) associated with it. This would mean that it is possible to import
(export) arbitrary quantities, but at variable prices, these prices increasing
(decreasing) when imports (exports) increase. These *price variations* could
express two phenomena : (i) the sensitivity of the world market, and (ii)
the asymmetric effects of trade deficits and trade surpluses on a collective
utility function. Such price variations would of course introduce non-
linearities into the model, but the model is already non-linear because it
uses probability distributions.

Now, concerning the constraints (*b*), we have to notice that they have a
physical meaning : Production is physically limited by the capacities as
measured by the capital stocks. I must confess that I have been puzzled
by the way in which Dr. Thore deals with these constraints. For *when a
physical constraint is encountered it can by no means be violated and hence
cannot be probabilized at all*, unless this probability is fixed at zero, in
which case we are back to the original constraint.

Thus, if we do distinguish between constraints (*a*) and (*b*), we cannot
probabilize the latter. This will do no harm because there is no constraint

(*b*) associated with imports and hence total demand is allowed to be met in every case, even if internal production is strictly limited by the constraints (*b*).

I now come to constraints (*d*). The only reasonable meaning I can find in these constraints is *not* that there should be no capital decumulation, but that the rate of decumulation, if expressed in value, must not exceed the rate of capital depreciation due to obsolescence ; this condition as a whole meaning that there must be no destruction of physical capital.

With this interpretation we see that the constraints (*d*) cannot be violated if we are looking for a collective optimum, for it could never be optimal not to use a sector's equipment as long as its scrap value is positive, this being true even if the sector cannot reach budgetary equilibrium without decumulation.

Here we find an important application of the analysis of dual variables. The scrap value of any equipment can, or must, be defined by the dual variables associated with constraints (*b*). This shows that constraints (*d*) need not be explicitly written in the primal model because they result from a correct understanding of the properties of dual variables when optimum is reached. I have always thought this was a serious criticism against the D.S.S. model, however classical it may be. The constraints (*d*) express optimal properties and therefore need not be written down.

On the other hand, it seems to me that there are other constraints which should be made explicit. First, there may be some sectors, such as hydro-electric power, where the total amount of equipment which can be built is physically limited. Second, capital stocks cannot be negative. (It may be noted that this allows aggregation of inventories and other types of capital, although it might be better to distinguish the two as they actually play somewhat different economic roles.)

Such new constraints will also have physical meaning and hence cannot be probabilized. Therefore, constraints (*a*) are the only ones remaining which might be probabilized.

But I said that the dual prices associated with constraints (*a*) are functions of the guarantee levels. I also said that a violation of one of these constraints implies a penalty for the economy, due, for example, to an increase in imports. All this strongly suggests that the correct way to express the requirement that production be able to meet demand is *not* to introduce such constraints as (*a*) but *to include in the objective function a term measuring the expected loss which will be incurred by the economy if internal production cannot meet demand*. An important word here is 'expected' : we require this term to depend on all the probabilities including the cross-moments of Dr. Thore's paper, and it shows the guarantee levels which will be obtained as a result of the optimization.

One of the main consequences of this method is that there is no longer any need to introduce guarantee levels into the model : question 2 vanishes. In fact, the whole *apparatus of chance-constraints vanishes*.

Record of Discussion

Constraints (*a*) were the only ones which could be probabilized, and we have just seen that they could be expressed much better in another way. It is only in cases where it is difficult to estimate the penalty due to violation of a constraint that the Charnes–Cooper method may be used. Indeed, in such cases we should parametrize the penalties to find how the optimum and, as a result, the guarantee levels, change when the penalties are changed. But the same results may be obtained by a parametrization of the guarantee levels in a chance-constrained programme ; this will show how the optimum changes as a function of the guarantee levels and, in particular, will give marginal penalties as dual variables of the chance-constraints.

It is to be noted that such parametrizations concern cases where uncertainty is connected with the utility function to be used (the penalties) rather than the probabilities which I assume, as does Dr. Thore, are known.

But all that I have said about chance-constrained programming could be repeated for any problem of this kind. That is why I think that *the Charnes–Cooper method is at best an approximation* which may or may not be good. When it is used it should be accompanied by a parametrization of the guarantee levels (a thorough sensitivity analysis).

And this will be my conclusion. It may seem as if my long discussion contains a hard criticism of Dr. Thore's paper. But it is not really addressed to *his* paper, but rather to those classical studies which inspired it : to Charnes and Cooper, who, as far as I know, have never written down with precision the assumptions under which their method can be really useful ; and to Dorfman, Samuelson, and Solow, for their analysis is not only oversimplified (which is quite normal in an otherwise excellent textbook) but it completely neglects to take into account such an important point as the economic interpretation of duality.

Mr. Baudier : I would like to mention that the work of Dr. Thore can be presented from a slightly different point of view, which would allow him to escape from the critique of Mr. Bessière as far as the probabilities of physical constraints are concerned. One may fix an arbitrary level of the objective function and similarly α and β, the guarantee levels. Then let α and β vary and maximize the objective function, thus obtaining a set of solutions which satisfy the efficiency condition. This will be equivalent to the Markowitz procedure for selecting efficient portfolios.

Dr. Thore : I would like to thank Mr. Bessière most warmly for his penetrating criticism of my paper and questions relating to it. Mr. Bessière has discussed the nature of many of the assumptions that I used in my paper, and thus has shed light on many issues which I dealt with perhaps too briefly. I have very little to add, and shall restrict myself to a few comments :

(1) As regards the interpretation of the chance-constraints, the present application admittedly involves an extension of the original idea as it was initiated in managerial applications. In the pioneering paper by Charnes,

439

Cooper, and Symonds (1959) for instance, the chance-constraints were to express the willingness of the management of an oil-refinery to be able to meet demand a certain proportion of the times. Presumably, then, when the refinery failed to meet demand customers would turn to a competitor. Admittedly, the situation is different and more involved in the present paper, where the chance-constraints are to express the willingness of a central planning authority for a whole country to be able to meet demand a certain proportion of the periods. When the planned economy fails to meet demand, where will the customers then turn ? Will they be able to cover their demand at all ? And if not, how will the customers react when they cannot buy what they want ? Will they switch their demand to the output of other sectors, so that there occurs a (non-planned) change in the vector of final demand ? What repercussions throughout the model economy would such a change lead to ? The nature of the adjustment processes called forth by a violation of the chance-constraints has been left unspecified. The chance-constraints just lay down the condition that the planner wants to avoid such a breakdown of consumption plans a certain proportion of the periods.

(2) Mr. Bessière brings up the question of the elimination of output X. In the deterministic case one has

$$X \geqslant A(\Delta S + C) \tag{i}$$

and

$$S \geqslant bX \tag{ii}$$

and combination gives

$$S \geqslant B(\Delta S + C). \tag{iii}$$

Similarly, in the stochastic case one could work with two sets of chance-constraints :

$$\text{Prob } [X_i \geqslant \Sigma A_{ij}(\Delta S_j + C_j)] \geqslant \alpha_i^* \tag{iv}$$

$$\text{Prob } [S_i \geqslant \Sigma b_{ij}X_j] \geqslant \alpha_i^{**} \qquad i = 1, 2, \ldots, n \tag{v}$$

or, as I have done, with one compact set of chance-constraints with output eliminated :

$$\text{Prob } [S_i \geqslant \Sigma B_{ij}(\Delta S_j + C_j)] \geqslant \alpha_i \qquad i = 1, 2, \ldots, n. \tag{vi}$$

Solow (1959) comments upon this elimination in the deterministic case : 'For most purposes I see no objection to the assumption that each output flow has positive value, so that no more will be produced than is necessary to cover the various demands' (p. 40). In that case there is an equality sign in equation (i) and any solution vector S can be uniquely converted into a corresponding solution output vector X. Now, if the same argument is accepted in the stochastic case, then $\alpha_i^* = 1$ for all values of i and the chance constraints (iv) collapse into the deterministic constraints (i).

Again it follows that any solution vector S can be uniquely converted into a corresponding solution output vector X.

(3) I have not discussed the properties of the dual system, but it is clear that there are defined dual variables ('evaluators') corresponding to α^t and β^t measuring the effect on the optimum value of terminal capital of a marginal change in the 'risk levels' α^t and β^t.

Chapter 21

APPLICATION OF STOCHASTIC CONTROL
PROCESSES TO ECONOMICS

BY

MILAN ULLRICH

IN this paper we shall deal with the general theory of stochastic-process control and its applications to elementary economic processes. As a special case of these applications we shall consider a simple model of a market and its control.

In the classical statistical decision theory it is supposed that there are given the sample space X, the parameter space A, and the decision space D. For every $a \epsilon A$ there are given the probability distributions $\nu(., a)$ on the sample space and a weight function $w(w \geqslant 0)$ defined on the Cartesian product $A \times D$. The probability measure μ defined on the parameter space A is called the *a priori* distribution on A. Let B be the set of all measurable transformations from X into D. The elements of B are called decision functions. For a given $b \epsilon B$ the function $w(a, b(x))$ defined on $A \times X$ is the loss corresponding to the decision function b provided the parameter equals a and the result of the experiment is x. The expected loss, called the risk, is defined by the integral

$$\int_X w(a, b(x)) d\nu(x, a)$$

and will be denoted by $r(a, b)$. The average risk for the given *a priori* distribution μ on A is defined by the integral

$$\int_A r(a, b) d\mu$$

and will be denoted by $r(\mu, b)$. The number $\rho(\mu) = \inf_{b \epsilon B} r(\mu, b)$ is called the Bayes risk with respect to the given *a priori* distribution μ. The decision function b_0, for which

$$r(\mu, b_0) = \rho(\mu),$$

442

is called the Bayes decision function with respect to the *a priori* distribution μ.

In a given statistical decision problem for which there exists an *a priori* distribution on A, it is natural to choose a statistical decision function the average risk of which is as small as possible, i.e. a Bayes decision function.

In the following we shall suppose that N is a given natural number, $A = E^N$, $X = E^N$ (E^N is the N-dimensional Euclidean space) and μ and v (., a) for every $a \epsilon A$ are absolutely continuous with respect to the Lebesgues measure on E^N. We shall suppose that the corresponding probability densities are given by

$$p(a_1, \ldots, a_N) = p_1(a_1) \cdot p_2(a_2 \mid a_1) \ldots p_N(a_N \mid a_1, \ldots, a_{N-1})$$

and

$$f(x_1, \ldots, x_N; \; a_1, \ldots, a_N) = f_1(x_1 \mid a_1) f_2(x_2 \mid x_1, a_1, a_2) \ldots$$
$$\ldots f_N(x_N \mid x_1, \ldots, x_{N-1}, a_1, \ldots, a_N).$$

Further we shall suppose that in this case the decision function is not of the form it has in classical statistical decision theory but that it is given by N decision functions $b_0, b_2, \ldots, b_{N-1}$ so that

$$b(x_1, \ldots, x_N) = (b_0, b_1(x_1), \ldots, b_{N-1}(x_1, \ldots, x_{N-1})).$$

where b_0 is an element of D and b_i ($i = 1, 2, \ldots, N-1$) are transformations from E^i into D; b will be called the decision policy; let us now suppose that the probability density f_i depends not only on $x_1, \ldots, x_{i-1}, a_1, a_2, \ldots, a_i$ but also on previous decisions, i.e. on $b_0, b_1, \ldots, b_{i-1}$ and therefore f_i is given by the conditional probability density

$$f_i(x_i \mid x_1, \ldots, x_{i-1}, a_1, \ldots, a_i, b_0, b_1, \ldots, b_{i-1}).$$

The weight function w will be considered also in another form than in classical statistical decision theory, namely in the form

$$w(a_1, \ldots, a_N; \; b_0, b_1(x_1), \ldots, b_{N-1}(x_1, \ldots, x_{N-1}); \; x_1, \ldots, x_N).$$

We shall say that a decision policy b is optimal if the average risk

$$\int_A \int_X w\{f_1 \ldots f_N p_1 \ldots p_N\} dx_1 \ldots dx_N da_1 \ldots da_N$$

is minimized.

Every decision policy influences the time course of the process and therefore we speak also about the control of the corresponding stochastic process or about the decision-process control.

We shall now determine the optimal control of the given stochastic process. For this purpose we shall use dynamic programming methods.

Let us suppose that b_0 and decision functions $b_1, \ldots, b_{N-2}$ are determined and that we know the actual values $x_1, \ldots, x_{N-1}$. It is necessary to determine b_{N-1}, so that the average risk is minimal. Let us denote this function by:

$$b_{N-1}(x_1, \ldots, x_{N-1}) = d_{N-1}^x.$$

Similarly we can determine for every $x_1, \ldots, x_{N-2}$ and given decision functions $b_0, b_1, \ldots, b_{N-0}$ a value d_{N-2}^x for which the average risk is minimal if b_{N-1} is optimal. In the same way we can determine $b_0, b_1, \ldots$

Now, we shall give the final expressions in the case:

$$a_1 = a_2 = \ldots = a_n = a,$$

with a given probability distribution $p(a)$, and a weight function w of the form

$$w(a_1, \ldots, a_N, b_0, \ldots, b_{N-1}, x_1, \ldots, x_N) = \sum_{i-1}^{N} (xi - c)^2$$

($c \geqslant 0$ is a given constant). Then for every $i = 0, 1, 2, \ldots, N-1$ and given $x_1, \ldots, x_{i-1}$ the optimal decision function b_i is given by

$$b_{i-1}^x(x_1, \ldots, x_i) = d_{i-1}^x,$$

where d_{i-1}^x is the value d from D, for which

$$\int_{-\infty}^{+\infty} (x_i - c)^2 \{\int_{-\infty}^{+\infty} f_1 \ldots f_i p(a) da\} dx_i$$

is minimal.

We shall now apply this generalization of the classical decision theory to the control of some simple economic processes. We shall deal with a simple model of a market with two participants and one product. Let us denote by A_i the number of units produced during the ith period, p_i the price in the ith period and y_i the inventory level at the end of the ith period. The consumer uses an unknown demand function $\pi(p)$, which we shall suppose linear, and constant in time, i.e. of the form

$$\pi(p) = \alpha p + \beta,$$

where α and β are two random variables with given probability distributions. Further let us suppose that for every $i = 1, 2, \ldots, N$

$$y_i = y_{i-1} + A_i - \alpha p_i - \beta + \xi_i,$$

where $\xi_i, \xi_2, \ldots, \xi_N$ are independent random variables, independent of α and β, distributed with probability density function $k(x)$.

We shall suppose that a constant $C \geqslant 0$ which denotes the desirable inventory level is given and that the weight function for every time period is given as the squared deviation of the actual inventory level from C.

In the following we shall solve three problems, and determine

(i) the optimal prices for given $A_1, A_2, \ldots, A_N$ and α;
(ii) the optimal production $A_1, A_2, \ldots, A_N$ for constant price p_0;
(iii) the optimal advertisement policy for given $A_1, A_2, \ldots, A_N$ and constant prices $p_1 = p_2 = \ldots = p_N = p_0$.

All these optimal policies will be derived from knowledge of the actual inventory level and the past history of the used policy. In all examples we shall suppose that the optimal policy is such that the risk is minimal. We shall suppose that the *a priori* probability distribution of the parameter (α, β) is given by the probability density $p(\alpha, \beta)$ and the probability density $k(x)$ is Gaussian, with the mean value μ, and the dispersion σ^2, i.e.

$$k(x) = \frac{1}{\sqrt{2\pi}\sigma} e^{-\frac{1}{2}\left(\frac{x-\mu}{\sigma}\right)^2}.$$

Problem 1: Let us suppose that $\alpha = \alpha_0$ is known and β is Gaussian, with mean μ_1 and dispersion σ_1^2, i.e.:

$$p(\alpha, \beta) = \delta(x - \alpha_0)\frac{1}{\sqrt{2\pi}\sigma_1} e^{-\frac{1}{2}\left(\frac{\beta-\mu_1}{\sigma_1}\right)^2}.$$

Then the risk for fixed initial inventory level y_0, for given prices $p_1, p_2, \ldots, p_N$, and production $A_1, \ldots, A_N$, is equal to

$$E\left[\sum_{i=1}^{N}(y_i - C)^2\right].$$

The optimal price p_i^x can be determined for given $y_0, y_1, \ldots, y_{i-1}$, $A_1, \ldots, A_i$, and $p_1, \ldots, p_{i-1}$. It can be shown that the optimal price p_i^x is given for every $i = 1, 2, 3, \ldots, N$ by the formula

$$\alpha_0 p_i^x = \frac{1}{\sigma^2 + (i-1)\sigma^2}[y_{i-1}(\sigma^2 + i\sigma_1^2) - y_0\sigma^2 + \sigma_1^2\alpha_0 \sum_{j=1}^{i-1} p_j +$$

$$\sigma^2\mu - \sigma^2 \sum_{j=1}^{i-1} A_j - \sigma^2\mu_1] + A_i - C.$$

Problem 2: Let us suppose that α and β are independent Gaussian random variables with

$$E[\alpha] = \mu_2; \quad E[(\alpha - \mu_2)^2] = \sigma_2^2$$

and

$$E[\beta] = \mu_1; \quad E[(\beta - \mu_1)^2] = \sigma_1^2.$$

Then the risk for fixed inventory level y_0 and fixed prices $p_1, \ldots, p_N$ is given by

$$E\left[\sum_{i=1}^{N}(y_i - C)^2\right].$$

The optimal production size A_i^x is determined so that average risk is minimal, for given $y_0, \ldots, y_{i-1}, A_1, \ldots, A_{i-1}$, and $p_1, \ldots, p_i$.

The calculations are similar to those of Problem 1, and we find

$$A_i^x = C - \frac{y_{i-1}(\sigma^2 + i\sigma_3^2) - y_0\sigma_3^2 + \sigma^2\mu - \sigma_3^2\sum_{j=1}^{i-1} A_j}{\sigma^2 + (i-1)\sigma_3^2},$$

where $\sigma_3^2 = p^2\sigma_2^2 + \sigma_1^2$.

Problem 3: Let us suppose that α and β are Gaussian random variables with

$$E[\alpha] = \mu^2; \quad E[(\alpha - \mu_\alpha)^2] = \sigma_2^2$$

and

$$E[\beta] = \mu_1; \quad E[(\beta - \mu_1)^2] = \sigma_1^2,$$

and that the effect of an advertising expenditure r on demand is given by the relation

$$\pi(p) = \alpha p_0 + \beta + r.$$

It is obvious that the problem has the same structure as Problem 2, and we can determine the optimal advertising policy.

Record of Discussion

DISCUSSION OF THE PAPER BY DR. ULLRICH

Professor Borch : To bring out the central idea of this paper it is convenient to start with the example.

If y is the inventory at the end of period i, we have

$$y_i = y_{i-1} + A_i - S_i + x_i.$$

Here

A_i = production during period i

S_i = sales during period i

x_i = a stochastic variable, independent of all other variables in the model.

Dr. Ullrich next assumes that sales depend on the price p_i through a relation

$$S_i = \alpha_i p_i + \beta_i,$$

where α_i and β_i are stochastic variables.

This gives us the equation

$$y_i = y_{i-1} + A_i - \alpha_i p_i - \beta_i + x_i.$$

The equation defines a stochastic process y_i, which depends on :

(i) three stochastic variables α_i, β_i, and x_i ;

(ii) two decision variables A_i and p_i, which can be chosen for each period by the decision-maker.

The problem of the decision-maker is then to select the sequences A_i and p_i, i.e. the control process, so that he obtains the 'best' of the attainable y-processes. It is not difficult to reformulate the problem so that it consists of minimizing an 'average risk function'.

Dr. Ullrich begins his paper by considering some far more general models. However, even the simple model in his illustrating example is very rich. It is easy to recast it, so that it will contain, as a special case, the chance-constrained model of the paper by Dr. Thore, without the multi-sector aspect. It is also possible to reformulate the model so that the problem is to find the production plan and the price policy which will maximize expected profits. This should make the model attractive also to my colleagues in business schools in Western countries.

Dr. Ullrich does not give any references to the work of others. It is, however, clear that by 'the classical decision theory', he must mean the theory developed by Wald[1] during the years 1945–50. Dr. Ullrich's paper is an obvious generalization of this theory. In fact Dr. Ullrich derives the

[1] Wald, A. (1945), 'Statistical Decision Functions which Minimize the Maximum Risk', *Annals of Mathematics* ; (1949), 'Statistical Decision Functions', *Annals of Mathematical Statistics*; (1950), *Statistical Decision Functions*, New York, John Wiley & Sons ; London, Chapman & Hall.

447

central parts of Bellman's theory of dynamic programming[1] from Wald's model by elementary manipulations with conditional probabilities. This is an achievement which commands respect and which has considerable interest. When it comes to practical applications, Dr. Ullrich's approach may be less useful.

In the example Dr. Ullrich assumes that the y-process is better the closer it lies to some constant c, i.e. that the problem is to minimize

$$E\left\{ \sum_{i=1}^{n} (y_i - c)^2 \right\}.$$

This may not be a very realistic objective, but it is useful as an illustration, and it leads to a relatively simple solution. It is, however, hard to see how one can solve the problem with a less special objective function without resorting to more powerful methods such as Bellman's 'principle of optimality'.

Mr. Baret: As Professor Borch has introduced Dr. Ullrich's model, I should only like to underline two points:

(1) Dr. Ullrich uses a demand function that is linear in price. Experience, in general, indicates that demand functions are not linear but convex, i.e. they have a positive second derivative. It is true, however, that as a first approximation and in a limited interval we can replace the corresponding part of the curve with a straight line.

(2) Dr. Ullrich applies his model to three problems differing only with respect to the known or variable parameters:

Problem 1: The initial stock level, a price system for the N periods, and the production in these same periods are known. We are to look for the optimal price p_i^* which will minimize the risk.

Problem 2: Stock levels for the different periods, the prices (which are all equal in these periods), and the production in the periods preceding those being investigated, are given. The task is to find, for each period, the optimal production which will minimize the risk.

Problem 3: The initial stock level, a system of fixed and equal prices in the different periods, a fixed production for every period; and a fixed advertising policy for the periods preceding that under study are given. The task is to find the minimum risk.

The expression for the minimum risk is found to be similar for all three problems. There may be an economic explanation of this result. I should like to ask Dr. Ullrich if he can give us such an explanation.

Professor Bühlmann: I have some basic doubts as to the applicability of Bayes methods in the case where the process to be controlled is that of a whole economy or a whole branch of economic activity. The difficulty lies in the fact that there is no objective way of establishing the prior distribution. If we then give the planner the freedom to define subjec-

---

[1] Bellman, R. (1957), *Dynamic Programming*, Princeton.

tively the *a priori* distribution we are introducing his personal feelings as probably the most decisive factor into the plan. This is — as I see it — not the intention of the plan.

Dr. Ullrich : To Professor Borch I may reply that although the general theory holds for any type of non-negative weight function and all possible probability distributions, the concrete evaluations of the optimum control can be very tedious when we assume other kinds of weight functions or probability distributions than those used in my paper.

Mr. Baret raised two points : (i) I have used in my examples only a linear demand function, but the whole theory can be used for other types of demand functions as long as we know the probability distributions of their parameters. (ii) The reason that I obtained the same expressions for the minimum risk in all three problems is that I used the same mathematical model and also the same information about the necessary values.

Professor Bühlmann had some doubts about the applicability of Bayes methods. In statistical decision problems where we do not know the *a priori* probability distribution but where we are able to make additional independent observations we can obtain some information about the actual values of parameters. It is then possible to use either the experience theory in statistical decision or the empirical Bayes solution. It can be proved that the average risk converges to the Bayes risk in both cases under very general conditions.

INDEX

Entries in the Index in bold type under the Names of Participants in the Conference indicate their Papers or Discussions of their Papers. Entries in italic type indicate Contributions by Participants to the Discussions.

Index

Index

Index

Index